PELICAN BOOKS
A889

MAN AND ENVIRONMENT

Robert Arvill is the pen-name of one of the few ex-
ponents of conservation planning and development to
have detailed, practical knowledge and experience on
local, central and international levels. After serving for
seven years in the army, being demobbed as a major, he
had two years on the development staff of a large county
borough and six years in one of the leading county planning and development departments, before, as he puts it,
'getting immersed' in conservation with national and
European authorities. In this work he has made important contributions as a member of teams which have produced many publications and has himself given numerous
papers to various conferences, including that of the
British Association. He believes deeply in the ability of
the ordinary person to contribute to a better environment. Forty-eight years old, Robert Arvill enjoys theatre
and music and keeps fit with walking and dancing.

ROBERT ARVILL

MAN AND ENVIRONMENT

Crisis and the Strategy of Choice

PENGUIN BOOKS

Penguin Books Ltd, Harmondsworth, Middlesex, England
Penguin Books Inc., 7110 Ambassador Road, Baltimore, Maryland 21207, U.S.A.
Penguin Books Australia Ltd, Ringwood, Victoria, Australia

—

First published 1967
Revised edition 1969

—

Copyright © Robert Arvill, 1967

—

Made and printed in Great Britain
by Richard Clay (The Chaucer Press) Ltd,
Bungay, Suffolk
Set in Monotype Imprint

CONTENTS

APPENDICES:

LIST OF PLATES

PREFACE

THIS book is about people; about their impact on land, air, water and wild life, and the environment they create; about the damage and destruction they cause and the measures they take as a society to remedy this. Above all it is about the possibilities they now have to re-shape and create an environment that fits their highest aspirations.

Environmental problems are being mentioned more and more frequently in the press and journals, and on television and radio. Such interest reflects man's dissatisfaction with what he is doing to natural resources and his search for knowledge on which to base his 'value' judgements.

Perhaps most important, this quickening interest – this recognition of the wrongs done and the groping attempts to prevent a recurrence of them – is an evolving acceptance by man of his personal responsibility for the state of this planet.

The great potentialities of modern science and technology and the new approaches in administration, education and information, offer man the ways and means for creating a high-quality environment. He will, however, often have to forgo short-term self-interest and take satisfaction instead from acting as a trustee for man's heritage.

Achievements in this field require planning – a much abused word for a good idea: forethought plus teamwork. Planning can be truly successful only if it is done for the people and carried out with the approval of the people. There must be a process of continual involvement: the planners and the people they are planning for must settle together the objectives to be sought, the limits to which the plans should go, what society should do and what is best for the individual.

Planning for posterity must be based on a full understanding of the interaction of human activities and natural forces, and of the ability of nature to sustain and to renew herself. Ecology is the science which seeks to elucidate the principles governing the interactions of the natural processes of land, water and all living things. Conservation involves the application of these scientific principles and a policy of trusteeship. Conservation requires planning of the factors of supply and demand and can itself be meaningful only if it is borne in mind when *all* human activities are considered.

This book seeks to give enough information about man's numbers and his impact on land, air, water and wild life to show the range of choices open to him. It stresses the interdependence of town and country but, because of the vast range of problems involved, does not deal to any extent with town planning and urban renewal. It proposes that, in future, government emphasis ought to be laid on conservation philosophy, principles and strategy rather than the detailed, negative, restrictionist planning which at present often bedevils individual freedom and irks so many. It proposes that what is essentially a process of reconciliation should be arranged between competing claims and individuals, between the forces of nature and our power to guide them, between man's baser and his finer capacities.

But so much depends upon the individual. Will he devote just that degree of personal interest and the few hours a year necessary to ensure that he does have a choice, that he can contribute to the strategy of choice, and that he will leave some choice for posterity?

I believe man can and will do this. He is concerned for the future of his children. But time is short. And posterity is with us now.

The major issues dealt with in this book have been kept under close review. Recent data and reports confirm the main trends and features and show that action is already under way on some of the proposals in the book. The text has been brought up to date with the latest readily available material, and a new Appendix 4 deals with the reform of planning.

ACKNOWLEDGEMENTS

FIRST, I must record my deepest thanks to Gerald Leach, who encouraged me to write this book, and to my family, especially my wife; their help and comments were invaluable.

For constructive observations on various aspects of the book, or on specific references to their publications or organizations, I thank most sincerely Dr R. H. Best, L. M. Blackmore, T. L. Burton, N. H. Calvert, D. Rigby Childs, Professor J. T. Coppock, Dr S. R. Craxford, H. Justin Evans, Lt Col. C. M. Floyd, O.B.E., P. F. Garthwaite, P. Gregory, B. H. Grimes, M.B.E., Dr P. Hall, J. R. Herbert, G. D. Harpman, K. J. Hilton, Dr L. Hoffmann, L. J. Lickorish, Dr N. W. Moore, P. Robshaw, Miss M. M. Sibthorp, Mrs J. M. Weingott and Miss O. Woodhouse.

I must acknowledge my appreciation of all those people and organizations who have in numerous reports, papers and conferences provided the basis for this book. The section on 'References and Further Reading' lists a few of those which I have found helpful and others which the reader may like to consult. Of especial value were the proceedings of the Assembly of the Council of Europe and the Conferences 'The Countryside in 1970', the literature of the voluntary bodies noted in the text and the reports of the research councils and other official and professional organizations concerned. My thanks are due to the staff of many libraries, particularly those of the Nature Conservancy and the United Nations.

For permission to reproduce the tables and illustrations in this book I am very grateful to the persons and organizations noted in the text. The permission of the Controller of Her Majesty's Stationery Office has been obtained to reproduce Plate 8 and Figures 8, 19 and 20.

This book covers a wide field. The compression necessary to provide an adequate synthesis has inevitably led to oversimplification and the omission of many relevant issues. I hope that for these and any other shortcomings I will be forgiven.

CHAPTER I

INTRODUCTION

I will show you fear in a handful of dust.
                    T. S. Eliot, *The Waste Land*

FROM primitive times man has been making an assault on his environment with fire, water and tools. Until a century or so ago, this attack took place over limited areas and in most cases at a relatively slow pace. Today there is a danger that man may use up the habitable and cultivable land. His activities increasingly outstrip the capacity of natural processes to restore the fertility of the land and water which has taken thousands of years to create. And through errors and misuse of his powers he is ruining or degrading vast areas of the globe.

The great driving force behind this new fierce assault is the population explosion. It took 200,000 years for man to reach his first thousand million, but only 100 years to reach his second. The world population in 1966 was $3\frac{1}{2}$ thousand million. By the year 2000 it is expected to be between 6 and 7 thousand million – in which case it will almost have doubled in 35 years. If present trends continue, 80 years from now, when many of today's children will still be alive, the figure could well be 12 thousand million.

Already we can see the devastation spreading, but what few people seem to realize is that the devastation to come may be so great that its scale will give it an entirely new quality – just as air-raids changed when the atom bomb replaced T.N.T.

There is no doubt that the spectacular increases in world population which have been forecast are inevitable except under two conditions: either a major catastrophe occurs – a pandemic, a plague, an all-out nuclear war – or man introduces severe population control. Since 1945, for example, the expectancy of life in India has risen from twenty to forty years. Its population increases by one million a month. Man has introduced 'death-control'; now he must find a replacement for the normal regulating processes of nature.

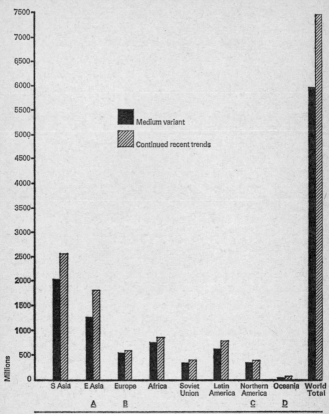

A Includes mainland China, Japan, Mongolia, Korea and China (Taiwan) B Outside the Soviet Union and Turkey C Includes Hawaii D Not including Hawaii

1 Populations in A.D. 2000 based on main trends
(United Nations)

All animal populations have a direct relationship to their environment, not only in connexion with food supply but also for living space. Man is no exception; but, unlike other animals, he has the power consciously to regulate his own numbers. Japan has shown since 1950 that this is possible on a large scale. But for the great masses of people in the under-

developed countries modern methods of birth-control are still
either unknown or too expensive. Then, too, in many countries religious sensibilities inhibit effective action by the State.
So we are faced with the dismal prospect that there may be
within our lifetime a substantial debasement of living standards
and of the environment.

Furthermore, the very pace of population growth poses
major problems of adjustment for man as a social animal.
When, during the nineteenth century, Europe's population
increased rapidly, tension there led to nearly sixty million
emigrating, notably to the U.S.A. A similar emigration today
from, say, China or India, would be almost unthinkable; the
suggestion alone could create dangerous international problems. Even the numerically minor emigrations from the East
now create great difficulties, but for the mass of Asiatic
peoples the problem is far worse: there is no place for them to
go to.

Estimates by the world Food and Agriculture Organization
(F.A.O.) suggest that one fifth of the population is well-fed,
two fifths are on a diet just adequate for subsistence and two
fifths are starving. The United Nations' (U.N.) *Third World
Survey* concluded that up to one half of the world's population
was suffering from hunger or malnutrition or both. The
urgent calls for wheat in recent years from India, Russia and
Africa, in order to prevent famine conditions, show what could
happen. The 1966 famine in India was called by Edward
Heath 'one of the free world's greatest challenges'. The
U.S.S.R. and China cannot survive without grain imports.
And, paradoxically, North America is the only region in the
world with a large unused capacity for export. This maldistri-
bution of the world's food production may itself be a factor
menacing the peace of the world. A starving man is often a
desperate one.

The increasing demands for food have led inevitably to over-
exploitation of the better quality and more accessible land.
The Dust Bowl disaster of the U.S.A., the problems arising
from the cultivation of the great plains of Kazakhstan in the
U.S.S.R., the agricultural settlement failures in Kenya and, on
a smaller scale, the shrinking peat fens of England, are all

...strations of man's mishandling. We are now faced,
...th a great increase in the numbers of pests capable of
...ng a crop. Pests in such numbers are largely the outcome
of man's agricultural systems, particularly the concentration
on single crops in large areas, which create conditions favourable to certain forms of animal and plant life.

Yet the paradox, both of demand and production, is that in
Western countries agriculture has reached such a pitch of
efficiency that in the U.S.A. many farmers have been paid not
to produce food but to conserve their soil – the 'soil bank'.
Despite such extra productive capacity, despite the prospect of
utilizing the relatively untapped resources of the sea and
despite the continuing achievements of science and technology,
the global food situation appears likely to get worse. To feed
the population of the year 2000 will require a spectacularly
increased production. The U.N. Survey considered that the
food supplies of the developing countries must be quadrupled.
Overall, world production of cereals must be doubled and that
of animal products trebled; in some of the presently under-fed
areas food outputs, especially of protein, will need to increase
four to six fold.

It is difficult to predict the long-term effects of these various
factors and trends. On the one hand, total food demand may
lead to a concentration on food production from every available acre. On the other hand, if population numbers can be
controlled, an increase in agricultural productivity may release
considerable quantities of land for other purposes, for example,
afforestation and recreation.

But there is little doubt that in either case the countryside
will change. Intensive farming may imperil the fertility of the
land; to maintain it is now the task of the great chemical
industry. The use of chemicals on land and water is further
extended by the need to keep down pests. Replacing traditional
practices of agriculture by the use of chemicals, factory farming, spray irrigation and the development of large fields without hedgerows and copses will remove much that has led to an
attractive landscape.

Many people today regard the countryside as unchangeable.
They do not know that there are very few natural areas,

certainly in Britain, and fail to realize that much of what they see is the result of man's activities over the centuries, particularly his search for food.

In the case of man's basic need of shelter the effect on the environment is more obvious. Vast proliferations of dwellings are to be found in every continent as the tide of population rises. In Europe, the overall population increase from 1956 to 1976 is expected to be around eighteen per cent. Since this increase is also accompanied by a desire for smaller family groupings, separate houses for different age-levels, and higher general standards of accommodation and living space, the effects will be tremendous. The great sprawl of bricks and mortar, ironically dubbed subtopia, and the constant battle over land for development, green belts and new towns, make daily headlines in press, radio and television. As far as Europe is concerned, it is prophesied that it will become a continuous conurbation from Manchester to Milan. In the U.S.A., the east and west coasts are developing into walls of brick and mortar greater than any built by China or Rome. And all over the world the giant cities of the twentieth century continue to spread remorselessly. In 1800 the world had fifty cities of over 100,000 people; today there are nine hundred. Once the land is sealed over with steel and concrete man cannot do much to restore it – his powers do not at the moment stretch that far. Even worse, within these expanding towns, factory sites, motorways and airfields, there are often large areas of neglected land and many sites are left degraded or derelict.

In the underdeveloped countries, although the living standards are low, pressures on the land and water are more intense as their populations increase at breakneck speed. In many of the urban centres of the world, in cities such as Hong Kong or Rio de Janeiro, vast ant heaps of people cling tenaciously to life in conditions so crowded and so primitive as to be beyond description – and all this within yards of skyscrapers and other symbols of twentieth-century development. In these areas, the nineteenth-century lesson that public health is everyone's business – for example, that disease is no respecter of persons – has yet to be learnt. The twentieth-century lesson, the need for planning and development directed to creating a healthy environment, is not yet on the curriculum.

But by whatever standards these areas of West and East are judged, they are symptoms of a general disease: man is degrading his own environment on a scale without historic parallel. Slums make no sense, they are not necessary, and their perpetuation is a sad reflection on man.

Even the waste in the slums is often exceeded by the devastation which man creates in his quest for the sources of fuel and power. Whole landscapes have been changed as men cleared forests to provide timber for fuel. Scotland grimly illustrates this, with its barren moors and bogs and eroded mountains – often the still visible results of forests being felled in the seventeenth and eighteenth centuries to provide charcoal for iron smelting. The enormity of the impact of man's search for coal can be seen in the torn and scarred valleys of Wales, the great opencast mining cuts in the Appalachians of eastern U.S.A. and the vast lignite areas of Czechoslovakia. Here the workings stretch for miles and have created a scene of devastation and pollution aptly described as 'the garden of Hell'.

More recent sources of power, such as oil, natural gas or electricity, do not so obviously degrade the landscape but their effect is still great. The countryside becomes a 'wirescape' for electricity and a conduit for pipelines. In just over a decade, 1,700 miles of large pipelines for oil have been laid in Europe and more are under construction. The skyline is dominated by massive power stations; coastlines are the site for nuclear 'temples of power', which may become monuments as lasting as the pyramids.

The twentieth-century quest for power is urgent. Nations have been frightened by current assessments of the known resources of power on land. These have revealed that at present rates of consumption (and more coal and oil have been used up this century than in all recorded history), several of the existing usable supplies of major fuels will last only for decades and not for centuries. Hence, vast numbers of scientific and technical staff and huge amounts of capital are locked up in the struggle to control the ultimate source of power – the atom – and to locate new supplies of natural gas and oil under the seas.

Success in these fields of endeavour could radically affect all man's activities and his environment.

But without question the most talked of, written about and glamourized of man's activities in the second half of the twentieth century are those relating to movement – his mobility on and off the planet. Today, its main feature is the race between the U.S.A. and U.S.S.R. to place men on the moon, a race that has created enormous new industries and insatiably devours vast resources.

Historically, population movements have taken many forms: a search for new pastures and new lands; a flight from scourges and persecutions; invasions of one nation by another. Nearly always these movements have had lasting effects on the natural environment. Today's movement, based largely on motor transport, is having an all-pervasive impact. More than any other factor motor transport has led to the sprawl of suburbs and to the relentless erosion of the countryside. It has led to the decay of many old urban forms and the merging of town and village into conurbations. In the U.S.A. in particular, the problem is causing great concern. The pressures arising from the arrival of a new baby every 12 seconds and a new car every 5 seconds are estimated to lead to the loss of 2 acres of country-side every minute.

Today, a new scale has been given to man's restlessness by his pursuit of leisure. A foretaste of what was to come was seen in the nineteenth century when much of Scotland was turned into a playground for the wealthy. The advent of the railway and the accumulation of wealth from the Industrial Revolution led to whole areas being devoted to pastimes like grouse shooting and deer hunting. The landscape was trans-formed within a few decades.

The rapid growth of travel by rail, sea and air during the past two centuries is now being surpassed in one generation. Enormous numbers of people possess a motor scooter or car and the money to travel at home and abroad. On public holidays, huge populations surge to and from the coast and the countryside is bestrewn with cars. Millions of people migrate from country to country in search of sun and sand or sight-seeing. The tourist industry is one of the world's largest. It dictates the economy of whole countries and demands ever-increasing numbers of roads, buildings and services.

These mass movements are like a floodtide in their impact on the environment. They are creating a wear and tear never before known. Probably hardest hit is the coastline. All over the world it is being developed and disfigured, primarily to cater for holiday-makers. In England, Wales and Northern Ireland already about a quarter of the 3,250 miles of coast is recorded as developed. In continental Europe, many believe it to be too late to save the coasts of Italy, Spain and Portugal. Those of Scandinavia seem likely to become the next victims. In many other areas sheer pressure of numbers has destroyed the original attraction. Once remote spots are being degraded by the pervasive forces of human erosion. Nature gets no chance to recuperate.

So, what is the outlook for the future? What is the lesson to be learnt about the impact of man's demands for food, shelter, power and mobility? It is that the natural environment can no longer survive without positive action by man to conserve it.

Changes in nature arising from man's activities over past centuries have been relatively gradual. Had there been satellites and modern photographic techniques in past centuries, they would have shown a pattern of continuous change in the countryside. Occasional flurries of activity, such as the deforestation of Roman times, were, until recently, the exception to the slow and apparently deliberate movement of zones of vegetation. For example, looked at from a satellite, the forests of the Mediterranean would have been seen steadily shrivelling in face of cropping by goats and sheep, erosion, burning and development by man. But today films from satellites would show a succession of arable lands being rapidly transformed into bricks and asphalt. Everywhere change is swifter and more drastic.

Many features of the 'natural' environment are threatened. The chalk grasslands of southern England are disappearing with changes in agricultural practice. The wetlands of Europe and North America, reservoirs of wildfowl and valuable for science and recreation, are being eliminated by drainage. In Africa and Asia, animals once found in great numbers are now on the list of rarities. And wild life everywhere is affected by the loss of habitats.

Change is, of course, inherent in the relationship of man and the rest of nature. What is now required is a purposive and regulated change to a design consciously formulated and reflecting man's highest aspirations. Has man the capacity for this? Do not 5,000 years of experience, since the days of the first pastoralists, suggest that he cannot live on this planet without degrading it? And, in any event, would not his efforts be in vain in view of the population explosion?

The answer is that to survive man must reject a counsel of despair. He must control his numbers; he has the capacity to do so. He has sufficient knowledge and means now, not merely to avoid debasing his environment but also to enhance and enjoy it more fully. He must assert his will to do so, and replace a generally *laissez faire* attitude towards his environment by positive, substantial and sustained intervention to manage all his resources.

How must man prepare this grand design? He must make his approach simultaneously on three fronts: political; organizational and administrative; and professional and scientific.

Politicians themselves need to become aware of the unity of the environment: that measures affecting it often have consequences beyond their immediate aims. They must cope with a public that cannot, or will not, perceive the long-term effects and values of environmental policies. Of course it is difficult to get the public's cooperation. Knowledge of the many factors involved in any decision on land or water use is rarely available to the citizen. Often only the politician in power can have access to all the knowledge and possibilities on which to make value judgements and take decisions. Yet, if a healthier environment is to be achieved, it is essential that the public become informed, aware of the issues, with attitudes and ideas based more fully on scientifically diagnosed facts. Leadership in politics must, therefore, be increasingly concerned with telling people and, in the broadest sense, of educating them about the implications of policies.

It is ironic that in this century – the age of the 'organization man' – there should be so many problems arising from faulty or inadequate organization. Without subscribing to Pope's view

> For forms of government let fools contest,
> Whate'er is best administered is best

there is, nevertheless, vast scope for improvement in the structure and content of central and local government; in the size of areas, membership of governing bodies and the quality of staff; in delegation at all levels; in the arrangements for cooperation between public and private enterprise; and, perhaps above all, in the ways of getting citizens to participate in decision-making.

For example, much of the twentieth-century industrial development is concentrated in extensive conurbations, often based on estuarine and tide-water sites, as at Rotterdam and on the Thames. Water is a vital resource for industry and where it is not locally adequate reservoirs have to be constructed, usually in upland valleys far beyond existing administrative boundaries. The resulting problems are complex and wasteful of resources. Nearly all these conurbations urgently need a structure of government related to their economic and physical hinterland.

Administration particularly requires new attitudes and ideas. New techniques for measuring the social cost and benefits of public projects and for assessing the value of amenity areas, open spaces and countryside must be developed if the money is to be found to manage them effectively for modern requirements. The social benefits to be derived from improving derelict and degraded land must be assessed, and the cost shared in an enlightened partnership between civic authorities and commercial firms. These and many other fields call for an administration capable of solving problems in a positive way, of bridging or eliminating the gaps between bureaucracy, technocracy and democracy, and of providing better intercommunication at all levels of society.

One of the major problems of our times is, in American terms, 'the collation, retrieval and dissemination of information'. Failure here leads to waste of the most vital resource – man's intellect. All over the world progress is delayed, research and studies are unnecessarily repeated, mistakes recur, because information is not spread effectively. Yet 80,000 scientific journals are published annually and the number is doubling every ten years; communication sometimes breaks down under the weight of its own processes.

Although scientists and technologists have provided the computer and are working with administrators to deal with this information-exchange problem, there are others very special to science and the professions which machines cannot resolve. The great specialization required in many subjects is leading to barriers between the disciplines and a failure 'to talk the same language'. The relationships of scientists with politicians, administrators and especially the public call for urgent and continuous attention. Scientists – and there are more of them alive today than existed in all history – must make a bigger effort to clarify and project their ideas to all sectors of society.

People who work in the environmental sciences and professions connected with the use and management of land, water and wild life must pay particular attention to the problem of how to spread their knowledge. Long-established and well-tested practices – for example, intensive irrigation to avoid soil erosion, and limitation of pests by growing mixed crops – are insufficiently known and acted upon. More advanced concepts, such as land capability, multi-purpose use, biological productivity and wild-life farming, and how to apply them, are not yet part of the practices of the average landowner and farmer. And one of the main reasons is the inadequate relationship between the man on the job and the scientists and professionals.

Of outstanding importance and urgency is the application of science to harvesting the natural resources of the sea. This could make a great contribution in food, minerals and energy, but prior ecological studies of fish and appropriate controls are essential to avoid denudation of stocks. Major barrage projects to provide power are already working successfully and their use could be extended to many parts of the world. Further research and development could rapidly bring the extraction of minerals and desalination of salt water within normal economic values and use.

Even now, in all these fields, there is sufficient knowledge and first-hand experience to effect a great improvement in the quality of the environment. Man has many successes to his credit – the Tennessee Valley Scheme, the agricultural settlements of Israel, and the recent exploitation of the mineral resources of the Sahara. During the past two decades substantial efforts have been made to cleanse rivers, to eliminate oil pollution of the seas, to prevent the misuse of pesticides and to safeguard wild life and landscape.

If the best policies and practices from these cases could be made widely known and acted upon, many lands could be radically transformed. The spur to action may be the great pressure of population itself. And developments in education have revealed a wealth of untapped human talent to be harnessed to the problems of production and distribution, to the wise exploitation of existing resources, and to the discovery of new ones.

Despite these promising lines of improvement, man must create for himself a better relationship within nature if he is not to have an irretrievably adverse impact on the environment. He must resolve the uncertainty and ignorance about the social factors of his habitat. He must exert the control over his physical environment which he now has in his power. And he must give greater priority to maintaining the long-term supply of land, water and wild life which are essential ingredients in the high-quality environment which posterity will expect. Time runs out rapidly. The future starts today.

CHAPTER 2

LAND

Any landscape is a condition of the spirit.
Henri-Fréderic Amiel

THROUGHOUT history land has been the most sought-after and yet one of the least understood of the earth's phenomena. Nearly always it has been regarded as wealth and something to satisfy a demand for food or living-space. Rarely has it been treated both as a living entity and a resource in very limited supply.

Land covers approximately one quarter of the earth's surface. But half of this is at present uninhabitable because it is in the polar regions or in mountainous or desert terrain. Man cannot do very much about the structure and disposition of the rocks underlying the land. He is able to alter the form of the land surface but only on a fairly small scale. He cannot yet transmute the vast deserts of the Sahara or the Gobi into fertile and habitable country, despite the pioneer work of Israel and projects such as those of the world Food and Agriculture Organization (F.A.O.) in Tunisia. Much of to-day's degraded land (like the dry wastes of North Africa, the arid, purple mountains of Greece and the wet moorlands of Britain) is, in fact, the result of previous misuse.

At present, the earth has about 25 million square miles of habitable and cultivable land, but vast areas of this, especially near the great cities, are being taken out of cultivation for urban expansion, mineral working and roads and by erosion. It has been calculated that every human requires the product from at least $2\frac{1}{2}$ acres per annum to support him. It is obvious, therefore, that with his rocketing population and the decline in the quality of his environment, man cannot afford to squander or misuse the land. What makes caution more necessary than ever is that the world's population is distributed so unevenly: for each citizen in the U.S.A. there are $12\frac{1}{2}$ acres, in France $3\frac{1}{4}$, and in Britain one.

The term land includes soil and topography, in fact, all the physical features of a given location. It reflects the interaction of physical conditions, natural processes, and man's response to them in social and economic terms. Very often it is the economic situation which dictates the planning and use of land. Sometimes in areas where labour and capital are readily available medium-quality soils are made highly productive while elsewhere better soils produce poor crops because no one can afford to farm them efficiently.

Over the centuries man has tended to find and to settle on the land with the best combination of qualities. Today it is even more essential that he finds and conserves the areas with the greatest value for food production. This may mean that in order to give the best soils special consideration, thousands of people, perhaps whole towns and cities, will have to be re-settled in less productive areas. Modern society has the mobility and means to do this.

One of the great problems about soil is that not enough is known about it – the distribution of the best soil, its quality and scope for improvement, and its suitability for various types of crops. Since 1960, the F.A.O. and the United Nations Educational, Social and Cultural Organization (Unesco) have been preparing a soil map of the world which will pinpoint the areas most suitable for food production and those where faulty agricultural policies and practices prevail. Some countries are preparing a map of the potential vegetation cover of their land – that is, the vegetation that would develop, given present flora, fauna and climate, if human intervention were to cease. Such a map will show the areas which would respond to similar development in agriculture or forestry, and it will facilitate the conservation of soil, water and other resources. In the U.S.A., the National Cooperative Soil Survey adopted in 1965 a new comprehensive classification system for soil based on its characteristics, and this may come into use in other countries.

But do we know enough about soil at the moment? And how is man treating it?

Soil

From our point of view, the most vital element in land is its wafer-thin outer layer of soil and sub-soil – a layer which is on average only 25 to 100 inches deep. The productive top-soil itself is little more than 10 inches thick over most of the earth.

What we call 'soil' is a highly complex and dynamic entity. It is composed of many substances and harbours an infinite number of living organisms; in fact, the weight of animals below the surface of a field usually greatly exceeds that of the cattle grazing upon it.

Soil is the end-product of a continuing and intricate inter-relationship and interaction between living things and dead matter, water, air and light. It takes nature centuries to create the productive soil which is the main feeding zone for plants and on which all life ultimately depends. Man cannot yet make soil in any quantity, and his fertilizers can only supplement or partly restore depleted soils. The primary importance of soil conservation to man *should* not, therefore, require further argument.

But, unfortunately, it does. For instance, it has been estimated that in England and Wales, if present trends continue, the remaining years of this century will see about six million acres of farmland developed for other uses, and as much derelict land will have been produced from mineral workings as in the previous two centuries. In or near most of the great urban centres of the world, the amount of ill-managed and neglected rural land increases as agriculturalists work under the threat of urban encroachments. Some of it is in green belts, and some is not yet ripe for development. Its existence brings out unpleasant features of human behaviour – trespassing, allowing dogs to interfere with cattle, the dumping of litter and old cars – and the landowner finds that working this land becomes increasingly uneconomic. It is a zone of 'rural twilight'.

Much of the earth's cultivable land has soil unfavourable to many crops; it suffers from adverse climate, a shortage or surplus of water, and much natural erosion. To mitigate these conditions and to enhance soil fertility in such areas requires expert management. Alas, this is often lacking, and many of man's activities only make the situation worse. Two special problems merit fuller study: these are soil erosion and pesticides.

Erosion

Soil erosion is a continual process in nature. Over the centuries weather and rocks interact to replace worn-out soil, much as man renews his outer layer of skin. But the accelerated soil erosion created by man often destroys faster than nature can renew. It usually results from rapid and thoughtless exploitation, an attempt to obtain the maximum product as quickly as possible. This attitude has led to excessive cultivation, deforestation, overgrazing, a failure to consider the nature of the soil and its environment, and a reluctance to devote labour and finance to maintaining its qualities. The results are seen in the barren lands of North Africa, the Middle East and South China. And soil erosion has been a factor in the downfall of past civilizations.

Perhaps the most frequently quoted example of soil erosion is that of the American Dust Bowl. This covers a large area of the Middle West – Colorado, Kansas, Oklahoma and Texas. Originally grassland in a semi-arid climate, its natural equilibrium was upset and the land reduced to near-desert conditions by over-cultivation and wind erosion accentuated by a succession of dry years. From this land, short of cover and of water, vast quantities of grain were produced earlier in this century. With the advent and rapid spread of farm machinery in the 1920s, the soil soon became worn and depleted. As its stability and holding capacity disappeared, it was swirled away in dust storms which left behind a degraded land and a defeated human population.

But there are many areas of the U.S.A. which have been similarly subject to wind erosion. Others have felt the impact of water erosion on land which, through misuse, had lost its porosity and coherence. Fertility in these areas dwindled at increasing speed.

The publicity given to erosion has undoubtedly helped to induce more conservation-minded leaders in the U.S.A. The graphic pictures of vast dust storms blackening the horizon, of derelict farms and silted-up rivers, awakened the conscience of the nation. Nevertheless, America's wasted land, difficult as it is to restore, is not now as serious a problem as the continuing active soil erosion in other parts of the world, especially in Africa.

A number of measures which help to conserve soil have been in use for centuries in many parts of the world. Their primary aim is to make the best use of rain. They include terracing, contour farming and strip ploughing, which control the quantity and pace of water run-off. Over the years, many of the best soils have been developed under grass. The soil itself must have a good biological content of minute organisms to circulate the nutrients and to maintain a healthy structure. With some crops soil conservation is facilitated by allowing weeds to grow or by cultivating leguminous crops. These help to protect the soil from wind and water erosion and can be ploughed back as manure. (It is ironic that the great increase in the use of heavy machinery in agriculture is giving rise to a new problem, the 'compacting' of soils on the wetter lands. This difficulty may, perhaps, be resolved through the application of the hovercraft principle to farm equipment.)

To restore vegetational cover to barren lands is a slow process, but the scientific and technical problems are far outweighed by those arising from man's legal, social and economic institutions, and his use of domestic animals, notably goats and sheep. These animals have caused soil erosion in many areas and it is urgently necessary to have more control over them. Quaintly dubbed 'nature's lawnmowers', goats and sheep have grazed large areas of Mediterranean countries into subsistence farming or desert; they prevent tree growth and have reduced the average tree-line by 1,000 feet in four centuries. Unfortunately, they and cattle are still being introduced into areas being cleared of forest in Africa. For example, the cattle of the Masai tribe in Tanzania, which serve as a status symbol, give rise to much erosion in their now restricted territories. In many instances, a far greater yield of protein could be obtained by 'farming' the wild animals in these territories. These animals and the plants on which their life is based have achieved a harmony or balance in their relationship which, history shows, is rarely achieved between the goat, as farmed by humans, and its terrain.

On the other hand, sheep and goats are probably the only practical way of maintaining many lands in their present condition – for example, some of the downland and grasslands of southern England. These well-loved amenity lands are the result of centuries of intervention by man, mainly through his use of grazing animals. With few rabbits about and the changes in agricultural practice which make 'close' shepherding on them uneconomic, these lands quickly revert to scrub, gorse and bracken. They become inaccessible to humans on foot and horse, and lose their character and charm. Chemicals can achieve some control but they have effects on the soil about which not enough is yet known. They cannot, therefore, be used to the extent necessary to control the natural succession of vegetation, which, in Britain, tends to cover many areas with scrub or forest, without unforeseeable effects.

Pesticides

Pesticides are part of the great chemical revolution of recent decades. Without them, world standards of food, health and hygiene would be incomparably lower. But they pose major problems and have created controversy the world over.

The great impetus to the use of pesticides was the discovery of the insecticidal properties of D.D.T. in the Second World War. This insecticide, and others based on the same element – chlorine – made fantastic inroads on the insect-carried diseases, like malaria and sleeping sickness, and on such scourges of the world as locusts. Thus, on the one hand, as a major factor in 'death-control', pesticides accelerate the population explosion. On the other hand, they appear increasingly indispensable: crops must be protected and the spectacular yields of recent years be maintained if we are to feed the world's growing population. But strains of insects have emerged which are resistant to pesticides. F.A.O. scientists report that during the past twenty years in approximately two hundred species of pests resistance has developed to the products devised to kill them. So new formulations are required.

Some chemicals persist in the soil of fields for a day or two, others for many years. Some chemical residues change in the soils: a very potent one, aldrin, is readily converted into a more persistent one, dieldrin. Chemicals can be taken from the soil by plants and animals and by physical action, such as leaching and by run-off. They have been found in fields, rivers and oceans many miles from their point of application.

Chemicals are stored in the fat of animals. Some species of predatory birds are particularly vulnerable to the harmful effects of this accumulation – their fertility and reproductive capacity have suffered and their numbers have been severely reduced by certain pesticides. And most humans in Europe and the U.S.A. now have at least some D.D.T. in their body fat, about 3 parts per million – probably harmless but worth keeping an eye on!

As man thus contaminates the soil, so he affects the whole environment. A major governmental review of persistent organochlorine pesticides in Britain in 1964 stated that these chemicals 'represent at least a potential danger to other plants and animals, including man himself'. It considered that 'the present accumulative contamination of the environment by the more persistent organochlorine pesticides should be curtailed'. A compulsory licensing scheme for all pesticide products used in agriculture, home gardens and food storage was issued for comment in August 1968.

In the U.S.A. and Europe, governmental bodies, national and international, with cooperation from the manufacturers and voluntary bodies, are seeking ways of ensuring that the many valuable chemicals now available are used wisely. It is probable that in time a balanced solution will emerge which will integrate techniques of rotation and cultivation, biological controls, chemicals and many other methods, but this will require of farmers and land-users an even higher standard of training and a much wider outlook than is common now.

Whatever the outcome, it is unlikely that large-scale 'chemicalization' of the soil will be the ultimate answer to food productivity. A leading British research chemist* engaged in the manufacture of agricultural chemicals said in 1963 that: 'The chemist can unwittingly create in one year a biological

* *Food Supply and Nature Conservation: A Symposium*, Cambridge-shire College of Arts and Technology, 1964.

problem so complex that his biologist colleague may need a decade to evaluate or solve it.'

Many lessons emerge from these studies of soil erosion and pesticides, but perhaps the most important one is that the soil must be treated as a living entity. It requires positive management carried out with an increasing knowledge of the many processes that go to create this vital element. This management should be based on a scientific assessment of how much wear and cultivation the soil can stand while yet maintaining its fertility. If he fails to make the right calculations, man may destroy the soil on which his existence depends; 'Nations live as long as their humus' – Henry Wallace.

In addition to the many changes in farming practice, such as mechanization and chemicalization, which may cause soil erosion or infertility, there are other inter-related developments. Already in some parts of the U.S.A. and Germany landowners are finding it necessary to replant hedgerows and copses which they once thought a nuisance – without their shelter, the tidy, efficient fields had begun to blow away. More difficult to renew are all those vast areas which, over the last century, have been denuded of their trees and left to decay. It is the trees which, with the soil, generally determine the character of the landscape.

TREES

> ... we cannot restore – once it is lost – the majesty
> of a forest whose trees soared upwards 2,000
> years ago.
> President Lyndon B. Johnson, 1966

Trees were once the main cover over most of the land surface. Today very little of the original forest remains except in parts of South America and Africa. For centuries man has stripped the earth of trees to develop land for cultivation and to provide his fuel, homes and ships. In every way man has been prodigal in his use of wood. Often he has been driven to seek new territory and to fight wars because he has denuded the forest and the soil. Wars in their turn consume vast quantities of timber. In the Second World War many forests were destroyed as part of a 'scorched earth' policy adopted by retreating armies. In Greece and Crete the invading troops felled and burned trees as part of their total, scientifically waged, warfare.

When the forest has gone the top-soil is soon washed away and deserts are created; floods and avalanches become seasonal; bogs and swamps develop; and the soil is impoverished as its nutrients are leached into the lower strata and water-courses. In many Mediterranean countries the mistakes of 3,000 years ago destroyed the tree cover, hot sun and arid wind did the rest, and the result is barren or degraded land.

But more important in the long term than the uses to which man puts the forest is its place in nature. It contributes substantially to the fertility of land and is the habitat of vast numbers of wild creatures. The root system of a tree is an intricate and incredibly lengthy network of main, secondary and minor roots and spurs – perhaps over 300,000 altogether. Masses of these roots in a wood can retain 1,000 tons of water per acre. A large amount (27 per cent) of rain or snow (precipitation) is held in the top of a tree and a further considerable volume passes from the roots to the top of the tree and is there evaporated. This water 'cycle' is important to water conservation and to climate. The fall of leaves helps to create the humus in the top-soil and reintroduces the minerals and other substances essential to fertility. The tree continually maintains and enriches the land on which it lives and is the only major raw material that can renew itself.

But suitable conditions are essential. Forests suffer greatly from natural events – fire (from lightning), tree diseases and pests – and require considerable management if their all-round values are to be realized. Unfortunately, until less than a century ago, man exploited timber very much as a mineral and only rarely cultivated and harvested it as a living thing. Enough is, however, already known about trees to make it possible for us to manage them and use timber more wisely. Intelligently planted trees can protect the soil and reduce the damage caused by rain and snow. They can act as 'nurses' to favour the growth of young seedlings, serve as shelter for

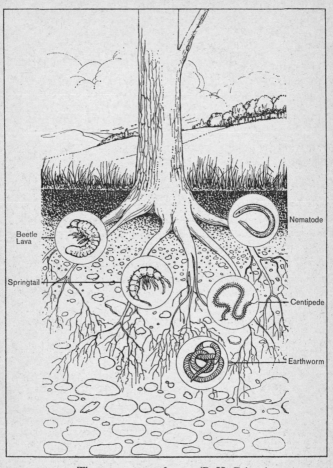

Beetle Lava

Springtail

Nematode

Centipede

Earthworm

2 The root system of a tree (B. H. Grimes)

cattle and provide windbreaks to protect crops. Hedgerow timber harbours many insects which can help to pollinate essential plants and will prey on other, less welcome, inhabitants.

Despite the many synthetic fibres now available, the uses of

timber increase and actually include providing cellulose for
synthetics. About 5,000 uses can now be identified. The
manufacture of paper alone consumes whole forests; every
Sunday issue of the *New York Times* devours the product of
150 acres. Forests are immense reservoirs of wild life. They
can provide a direct crop from the sale of animals, such as deer,
culled in accordance with a management programme. The
fees from licences for hunting, shooting and fishing within
forests are an important source of revenue. Millions of people
visit forests all over the world, most being content to stroll in
them leisurely and enjoy the scenery. For increasing numbers,
forests are open-air classrooms or laboratories for education
and research. And overall, the forest is a major feature in the
landscape.

For these and many other reasons, most countries now have
afforestation programmes. For a century the Swiss and
Austrians have planted trees systematically in the Alps as a
protection against avalanches and erosion. Defence and
economics have also influenced tree planting in many countries. In the last sixty years in the U.S.A. and Germany, and
since the First World War in Britain and many other countries,
timber has been planted and managed scientifically and cropped
in a way which favours its renewal. Afforestation is, however, a
costly and time-consuming process. The rewards do not
usually come within a generation and man does not yet know
enough about the wonderful and complex life of the forest to
ensure that he always plants every species in the most appropriate soil and situation. From seedling to harvest, a timber
crop rarely takes less than thirty years even for some of the
quick-growing conifers and poplars. Although the rate of tree
growth can be increased for some species and younger and
lower-grade trees may be acceptable for some modern industries, plantations designed to give quick results can supply
only a part of the total requirements, and do not contribute
wholly satisfactorily to the landscape.

Felling trees meets a demand for the uses already mentioned, and provides a cash return; afforestation usually does
neither until the next generation has taken over. Hence the
tendency is for forests to be destroyed faster than they can be

replaced. It has been suggested that, at the present rate of use, all the supplies of timber in the world will have been exhausted within a century. The position in the U.S.A. was reviewed in 1958 in a report *Timber Resources for America's Future*. It showed that although afforestation was increasing, the quantity and quality of trees were declining. Substantial increases in timber growth would be needed to meet the vastly expanded requirements of the twenty-first century.

The situation in Europe was reviewed in a joint report by the F.A.O. and the U.N. Economic Commission for Europe, published in 1964. It showed that by A.D. 2000 the gap between consumption of wood in Europe and production from its own forests would be large, perhaps between 3,500 and 5,600 million cubic feet. And contrary to popular belief, the great tropical and monsoon forests of South and Central America, Africa, Indonesia and South-East Asia are unlikely to meet the demands of the temperate, populated areas. Commercial exploitation is handicapped by the inaccessibility of much of the timber and its distance from markets; the wood is dense and difficult to season; and the climate creates labour problems. Few of the trees are in much demand apart from special woods, such as teak, mahogany, rosewood and ebony, whose qualities make them worth the extra effort. The great centres of population and industry must, therefore, soon look to their own plantations to meet their vast and seemingly insatiable demands for timber.

ETHICS

These main components of the land – soil and trees – are obviously not easy to create or to replace in the desired quality or quantity. They should be regarded as what in fact they are, natural resources vital to all life on earth. To appreciate their full significance requires more, however, than an understanding of their part in the energy cycle, more than a detailed scientific knowledge of their constituents and how to conserve them. It requires what has been called a *land ethic*. The late Aldo Leopold stated in *A Sand County Almanac*, first published in 1949 . . .

That land is a community is a basic concept of ecology, but that land is to be loved and respected is an extension of ethics. That land yields a cultural harvest is a fact long known, but latterly often forgotten. . . .

A land ethic, then, reflects the existence of an ecological conscience, and this in turn reflects a conviction of individual responsibility for the health of the land. Health is the capacity of the land for self-renewal. Conservation is our effort to understand and preserve this capacity. . . .

The 'key-log' which must be moved to release the evolutionary process for an ethic is simply this: quit thinking about decent land-use as solely an economic problem. Examine each question in terms of what is ethically and aesthetically right, as well as economically expedient. A thing is right when it tends to preserve the integrity, stability and beauty of the biotic community. It is wrong when it tends otherwise.

If such an awareness of the deeper relationships of man and the land were to become widely diffused throughout the community, it would do much to create and maintain the high quality environment man now has the capacity to achieve. And it would conserve the good earth.

But do the policies and practices of governments and the behaviour of peoples give any hope for such an ethic? Britain has many problems typical of those of the developed countries. What are her policies and practices? How do Britons treat their land? And what are the new trends and patterns? These are some of the issues examined in the next three chapters.

CHAPTER 3

LAND IN BRITAIN – I

Land is the ultimate platform of all human activity.
Lord Robens, 1966

OUT of Britain's total land area of 56 million acres, approximately 29 million are under crops and grass; 17 million are under rough grazing of little value for agriculture, except for the rearing of hardy sheep and cattle, and are increasingly used for afforestation and recreational pursuits; about 4 million are under woodland; and the remaining 6 million cover urban and residual uses.

TABLE I

Major Land Uses, 1960

	England and Wales	Scotland	Great Britain
	millions of acres		
Agriculture			
arable	13·7	3·4	17·1
permanent grass	10·7	1·0	11·7
rough grazings	5·0	12·5	17·5
TOTAL	29·4	16·9	46·3
Woodland	2·5	1·6	4·1
Urban	4·0	0·5	4·5
Other uses *	1·2	0·1	1·3
TOTAL	37·1	19·1	56·2

* 'Other uses' includes mineral workings, military sites and areas not within the other categories.
SOURCE: *The Changing Use of Land in Britain*, R. H. Best and J. T. Coppock, 1962.

Within these main categories, there are many features, such as wetlands, moors, downs, copses and the pattern of farms, which are the product of man's interaction with nature over the centuries. By the seventeenth century, a considerable part of the woodland had been replaced by agricultural land – in small enclosures, large common fields or open moorland. The eight-eenth-century revolution in agricultural techniques led to the disappearance of most open fields so that the lowlands came to be characterized by small fields, separated by hedgerows or stone walls, which are part of the attractiveness of that type of countryside today. A strong corps of landscape specialists, such as the legendary 'Capability' Brown, developed many estates and landscape parks which helped to create new standards of visual beauty. From Tudor times onwards oak was planted for the Navy. John Evelyn was prominent in this work in the seventeenth century. In 1664 he wrote *Sylva, or a Discourse of Forest Trees*, purposely directed to preserve the English woods which were later to provide the ships for Trafalgar. At the end of the eighteenth century, Lord Nelson insisted that the Forest of Dean should be replanted with oak. During and after the Napoleonic Wars there was also some planting of the hard-woods treasured so much today. Generally, much of what is to-day regarded as beautiful or 'natural' landscape reflects these relatively recent developments.

Many of the features which gave rise to the accepted aesthetic qualities of the countryside are now disappearing, despite their new values for amenity and recreation. Often changes are taking place without any thought or consideration of their effect on the landscape and the ecology of the countryside. New tech-niques in agriculture and forestry are likely to bring a revolu-tion in our landscape greater than the one experienced in the eighteenth century. What, then, are the major trends of signi-ficance to the countryside?

AGRICULTURE

Agriculture in Britain accounts for about 80 per cent of the land surface. Farm sales in the mid-sixties were about £1,800 million and expenses £1,500 million. Net income in the in-dustry (i.e. the reward for the manual and managerial labour of the farmer and his wife, and for the occupier's investment) was around £460 million. National policies led to agriculture receiving about £260 million from government funds. Despite a drop of nearly 25 per cent in the labour force over the past

decade, it employs half a million and has increased net
output in this period by about 33⅓ per cent. Agriculture is
clearly a vital factor in the economic and social life of the
nation.

Since 1940 there have been vast changes in agriculture. The
major alteration, affecting the whole economy of farming and
its operations, has been mechanization, particularly the ousting
of the horse by the tractor. The one million horses used in 1918
have been largely replaced by tractors, combine harvesters and
a vast quantity of agricultural machinery (enthusiasts should
see the tables in the annual *Agricultural Statistics*). A team of
two horses could plough on average an acre a day; a tractor
will do eight or nine acres, it can operate on steep slopes and
enables more land to be utilized. One of the fundamental
results of mechanization was that the discipline of rotational
farming was eased. In consequence, the famous Norfolk or
'four-course shift' has been superseded in many areas. Its
objectives – to prevent disease and weeds and to maintain
fertility – are now largely achieved by fertilizers and herbicides. Intensive crop rotational systems are practised in the
southern and eastern counties of England; on Salisbury Plain
barley has been grown in some fields for eleven years in succession. Cash crops – wheat, barley, peas, beet – are interspersed with ley – land temporarily under grass – which
provides an income from the cattle which graze it.

The break-up of many large estates and the shortage and
high cost of manpower all affect the structure of farming.
The spread of owner-occupancy and large capitalized concerns
leads to new approaches. Factory production techniques are
applied to the rearing of poultry and livestock. Producers are
having to follow market requirements closely and to organize
themselves so that they can respond rapidly to new needs.
Increasing population and higher incomes are leading to a
demand for more food. Consumers require better quality and
luxury products. Satisfying these demands in turn accelerates
the pace of change in agriculture and influences the shape
of the new emerging landscape. All these factors are interacting to give an agricultural revolution greater than any
before.

The Agriculture Acts of 1947 and 1957 laid down certain principles directed to promoting and maintaining

> a stable and efficient agricultural industry . . . capable of producing such part of the nation's food and other agricultural produce as in the national interest it is desirable to produce in the United Kingdom.

The objectives set for agriculture in the National Plan (Cmnd 2764) are to save imports of food that would otherwise be necessary to meet increasing demand and to release manpower to other sectors of the economy. In the mid-sixties the aim was to give further stimulus to the expansion of beef production. The Annual Reviews under the Agricultural Acts show that the nation produces over half its total food supply, including about 75 per cent of its requirements of temperate foodstuffs. For example, the estimates given for the mid-sixties for the United Kingdom were as follows:

TABLE 2

	Home produced	Imports	Approx. percentage home produced	Approx. percentage imported	Approx. ratio
	thousands of tons				
Sugar	890	2,179	29	71	3–7
Milk products	613	683	47	53	1–1
Grain	13,494	8,225	62	38	3–2
Meat	2,297	1,050	68	32	2–1
Potatoes	7,457	310	96	4	24–1
Egg and egg products	1,166*	47*	96	4	24–1

* Million dozens.

Clearly, changes in the ratios of home produce to imports will directly affect not only the agricultural industry and land use in Britain but also the country's balance of payments. The nation's 'antennae' to anticipate and detect factors influencing the level of imports must, therefore, be highly developed if planning is to be effective. But the problem is complex and sophisticated, unlike that in the underdeveloped countries where the primary need is a rapid increase in food production. In Britain, as in other advanced countries, a harmonious relationship of supply and demand is required to ensure stability and adequate returns to farmers, farm workers and investors.

To make any adjustment in the intricate pattern of agreements and traditions is a complex task. There are many agencies involved in this vital industry: official departments of agriculture, a government research council, an influential association of landowners, a powerful farmers' union, a strong agricultural workers' union and a highly professional body of land agents. The farmers' and workers' organizations may wish to plan well ahead but they have to safeguard the interests of their members and they must inevitably remember the dictum, attributed to Lord Keynes, to the effect that 'in the long term we are all dead'. So that to take a total view – an ecological view – is not always practical politics. But long-term agricultural planning, integrated within overall social and economic objectives, is increasingly part of the pattern of State activity in Britain and other developed countries as the need to ensure the wise use of the limited natural resources of the land becomes urgent.

In August 1965 the Government issued a new statement of policy (Cmnd 2738) to deal with the problems of the small farmers who form about 75 per cent of the 455,000 holdings and produce only about 30 per cent of the home-grown food. According to the Report of the Land Use Study Group, *Forestry*, *Agriculture and the Multiple Use of Rural Land* (*F.A.M.*), published in March 1966, the present structure of farming in Britain 'adversely affects the national allocation of land between alternative activities in a number of ways', and leads to 'a less efficient pattern of production than would otherwise be the case'.

Following European experience, the Government intends to encourage attempts to increase the size of farms and co-operative enterprises. Grants and other practical help will be given and the existing Farm Improvement Scheme will be extended to speed up the adoption of better techniques and the construction of labour-saving buildings and devices. Rural Development Boards are being set up for selected hill and upland areas in England and Wales to prepare and to promote programmes covering agriculture, forestry and other uses of land, such as outdoor recreation and tourism. These Boards are to work in close touch with the regional and local bodies concerned. In Scotland a special Development Board was set up in 1965 to help the Highlands and Islands to play a more effective part in the economic and social development of the nation. The Board is to review all relevant issues and has been given wide-ranging powers.

The *F.A.M.* Report welcomes the proposal for Rural Development Boards. It stresses the importance of coordination on a regional basis, which it believes to be essential to achieve the best results in terms of the development of landscape amenities and the social fabric of the countryside. Those opposed to the Boards contend that they will be too limited, having experience mainly in agriculture and forestry, and that their functions should be given to the local planning authorities. These are held to be better equipped to relate the primarily economic interests of agriculture and forestry to the social values of recreation and amenity and to create new, imaginative landscapes. The need for these Boards may, in fact, reflect the absence of effective regional government (see Chapter 18).

The Government's proposals – so vital to countryside planning – are in the Agriculture Act, 1967. This embodies provisions for stimulating cooperation in marketing and in farm production. Other measures include activities to promote greater business efficiency and the training of managers. One significant sentence in Paragraph 2 of Cmnd 2738, referring to the small farmers who at present look to their farms for only part of their livelihood and who may wish to continue, states 'If they do, however, they cannot expect farming to give them their main livelihood.' This suggests that there may soon be an intensification of multiple-use farming on the one hand and large-scale farming on the other. There are, however, counter-trends.

Some are based on the proposition that changes in world markets will require Britain – and the rest of Europe – to become as near self-sufficient in food as possible. Proponents of this view refer to the F.A.O. statistics. These show that the impressive increases in world food production over the past decade have been counterbalanced by the rise in population, which is now outstripping food supplies. If such trends continue Britain would be unwise to rely upon the idea that she can continue indefinitely to import fifty per cent of her food supply. It would be necessary to provide food from every available acre, although it seems at present unlikely that Britain could ever be self-supporting in the wide range of produce required by modern standards of living.

As technical and other improvements lead to greater agricultural production, land which at current prices becomes marginal should be regarded as a long-term 'bank of fertility'. Any uses to which it is put should be compatible with maintaining and enhancing its quality for future production of food. This obviously cannot happen if it is taken for urban-type development. Between 1900 and 1960 the area of urban land in Britain doubled. In the decade to 1960, about 363,000 acres (just under one per cent of the total acreage of England and Wales) was taken for urban uses. Currently these are responsible for the average loss to agriculture of 35–40 thousand acres a year. Professor G. P. Wibberley and his colleagues at Wye College have calculated that the increasing efficiency of British agriculture will enable it to meet the demands of the greater population of the 1970s with 5 per cent less land than in 1960, provided that the better-quality land is not taken and assuming that Britain can continue to import at roughly the present levels. But as much of the land lost to urban uses has been best-quality farmland, the losses and trends are more serious than the statistics disclose.

Some people, more optimistic about international prospects, consider that Britain should concentrate on those industrial activities in which she can maintain exports adequate to pay for her imports of raw materials and food; such a policy invites an even more selective approach in agriculture. The Report of the Scott Committee on Land Utilization in Rural Areas in 1942, mentioned in Chapter 16, reflected the two main points of view: the one favouring strong safeguards for the better-quality land, and the other (a minority report) contending that agriculture should not have a prior right over other interests. Since then the arguments have been intensified and have been affected by new developments. Comparatively speaking, modern aids and techniques have made the physical quality of the land for food production less dominant in relation to labour and capital than it was a few decades ago. Although land has acquired new and extended social values, these may be relatively short-term factors. Land is a long-term commodity and the best soils are a vital resource.

There are other viewpoints. One is that agriculturalists and foresters should be encouraged to develop an ecologically healthy and balanced countryside. Some of its proponents favour the term 'sacramental agriculture', believing that the land has special qualities of its own, living and enduring and playing a vital part in all man's relationships. Others regard agriculture as a 'public-service' industry, pointing out that it provides a landscape for amenity and recreation and maintains land for water conservation and multiple uses. Both attitudes seek to prevent land from being used purely for the intensification of food production and would not treat agriculture and forestry solely as economic activities. They aim to conserve a good proportion of the land for traditional vegetational cover and to design and manage the landscape to the highest standards.

Changes in any of the directions proposed will have a substantial effect on the land and its appearance. The spread of large-scale farming and mechanization eliminates hedges and copses and leads to large open fields, like those found in Lincolnshire. Drainage – so often essential to the fullest exploitation of modern farming techniques – eliminates meadows, alder and reed. More buildings for 'indoor' farming – for example, chicken broilers or sheds for calves – are being erected, and technical aids, such as spray-irrigation, will become a feature of many parts of the countryside. In future agricultural lands may no longer provide major reservoirs of wild life. With present policies and Britain's capacity to import, the amount of land which it will not be profitable to farm solely for agricultural produce may increase. No one will bother to manage marginal land adequately unless it is developed for other worthwhile and lucrative uses – for example, game rearing and outdoor recreation. Membership of the European Common Market could also profoundly affect agriculture in Britain, especially horticulture, and lead to new land-use patterns.

Change is inherent in all these trends and proposals. Growth and decay are inevitable cycles in nature. The countryside should evolve, but now that man can guide and re-shape this process, he should make sure the changes follow conscious and desired patterns. It is particularly essential that agriculture should be developed on a strategic basis, taking account of wide physical and economic conditions and reflecting its predominant place in the countryside.

FORESTRY

In much of Britain trees represent what some scientists call the 'climax' type* of vegetation, that which is most likely to emerge in existing physical conditions without human interference. Heavily wooded until the Norman Conquest, England has since lost much of its woodland. Great inroads were made for cultivation, grazing, housing, shipbuilding, charcoal – for use in smelting iron ore and in cottage industries – as well as for fuel. Statutes of the fifteenth and seventeenth centuries disclose the concern of the governments of the time. During these centuries the first major replanting of woodland began, mainly by the large landowners, and this continued until the new uses for capital of the Industrial Revolution diverted effort. Nevertheless, the total area of woodland shrank, particularly when in Scotland further clearing of woodlands took place in the eighteenth and nineteenth centuries, much of it for sheep farming and later for sport. Measures to conserve the hardwoods of southern England and the increasing difficulty and cost of getting fuel undoubtedly contributed to the pressure on industrialists, such as Abraham Darby, to find an alternative to charcoal for smelting iron ore, and thus led to the Industrial Revolution, which was to change the land even further. By the twentieth century, Britain was one of the few major countries in Europe

* This concept involves arbitrary judgements and is not acceptable to all ecologists.

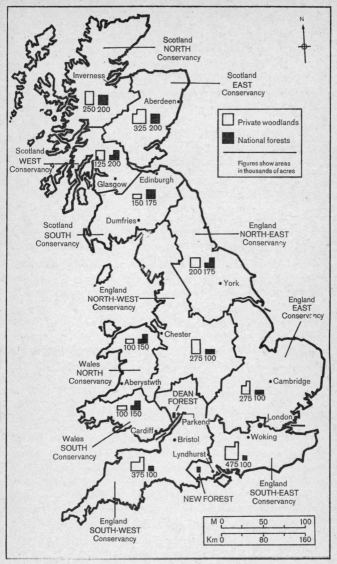

3 Forest areas shown in the conservancies of the Forestry Commission, 1968 (Copyright Forestry Commission)

without any large-scale state programme to replenish its vital woodland resources.

What is the position today? The map on page 47 shows the forest areas in the conservancies of the Forestry Commission and Table 3 gives the main categories of woodlands.

TABLE 3

Woodland Distribution, 1967*

	High forest,† coppice and coppice with standards	Scrub and felled areas	Total
	millions of acres		
England	1·6	0·5	2·1
Wales	0·4	0·1	0·5
Scotland	1·3	0·4	1·7
TOTAL	3·3	1·0	4·3

* This Table is based upon later figures than Table 1, and is derived from Forestry Commission data.

† 'High forest' usually relates to trees having a canopy density of more than 20 per cent.

The area of woodland in Britain is about one acre per thirteen citizens; in Germany it is an acre per three; but in the U.S.A. it is about four acres to each person. Only about 7½ per cent of the land is devoted to trees, one of the lowest figures in Europe, and as Britain imports about 92 per cent of her timber requirement, it is questionable whether on any basis she has enough trees. Estimates of the total United Kingdom output for the year 2000 are 300 million hoppus feet (the measure of volume; 1 H.F. = 1·273 cubic feet) per year but the demand is expected to be 2,190.

The 2·1 million acres of woodland in England are divided approximately into 800,000 acres of conifer, 700,000 of hardwood, 100,000 of coppice with standards and 500,000 of scrub. This last category is generally inferior growth unlikely to develop into forest or coppice. It includes derelict coppice, felled

areas and some miscellaneous, often unmanaged, sites. Changes
in the balance of the three main categories reflect developments
similar to those described earlier in agriculture.

Coppices are tree crops from stool or vegetative shoots, usually hazel. The standards (trees of seedling origin) with which
they are associated are usually oak. The original demand for
these products – for sheep hurdles, pea and bean sticks, and
thatching, for example – have largely disappeared and the area
of these woodlands has dwindled rapidly in recent decades.
Many are now neglected and their main interest is often amenity, educational or scientific. Coppice of sweet chestnut is, however, still a commercial proposition – for example, for hop poles
and fencing – in the limited areas climatically suitable for it;
these are mainly in Kent and Sussex and the South-West.

Hardwoods – ash, beech, oak and sycamore – have been
strongly affected by economic changes. Only the best quality
hardwoods can command a worthwhile price. Also they are a
very long-term investment – beech takes approximately 100
years, oak 120, to mature. Oak thinnings cannot be sold for
about 30 to 35 years, while some fir plantations can be thinned
after only 15. A further factor has been the great impact of grey
squirrels, which can rapidly kill or ruin a hardwood plantation
by eating the bark from young trees.

The acreage of conifer high forest has increased greatly and
will continue to do so as these trees – mainly larches, pines
and spruces – are well-suited to modern needs. Although large
areas of these economically important forests are under thirty
years old, many of them are now being managed for multiple
uses. Some of the woodlands contain deer which provide sport;
several species of birds have colonized the rides and fringes;
and increasingly these forests become important for amenity
and science. Generally, the new conifer forests offer fresh opportunities for creative landscaping. This is particularly obvious on the windswept, thin soils of Breckland in East Anglia
and over the bracken- and heather-clad hills of Wales.

In 1919 the Forestry Commission – a government agency –
was set up to help restore the timber resources of the country
depleted by the First World War and to create a national
strategic reserve of timber. In the following twenty years the

Commission planted about 370,000 acres and private land-owners about 200,000 acres. The Second World War led to further depletion of the national timber stock and post-war policy was based on an estimate that by the year 2000 Britain would need five million acres of woodland (about ten per cent of the land surface). Three million acres of this would be provided by the afforestation of bare land, mostly in Scotland. The privately owned areas of the existing woodlands were to be dedicated to forestry or acquired by the Commission. At present, it manages about 2 million acres of national forests. The general aim is to review the position every five years and to agree a planting programme for the following ten years. For the period between 1964 and 1973 the Commission intends to plant about 450,000 acres, mainly in upland areas of Wales and Scotland. Liaison between the Forestry Commission and the government departments concerned with agriculture ensures that new planting is usually on the poorer farming land, which is, in any event, often the only land that the Commission can afford to buy. Afforestation has not seriously affected sheep breeding. Generally agriculture benefits, especially in upland areas.

In 1965 the Forestry Commission was reorganized for its increasingly important role as a timber seller, now that the large areas of woodland planted about thirty years ago have begun to reach maturity. The main objective is still to increase the supply of timber but now it is industry which finds it a vital raw material. Currently Britain produces rather less than 10 per cent (in money terms) of her wood requirements. By the year 2000 home production is intended to meet about 15 per cent of the demand. Thus the concept of a strategic reserve of timber though no longer, perhaps, valid for defence purposes, certainly remains important for industry owing to the world shortages expected in the next century. Timber is one of the bulkiest cargoes and is expensive in terms of shipping space – a factor important in peace and war. Transport costs also suggest that, other considerations apart, some timber should be grown in the Home Counties.

The Commission is now the biggest landowner in Britain and is responsible for the uses of its woodlands. Amenity considerations are an important factor and for some time the Commission has been giving more attention to the quality of the landscape. Since 1963 it has retained as consultant one of Britain's leading landscape architects. With the decline in demand for hardwoods since the nineteenth century and the rapidly rising demand for softwoods – 90 per cent of the timber used – much of the acreage planted was inevitably coniferous. Some people have not looked favourably on this and have strenuously opposed having the 'tree factories' in their areas, especially in Dartmoor and Exmoor. As, however, the new woodlands reach maturity and their appearance improves there has not been so much criticism – though doubtless this will be revived if large-scale felling takes place of the stands of trees of similar age.

In the New Forest and seven Forest Parks, the number of campers using the Commission's sites rose from 50,000 in 1957 to 700,000 in 1967. Over 4 million picnic in its forests. It maintains a number of Forest Nature Reserves in cooperation with the Nature Conservancy and provides nature trails and viewpoints. It also gets a small but increasing income from the sporting facilities in the forests. Generally, the economic and ecological balance of the countryside is increasingly improved as the nation's forests expand. They make use of poor land, contribute to the economy of farming, play an important, if not yet fully understood, part in water catchment, provide good recreation areas and sanctuaries for wild life.

Privately owned woodlands cover around $2\frac{3}{4}$ million acres, and about 35,000 more acres are planted each year. The nation helps the private woodland owner in many ways. The Commission gives expert advice and it makes financial contributions in areas dedicated by their owners for management under an agreed plan. Tax allowances are available for forestry under Schedules B and D; estate duty is calculated not on the maturity value of timber but on its value at the owner's death, and tax does not have to be paid until the timber is sold. Thus persuaded, private owners are taking more interest in the development of new forests. Officially encouraged associations, such as the Timber Growers Association in England and Wales and the Scottish Woodlands Owners

Association (both formed in 1959–60) look after the interests of
private landowners and work closely with the Commission.

The Forestry Act, 1967, is an important consolidating
measure. The Countryside Act, 1968, strengthened the
Forestry Commission's powers to provide recreation and other
facilities on their land and to acquire land and plant trees
specifically for amenity purposes.

As the largest single land-user in Britain, and as one of the
organizations best-suited to obtain and give out information
about tree-planting and afforestation, the Forestry Commission has great responsibilities. It must see that the best
possible professional and scientific advice is used when policies
are determined that will substantially affect the character and
interest of the landscape. In all this it requires the support
and goodwill of the people.

MARGINAL AND OTHER LANDS

Large areas of land in Britain fall within three main categories:
common lands; the 'minor' sites, such as village greens and
roadside verges; and 'true' marginal land. If the pressures on
space continue to increase it will be necessary to examine very
carefully the management of these lands to ensure their
optimum use.

Estimates of common land vary: there may be one and a half
million acres in England and Wales. Although some of it is of
poor quality, common land is a heritage of considerable
importance. It provides many wooded areas, which with good
management could be made more valuable; its open spaces
are vital 'lungs' to many towns; its soil and trees, being largely
untouched by modern fertilizers and pesticides, should provide
good material for scientific and educational studies; and it
supports many animals and plants which can no longer flourish
in agricultural or urban areas. Fuller details of common land
are given in Chapter 13.

The second category, 'minor' lands, could also become
important. The area taken up by road verges in England and
Wales may be as much as 200,000 acres. Every new motorway
adds hundreds of acres to that total. Even so, the acreage,
however large, does not indicate the real importance of road-

side verges. They are a source of pleasure to residents and to
the travelling public. Often they are the 'shop window' of the
country to tourists. Roadside verges are also a significant
reservoir of wild life and their hedges and vegetation function
as wind- and snow-breaks. Intelligent use of modern techniques and the application of scientific knowledge, especially
about plants, can reduce the destruction of roadside vegetation
arising from measures carried out for road safety. Skilful
management – planting the right trees and shrubs in lay-bys
and selecting plant species – can enhance the appearance of
verges. Village greens, semi-urban parks and some of the
great estates are obviously precious open spaces. For amenity,
recreation and essential living-space they make a valuable
contribution. But not all of them are adequately cared for.

The 'true' marginal lands – the areas of low population and
deteriorating soil and vegetation – are to be found mainly in the
Pennines and Lake District, Wales and Scotland. Many of
them are at high altitude, have steep slopes and are in the
wetter parts of Britain. Since the original vegetational cover –
generally woodlands – has been destroyed by man, these lands
have deteriorated badly. Now they are not only inaccessible
and awkward to cultivate, they are infertile as well. And the
less money that can be wrung from them, the less money
people are willing to spend on them. It is this type of marginal
land which accounts for most of the rough grazing in Britain
(17 million acres) and also for some of those acres remaining
unclassified. Its main use in farming is as a breeding ground
for cattle and sheep and as seasonal pasturage. In these ways
many hill and valley areas are complementary and the loss of
one often affects the economic value of the other. Today, the
uplands offer great scope for forestry, water catchment and
recreation. In the Peak District National Park, the uses of
the marginal land are summed up as the '4 G.s' – that is,
grazing, gathering grounds (for water), game (grouse and
partridge) and gold awards (the Duke of Edinburgh's Award).
The need for coordination of effort in these areas is probably
greater than in the more prosperous localities and should be on
a large enough scale for proper long-term planning. The
work of Rural Development Boards, if implemented with a

real 'land ethic', should, however, provide a useful basis for action.

Appraisal

Clearly the future development and management of agriculture, forestry and marginal land have to be related to many factors, in addition to the obvious demands for food and timber. They should reflect the greatly increased need for access to land for enjoyment; they must be considered within the visual framework and unity of the landscape; and they must be part of a national policy for the land related to the whole social and economic life of the countryside.

But whatever problems arise from them, agricultural practices and afforestation are generally helping to maintain a 'natural' countryside. Obviously other demands on land – for housing, industry, mineral extraction, communications and services – do not do so. Once the land is sealed over, once the under-surface world of pipes and cables has been laid and, perhaps above all, once people have accepted an area as built-up, there is little prospect of restoring it to 'natural' countryside.

CHAPTER 4

LAND IN BRITAIN – II

Britain has not, like Holland, France or America,
developed an urban bourgeoisie which is content
with a luxury flat.
                    Anthony Sampson, *Anatomy of Britain*

URBAN LAND

IT is difficult to give accurate figures of the land used for urban
development in Britain. The last complete check was by the
Land Utilization Survey of the 1930s (a second is nearing
completion in 1969). It is also of little help to consider local
government areas with their historically acquired titles (rural
and urban districts and so on) as these names are often misleading. A 'rural district' may include a medium-sized town
and many areas of land having multiple uses. Towns and once-
rural settlements have frequently merged in suburban diffuse-
ness, and some city boundaries contain large areas of farmland,
as well as great stretches of rural-looking commons.

Accepting these difficulties and applying a variety of
methods, Best and Coppock have estimated that the total urban
area in 1960 was about 4,000,000 acres for England and Wales
and 500,000 acres for Scotland, a total for Great Britain of
about 4,500,000 acres (see Table 1, p. 38). This urban acreage
covers all built-up land and includes the main areas used for
housing and industry, roads and railways, and education and
open space, all of which tend to move in relationship with
population numbers. It also includes built-up land in the
countryside which accounts for about $1\frac{1}{4}$ million acres. In
England and Wales urban uses take about one acre in every
nine!

Housing absorbs the most, covering up to 50 per cent of the
area. Open space takes about 20 per cent, although if house
gardens and school playing-fields are included the percentage
may rise to 45 in the cities and towns of over 10,000 population.

Industry accounts for around 6 per cent – in the larger industrial towns of the north the figure is about 8 per cent. The statistics are complicated by the fact that commercial and service facilities – for example, railways, docks, warehouses – are not included in the figure for industry. Railways occupy about 5·8 per cent of the urban area; roads a still larger pro-

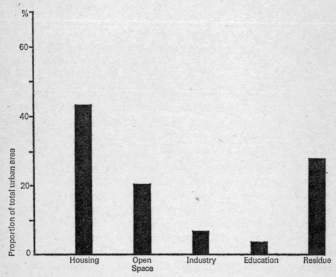

4 Composition of the urban area in England and Wales, 1950
(SOURCE: R. H. Best and J. T. Coppock op. cit., page 38)

portion, some of which is included in the figures for other categories and some in residual uses.

Figure 4 gives the picture for county boroughs and large settlements (population over 10,000). There are no adequate figures for settlements with a population of under 10,000 although sample estimates suggest that housing may take more of the urban area, and that acreages listed under other headings will inevitably reflect the varying population composition and the importance of agriculture.

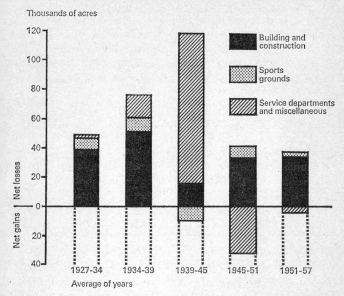

5 Gains and losses in agricultural land in England and Wales, 1927 to 1957 (SOURCE: R. H. Best and J. T. Coppock op. cit., page 38)

Best and Coppock calculate that the net loss of farmland to all other uses in England and Wales between 1900 and 1950 has been about 7 per cent; this covers an 80 per cent growth in the urban area, the rest being for other uses. Figure 5 shows the net losses and gains of agricultural land; it reflects the great spread of suburbia between the World Wars and the sharp demand for land for defence purposes (airfields, camps, training grounds) during the Second World War.

Current social and economic pressures and population trends, discussed in Chapters 14 and 15, suggest that more and more land will be wanted for urban uses. It is thought likely that urban development will take 750,000 acres of farmland in England and Wales between 1951 and 1971, while forestry and other uses may take a similar proportion, though mainly in areas of poorer quality soil. Continuation of present trends may well lead to a greater loss of farmland in the second half of the twentieth century than in the first. In this period, the urban area may extend by nearly 2 million acres. In other terms, Britain may have to find housing land for an extra 20 million people by A.D. 2000 – space for twenty cities the size of Birmingham, seventy the size of Newcastle upon Tyne, or 280 towns the size of Shrewsbury. Within this period, room must also be found to rehouse the people now living in slum areas. With the new and higher standards expected a total urban area of $6\frac{1}{2}$ million acres may not prove enough.

Although, therefore, a substantial area of farmland is likely to be taken, this loss in itself need not be too alarming provided that the increased productivity of agriculture and present import of food can be maintained. What is vital is the *quality* of the soils taken and the *location* of the land being developed. The late Sir Dudley Stamp, writing about the quality of soils, evolved a measure he called a potential production unit (P.P.U.) for good average farmland, such as exists in East Anglia. The best soils get a ranking of, say, 2 P.P.U. per acre but some of the poorer mountain soils only 0·1 P.P.U. If, therefore, a new town of 5,000 acres is sited on the finest land the loss is 10,000 P.P.U. whereas if it is built on poor or marginal land the loss is only 500 P.P.U. He also pointed out that light sandy soil, of little value to farmers, is very suitable for house gardens. As to location, if all new major urban development could take place on degraded land in, say, the Pennines or Scottish Highlands thousands of acres of best-quality soil would be saved. But such a scheme is not practicable on a large scale, and a further complication is that much of this poorer land is important for amenity and recreation (see map on p. 211).

The complex problems of the South-East region – south of a line from the Wash to Dorset – reveal the pressures placed on an area containing some of the best soils in the country. *The South–East Study, 1961–81*, published in February 1964, was undertaken by the Ministry of Housing and Local Government, in close consultation with numerous central government departments and many local planning authorities and other bodies. It showed that the South-East faces four huge problems: a tremendous population increase; a strong employment growth; a large overspill problem; and an acute shortage of land in and around London.

About 18 million people live in the area – 35 per cent of the people in Great Britain. The Study assumes that by 1981 the population will grow by 3·5 million, of which 2·4 million will be from excess of births over deaths and about 1·1 million from net inward migration. The various estimates are widely criticized; some assert that they are too low; others contend that any acceptance of these figures as inevitable will lead to defeatism. Some think that instead of suggesting that new cities and towns be developed to accommodate these populations within the South-East area, the Study should have proposed to disperse them to other regions. Other criticisms hinge on the congestion to industry, the choking of communications and the inadequacy of the measures for conserving green belts and agricultural land.

The loss of the good-quality soil in the region, with its excellent yields, could have a serious effect on agriculture and the economy of the country as a whole. Many of the propositions touched on in Chapter 3 would be substantially affected.

In effect, a national strategic plan is required. This should correct the imbalance between regions in the distribution of population and industry. In particular, a large number of the present activities in and around London should be dispersed to the North, Scotland and Wales; to achieve this it may be necessary to place Parliament in a new city on the York Moors (as has been suggested), or near the Humber. The trends revealed in *The South-East Study* should be assessed in relation to the whole country and the measures to deal with them should be harmonized with the interests of all other areas. Unfortunately, before a full-scale national plan can be prepared or carried out by regional authorities, the population and industry in the South-East will have increased substantially, and therefore many of the other developments foreshadowed by the Study will already have taken place.

In January 1966 a Ministry circular gave further estimates of the population increase and the measures required to provide for London's overspill. In March, the Standing Conference on London and South East Regional Planning reported on the estimates. It seems that population in the South East may not increase much faster than elsewhere and that much of the increase must be provided for by local authorities and private developers, with no town expansion schemes promoted within the Metropolitan Region (within forty miles from Charing Cross).

The grave problems facing the South East were confirmed by the first report* of its Economic Planning Council (November 1967, see p. 262). Its strategy for star-shaped growth corridors from London has been criticized, but the report led the ministries concerned to undertake a comprehensive physical planning exercise to forward the work of the Council and the Standing Conference. The prime weakness is still that this is not within the framework of a national physical plan.

Fortunately, regional studies and planning projects show the capacity of areas like Cumberland, Westmorland, the Solway, and mid-Wales to absorb populations and industry in pleasant surroundings, without eating into best-quality land.

A more strategic approach at national and regional level to the selection of land for urban development is vital. Nibblings into the countryside by existing towns, and the periodic forays of the larger cities, must be stopped. Land-use planning, especially at regional level, should be related to the variety and qualities of land required and available. There exist large areas of land in Britain which are already spoilt, low-grade or half-committed to urban use. Ian Nairn has made a pragmatic appraisal of such areas and has suggested sixteen sites for new cities (*Observer*, 8 August 1965, see map on page 61).

It should be possible to find more of these sites and, given the help of the Land Commission (see Chapter 20) in making them readily available, to encourage their development both by local authorities and private organizations. The positive deployment of the resources of the building industry in such a way would greatly reduce the pressures on the better land.

Whatever the wisdom shown in planning and managing the use of the land required for urban purposes, there are certain major problems which cannot be fully resolved in the present

* *A Strategy for the South East.* A first report by the South-East Economic Planning Council. H.M.S.O.

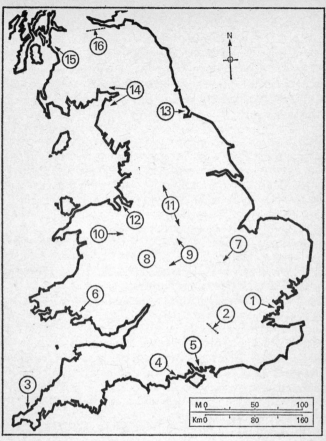

1. South-east Essex, between Billericay and Southend. 2. The battered fields and heaths between Reading and Aldershot. 3. The Camborne–Redruth area of Cornwall. 4. Bournemouth–Poole and its hinterland. 5. Southampton–Portsmouth (already nominated in the S.E. survey). 6. Between Carmarthen and Swansea, around Cross Gates and Tumble. 7. Eastern Northamptonshire, between Kettering and Rushden. 8. The southern half of Cannock Chase. 9. North Warwickshire around Nuneaton and Western Leicestershire, between Burton-on-Trent and Charnwood Forest: a kind of twin town with genuine countryside in between, at Bosworth. 10. Wrexham–Oswestry on the Welsh border. 11. Almost the whole of the land between Nottingham–Derby and Wakefield–Castleford: a colossal area this, more than 50 miles long but rarely more than six miles wide – and with the Dukeries on one side and the Peak District on the other. 12. The Wirral – already proposed, far too late, for the wrong kind of Green Belt. 13. South-east Durham. 14. The land from Annan to Gretna and from Gretna to Carlisle, around the Solway Firth. 15. Western Ayrshire: the area between Kilmarnock and the coast. 16. The hills between Glasgow and Edinburgh.

6 Sites for new cities suggested by Ian Nairn (*Observer*)

state of technology and economics. For example, the location of nuclear power stations is governed by safety factors (although, technically, these could be relaxed) and the need for large supplies of water for cooling purposes. Pipelines for gas and oil, and overhead lines for electricity, are still inevitable. Some industries – for example, mineral extraction – completely depend on physical factors; and the discovery of gas under the North Sea will obviously lead to tremendous changes on the north-east coast. Generally, large-scale industry tends to develop in estuaries for the sake of easy communications and supply of raw materials; this can be seen on the major rivers of Europe, such as the Rhine, Thames and Tees. This concentration is good to the extent that it leaves other areas free, but bad when through faulty planning it creates vast blotches on a coastline or heavy pollution.

The operations of the Central Electricity Generating Board (C.E.G.B.) illustrate some of the problems. Undoubtedly the supply of cheap power throughout the country is a great boon to people and industry. Its use leads directly to more comfortable homes and more efficient factories. The demand for electricity doubled between 1955 and 1963 and is expected to double again by 1970. The C.E.G.B. has, therefore, seven years in which to double the output of a system which took seventy years to build up. To quote its leaflet – 'In terms of private industry it means building an organization with plant and equipment the size of the British Motor Corporation every three months.' The great new oil- and coal-fired power stations required for this will need vast quantities of cooling water and must be sited on or near main rivers. To save transport costs, the coal-based ones must be near the most efficient coalfields. Thus there is a limited choice of sites and this in turn predetermines the routes of the 'wirescapes' along which the power is distributed. Vehement demands are often made that power lines should be put underground. In an average rural area a 400 kv line costs £54,000 a mile if it is strung overhead, but £1,182,000 a mile if it is put underground – three times more per mile than the M1 motorway.

The by-products of the electricity industry are also of some importance. What can be done, for example, with the millions of tons of pulverized fuel ash (P.F.A.) which the industry produces every year? One large-scale scheme for its disposal – the Peterborough Project – has already begun. Here thirty million tons of P.F.A. from the Board's power stations in the Trent Valley are to be used to fill in waterlogged holes and pits left from derelict brickworks and clay excavations. This vast reclamation will create new landscapes and is being carried out to a master plan by a leading landscape architect.

Several major discoveries of natural gas under the North Sea and in Yorkshire in 1966 and 1967 open up the prospect of a national energy policy related to the long-term use of natural resources. This has profound and far-reaching implications for the environment – urban and rural. Inevitably, the problem of exploiting the gas without disfiguring the landscape arises. Proposals for development on the Norfolk coast, where some of the gas is to be brought ashore, led to public inquiries in 1967–8.

Another industry which has to construct prominent objects with a strong visual impact on the landscape is the General Post Office. It must meet the rapidly increasing demand for radio and television transmission as well as the phenomenal growth in all the media of communication. Sites for over 100 towers are needed to transmit microwave signals. These signals travel in direct lines and must have unobstructed passage for a distance of about thirty miles. The towers themselves have a concrete core and are about 100 to 300 feet in height. They obviously need high ground and will tend to dominate the countryside. Where possible, these should be sited in despoiled areas rather than adding yet another feature to the 'skyscrape' of rural areas.

But probably the industry with the most widespread impact on the landscape is the sand and gravel industry. According to estimates published in the January 1966 *Newsletter* of the Sand and Gravel Association (S.A.G.A.), it is likely to surpass coal as Britain's largest extractive industry by the late seventies. This material, basic to concrete and extensively used for houses, factories and roads, has to be won from locations within economic transport distance of its markets. S.A.G.A. point out that transporting it for an extra fifteen miles can

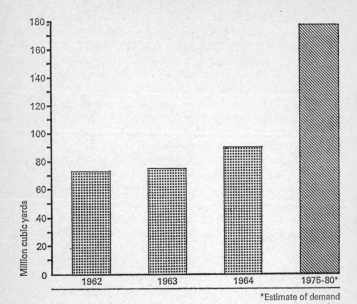

7 Demand for sand and gravel; estimates in 1966 based on current trends (Sand and Gravel Association of Great Britain)

double its price. Inevitably, it becomes difficult to reconcile the urgent and increasing demands for sand and gravel with the conservation of high-quality soils and amenity. In many localities, the workings give a frightening, often eerie, look to the landscape and this has a strong effect near housing estates or in the countryside. But luckily modern equipment makes it possible for good use to be made of this industry's worked-out sites. S.A.G.A. has issued booklets on how to tackle this work and gives guidance not only to members but also to civic bodies and societies. Already some sites have been used excellently – they have been turned into well-managed refuse pits, fertile fields, nature reserves and playing-fields, and wet pits have been developed for water ski-ing, angling, wild-fowling and many other recreations. Sometimes these sites are more valuable and useful to the community now than they

were prior to mineral excavation. Unfortunately, there are
too many old, still derelict sites; in some localities developers
and planners have failed to cooperate, and little has been done
to interest the public in the possible uses of these pits. Perhaps
the problems of the South-East region will bring these issues
to a head, as the nearest major sources of sand and gravel are in
the middle and upper Thames area and middle Anglia, where
much of the land is of high agricultural and amenity value.

There are a number of other industries which exercise a
significant influence on the countryside. Water supply is one,
through the siting of its dams and the extraction of water from
reservoirs, lakes and rivers. Granting the public access to and
recreational facilities in such sites can change pressures over a
whole area; fuller details are given in later chapters.

One aspect of the use of land which tends to be overlooked
is that organizations often have to acquire space incidental to
their primary objectives. For example, they may have to take a
complete ownership or a large homogeneous area which includes land surplus to operational needs. Or it may be desirable on grounds of public safety or for amenity purposes to
include 'buffer' land. The total area of this 'institutional' land
held by commercial or public bodies has been calculated by
C. R. V. Tandy as in the order of 990,000 acres. Although all of
it has not been surveyed, sample checks indicate that much of
it is not fully used.

These few examples show that although industry's demand
for land may be relatively small the location, management,
design and type of industrial buildings and related equipment
can greatly affect the appearance of the countryside, particularly on high ground and at the coast.

DERELICT AND WASTE LAND

The definition of derelict land given by the Ministry of Housing and Local Government can be summed up as follows:
'Land so damaged by industrial or other development that it is
incapable of beneficial use without treatment.' During the past
decade the public conscience in the U.S.A. and Europe has
been awakened to the effects of the scars and aftermath of the

Industrial Revolution and the insidious twentieth-century blight appearing on much of the land surface. In Britain two major reports have contributed to creating the public support necessary for action: *New Life for Dead Lands* published by the Ministry in 1963, and *Derelict Lands* published by the Civic Trust in 1964.

The Ministry more recently estimated that, by 31 December 1964, about 99,000 acres were derelict in England* and Wales. They suggest that 59,000 acres justify treatment; of these approximately 23,000 acres are spoil heaps, 15,000 are holes and 21,000 are other forms of dereliction or miscellaneous wastelands. Derelict land is distributed fairly evenly over the main regions, although the South and South-Eastern have much less than the average and there are 16,000 derelict acres in the South-West. The bulk of this land is north of a line between the Wash and the Severn and in certain localities, such as the West Riding of Yorkshire, industrial Lancashire and the Black Country, the average is very high.

With the inevitable and continuing economic need to exploit the minerals now under the land – coal, potash, iron ore, sand and gravel, chalk, limestone, brick and china clay – it is obvious that, without consummate care by all involved, the total area of derelict land will increase. The Civic Trust has worked out that Britain's wasteland increases by about 3,500 acres a year. Planning Authorities attach stringent conditions to permission to extract other minerals. The conditions are often technically difficult to comply with; then, too, once an area has apparently been abandoned by a firm, it may not always be possible to enforce these regulations for financial or legal reasons.

The National Coal Board have a finely attuned organization for restoring lands used for opencast coal. They have, however, a serious and almost intractable problem in dealing with spoil tips inherited from past workings, and also find it difficult to dispose of the increasing waste resulting from greater mechanization in the deep mines.

Several local planning authorities have set up environment

---

* Recent returns show no significant changes. In England, only 1,641 acres of derelict land were reclaimed or landscaped in 1966 and 3,910 acres proposed for treatment in 1967.

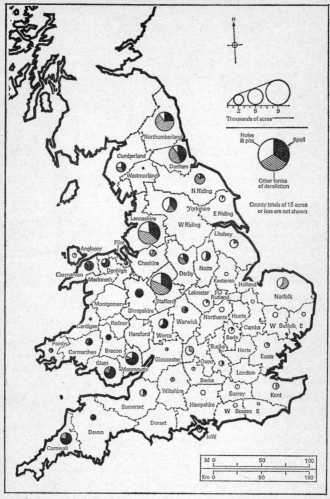

8 Derelict land in England and Wales, 1964. Acreage justifying treat-
ment. Compiled from returns submitted by local authorities to the
Ministry of Housing and Local Government and to the Secretary of
State for Wales in response to Circular 55/64 (Reproduced by permis-
sion of the Controller of Her Majesty's Stationery Office. Crown
Copyright)

conservation groups in their planning departments. These are studying and evaluating resources, landscape and rehabilitation of derelict land, as part of programmes for raising the quality of the environment of towns and country. In Lancashire the Community Council, supported by the Calouste Gulbenkian Foundation and the Planning Department, ran a course in 1966 on re-vegetation of eyesores – for example, colliery shale. Both Lancashire and Staffordshire County Councils – and others – are active in rehabilitating derelict land in a creative modern manner.

Despite such activities and initiatives, the major problem remains: how to get rid of blight and eyesores which have an effect far beyond their actual areas on the landscape and the morale of people. Fortunately the answer to 'Can anything be done about the existing wastelands?' is 'Yes'. What are needed most are finance and skilled staff. At present, where reclamation schemes are eligible for Government aid (and many of them are not), about eighty-five per cent of the cost is recoverable by local authorities in the development areas and seventy-five per cent in National Parks and Areas of Outstanding Natural Beauty. But this very definition excludes many areas which need most help; and local authorities in Britain in the mid-sixties have so many pressing claims on their limited resources that much of the work is beyond them.

Local authorities in England with substantial acreage of derelict, neglected or unsightly land were asked by the Minister of Housing and Local Government in 1967 to prepare schemes for its treatment. Priority is given to schemes in development areas (where special measures are being taken to stimulate industry), and the local authorities concerned are urged 'to reclaim or improve such land wherever treatment is justified'. Grants are available under the Industrial Development Act, 1966, or the Local Government Act, 1966, and a wide range of technical and advisory services can be provided by the Opencast Executive of the National Coal Board.

Although much further research is required on the properties of the waste products to be found on derelict land, and the uses to which they can be put, enough is known to enable substantial inroads to be made on the worst areas. There are a number of ways, for example, in which old spoil-tips can be

reclaimed. Trees can be planted on them. Recently ski enthusiasts have even suggested some of them should be covered
with artificial snow and used for year-round 'winter' sports.
Some heaps have been bulldozed and used to fill up unwanted
holes in the ground. But not all of them can be moved by
normal equipment; some of those in the Lower Swansea
Valley require blasting. Occasionally, old quarry holes are too
deep or are sited in such awkward positions that they are
extremely expensive to fill in. For example, in Lancashire,
38 acres of land were bought for only about £3,700; but to
reclaim and landscape them cost nearly £15,000.

Apart from the financial and technical difficulties, there are
many legal problems of ownership to be overcome. Arguments over who shall develop the land after it is reclaimed, and
the overlapping of local authority boundaries, render a complex
task even more discouraging. Planning authorities are now
surveying the extent of dereliction in their areas and will check
on this annually. There is, inevitably, a shortage of scientists,
landscape designers, foresters and technicians qualified in the
specialized work of reclamation. And overriding all is the
absence of any central driving force determined to clear up the
mess of past decades and to prevent new horrors from developing.

About £30 million might be enough to restore most of the
derelict land in England and Wales. The land reclaimed would
be valuable for many purposes and probably be worth at least
£10 million straight after the work was finished. If the public
could be made to appreciate these possibilities then, in these
days of macro-economics, they would surely press their politicians to have this land cleared immediately.

The definition of waste land which was given earlier did not
include a large amount of 'twilight' land in and near the
towns. It did not take into account the great and increasing
problem of how to dispose of waste and by-products without
threatening more land. Where, for instance, can surplus persistent pesticides be thrown away? What about the refuse
spewed out every day by the towns? What about nuclear
waste? What about those vast quantities of pulverized fuel
ash and the other major by-products of industry? These issues

should be dealt with as part of a major national assault on land reclamation and the use of refuse and waste or by-products.

All policies for land and water use must recognize the interdependence of town and country. It is absurd to let whole districts in town areas lie derelict – ignoring places like the Lower Swansea Valley, the West Midland tips and quarries, and the many bomb-sites of London makes no sense at all. Such renewal in urban areas is much talked about but work on rural areas is no less urgent – in fact, a total renewal of our physical environment is now overdue. It is a pity that, at the moment, we lack techniques for assessing effectively the social cost and benefits accruing from alternative policies. For example, a financial 'weighting' of the long-term value of the rural areas around Swansea for agriculture, amenity, recreation and so on, would probably reveal that it would be cheaper to develop the waste lands in the urban area than to take more of the (apparently cheaper) countryside. But the individual can hardly be expected to make these assessments; they require a strategic approach by an appropriate authority. Organizations of any kind should not be allowed to effect large-scale changes in land use until the overall value to society of the various possibilities has been assessed.

In many ways action over derelict land offers the key to man's intentions. So much dereliction is glaringly obvious. It conduces to squalor. At the same time this type of land offers fewer obstacles to the really imaginative and energetic developer – radical new techniques can be used to solve both old and new problems. Reclaimed and put to fresh uses, derelict sites would save good land and be a stimulus to everyone who seeks a high-quality environment.

Appraisal

It is obvious that the growing demands for land for urban and industrial development must, theoretically at least, absorb a substantial part of the land surface in England and Wales. Scotland has a greater total acreage of land; the figures, however, tend to be misleading, as the localities suitable for urban and similar development are relatively limited. But the actual total acreage of land to be consumed for urban development in

Britain in the next few decades is not in itself so crucial as is the choice of the sites and the manner of their development. We can afford to build houses and factories on poor land; it is unlikely that we can afford to- put them anywhere else. Much more strategic planning is required nationally to create balanced regions; much more research is necessary into the problems of siting development and the use of marginal and derelict land; and much more effort must be made to apply existing and new knowledge to environmental problems.

The demands on land and water so far considered are not, of course, the whole of the picture. The Defence Departments clearly require a large area of land and water for training and other purposes, but, in the absence of a major war, this demand is diminishing. In any case, the Defence Departments sometimes help, rather than hinder, land conservation, for much of their property, like Salisbury Plain, stays in a relatively wild state, whereas it might otherwise be developed or despoiled. Nevertheless, constant vigilance is required to ensure that no land is retained unnecessarily and that all its possibilities are exploited. There are, however, other uses of land and other forces at work having a substantial impact on many areas. What is loosely called the 'leisure boom' may give rise to even greater changes in some ways than those so far considered.

CHAPTER 5

LEISURE ACTIVITY

Leisure is the time for doing something useful.
Nathaniel Howe

LEISURE activity is as old as trade. All the great civilizations have bequeathed some legacy; the Greeks their theatre and olympiads, the Romans their *panem et circenses*, and Britons today still enjoy some of the deer forests and chases of the Saxons and Normans. Whenever man has had time and facilities he has indulged in some form of active recreation: hunting, shooting, fishing – the traditional trio – travel, entertainment, all have been pursued. But these activities were usually the prerogative of a few and, both because of this and the very small size of the populations they did not affect much land, water or wild life. Today, with vast numbers seeking holidays and outdoor recreation, and with tourism the biggest item in international trade, the impact is dramatic.

All the factors determining leisure pursuits – population, free time, money, mobility, inclination – have grown rapidly since 1945 and are still rising. The classic survey of outdoor recreation (*The Report of the Outdoor Recreation Resources Review Commission*, 1962 – the Rockefeller Report) predicted that the U.S.A. demand would treble by A.D. 2000. All European countries, especially the Scandinavian, report a great expansion in outdoor recreation.

Many of the traditional recreations, such as cycling, football and cricket, have declined relatively as greater wealth, time and mobility enable more varied and often expensive activities, such as ski-ing, sailing and golf, to be pursued. The increases have been exceptional in water sports, climbing, caving, riding and bird-watching. Camping, caravanning and motoring for pleasure have also greatly increased (over 7 million Frenchmen go camping each year); and field sports such as hunting, shooting and fishing, have continued to grow steadily.

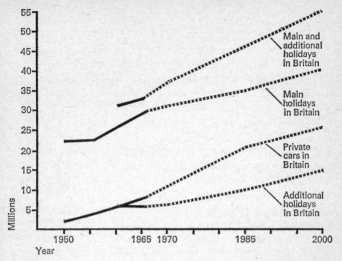

9a Trends in holidaymaking and private cars in Britain 1950–2000
(T. L. Burton)

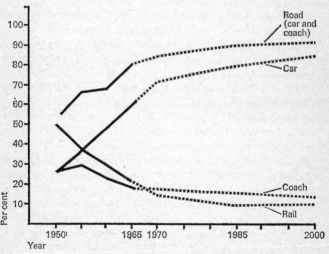

9b Trends in holiday travel by road and rail in Britain 1950–2000
(T. L. Burton)

The graphs on page 73 show the vast numbers of people mobile and the upward trends of the related factors; 9b does not take account of the numbers who travel by air transport. If the Duke of Wellington were alive now, he would no doubt feel the situation called for an even stronger remark than the one he made on seeing the first train: 'Progress be damned. All this will do will be to allow the lower classes to move around unnecessarily.' This may be contrasted with the statement attributed to Henry Ford: 'I will build a motor car for the great multitude . . . so low in price that no man . . . will be unable to own one – and enjoy with his family the blessing of hours of pleasure in God's great open spaces.'

The number of people seeking active outdoor recreation is multiplying rapidly. At the first conference on 'The Countryside in 1970' held in 1963, Jack Longland, County Education Officer for Derbyshire, spoke of '. . . this quite astonishing shift of the whole range of subjects which we call physical education towards outdoor pursuits . . .'. Since 1945 there has been a five-fold increase in coastal sailing and there are now a half million dinghy sailors, at least three million anglers and over 100,000 naturalists. At least fifty activities are represented on the Central Council of Physical Recreation (C.C.P.R.). There are vast crowds taking more passive enjoyment in the countryside or at the coast: in 1963, 56 per cent of the population took at least one short pleasure trip during the Whitsuntide holiday. All the indications are that leisure pursuits – both active and passive – will treble in Britain by A.D. 2000. And the resources available are limited.

Tourism is now a major industry in the world; the map on pp. 76–7 shows some of the colossal numbers involved. In 1967 there were around 3½ million overseas visitors to Britain, an increase of 8 per cent on the previous year, and they brought in over £350 million. Their average length of stay here was 18 days – compared, for example, to about 5 days for a tourist in Italy. Britain's tourist industry now employs around 5 million people and has an annual turnover of about £1,000 million. Tourism is already the country's fourth largest export industry and about the largest in terms of American dollars. The British Travel Association (B.T.A.) estimates that in the

1970s Britain will be attracting about five million visitors a year. Included in the features which give Britain 'its own special appeal' is beautiful countryside. Tourism is increasingly intermingled with outdoor recreation. The B.T.A. notes that sporting holidays are growing in popularity, notably boating, pony-trekking, fishing, golfing and other open-air activities, including ski-ing in Scotland. It is obvious that these trends will continue to accelerate since most countries are making a determined effort to increase interest in sport.

The B.T.A. figures for holidays give further evidence of the pressures on countryside and coast. In 1967, 30 million Britons took holidays away from home. They made a total of 35 million holiday trips of which approximately 5 million were abroad. The Association refers to second holidays during a year having more than doubled within a decade and states that the demand for holiday services grows faster than that for most other products. In addition, it seems that the length of the average holiday is extending and more people are taking 'long weekends'. All these developments are placing great pressures on favoured localities. They should be studied and their significance assessed in relation to each area's capacity to sustain them without becoming degraded. The B.T.A., in fact, urges national surveys and the preparation of a national recreational plan, to be implemented through close cooperation between the many bodies concerned. In Parliament, on 2 February 1966, Lord Geddes (Chairman of the B.T.A.) stated that: 'The shape which our environment takes is of supreme importance to the domestic holiday trade, which is the backbone of British tourism.'

One of the main problems is to know what the public really wants and what it would pay to get it! The underlying trends and motives need to be investigated by the Social Science Research Council; the implications in terms of planning and commerce by the local authorities and specialist firms; and the effects on land and water by the Natural Environment Research Council. The lack of reliable information about the facilities required is one side of the coin; the other is that many landowners and planners are not sufficiently aware of the demand for facilities, nor do they understand how best to provide

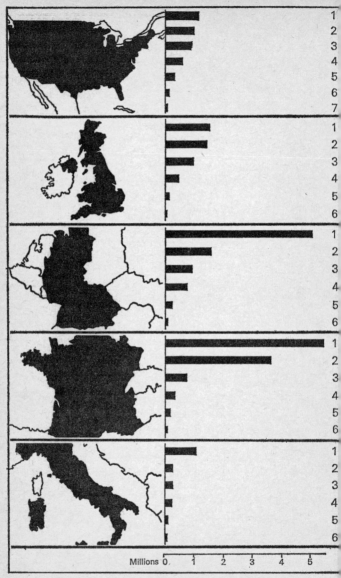

10 Tourism in Europe, 1964 (*Observer* and E. Jeffery Lacey)

4,167,752 Americans to	1	Italy	1,104,800
	2	W.Germany	992,114
	3	France	920,000
	4	Britain	589,200
	5	Spain	351,212
	6	Greece	140,965
	7	Yugoslavia	69,461
4,845,442 Britons to	1	France	1,550,000
	2	Italy	1,473,100
	3	Spain	998,094
	4	W.Germany	596,994
	5	Yugoslavia	156,980
	6	Greece	70,274
8,579,529 W.Germans to	1	Italy	5,026,000
	2	France	1,560,000
	3	Spain	917,749
	4	Yugoslavia	759,389
	5	Britain	227,800
	6	Greece	88,591
10,344,776 Frenchmen to	1	Spain	5,476,831
	2	Italy	3,665,200
	3	W.Germany	652,214
	4	Britain	325,500
	5	Yugoslavia	156,980
	6	Greece	68,051
1,918,917 Italians to	1	France	1,060,000
	2	W.Germany	288,948
	3	Yugoslavia	253,303
	4	Spain	202,490
	5	Britain	76,100
	6	Greece	38,076

them. Too little is known about the returns possible from recreation.

These factors are particularly important to the recreational use of rural land. Positive management is essential to promote the multiple use of land for food, timber, sport, rambling and other activities. How vulnerable various soils are to erosion from intense recreational pressures should be assessed. The potential uses of the land – for example, for camping sites, pathways and walking – must be known, and such matters as site drainage and water disposal wisely arranged. Trees are very important to the landscaping of sites, but they must allow light through to encourage ground cover. Rotation of camp sites, climbs and walks may be necessary to allow natural renewal. Some landowners are now denying the public access to spaces which were once open; in some cases the difficulties arise from lack of knowledge of both trends and the management necessary to cope with them. Others are infuriated by visitors' carelessness or their failure to contribute to upkeep costs. The point of the leisure boom is that a mass of people cannot enjoy, in the same places and at the same time, the pleasures that once a few enjoyed. As demand increases, so must planning and consideration for others.

Unfortunately, not enough is known about how much land is accessible to the public for recreation. Open lands managed by the Forestry Commission, the National Trust and the Nature Conservancy, plus the commons, probably add up to about three million acres; some details are given in Table 4.

Land available for recreation in Britain includes much of the hill and upland areas of Scotland, Wales and the Pennines. As they contain many of the National and Forest Parks and are scenically very beautiful, they also attract many tourists, as well as the ramblers, climbers and cavers who frequent them. With the development of motorways many of these areas are within weekend reach of the great cities.

Better access by road, rail and air undoubtedly contributes to the rapid expansion of Scotland's booming ski industry. In 1968 about 50,000 people stayed some days for the ski-ing, but a quarter of a million made day trips to the leading ski areas of the Cairngorms, Deeside and Glenshee. For the seventies the

TABLE 4

Areas of Rural Land Available for Public Recreation, England and Wales, 1962–3

Category of land	Lowland England	Highland England	Wales	Total
	acres	acres	acres	acres
National Parks Statutory Access areas	nil	30,390	nil	30,390
Nature Reserves	6,000	7,260	4,100	17,360
National Trust properties	65,000	146,500	52,500	264,000
Common lands minimum	(Distribution not known)			265,000
maximum	210,000	820,000	450,000	1,480,000
Woodland minimum*	287,000	227,000	256,000	770,000
maximum	1,220,000	640,000	440,000	2,300,000
Total minimum	358,000†	411,150†	312,600†	1,366,750
maximum	1,501,000	1,644,150	946,600	4,091,750
Inland water	96,500	80,000	31,500	208,000

* Estimates.   † Regional figures incomplete.
SOURCE: T. L. Burton and G. P. Wibberley, Wye College, 1965.

The main categories noted here are discussed by T. L. Burton and G. P. Wibberley in their study *Outdoor Recreation in the British Countryside* from which this table is reproduced. They point out that the public has *de facto* access for recreational purposes to a much larger area than that to which it has legal access. In the case of common lands, the minimum acreage is legally available for recreation; the maximum area is physically capable of being used for recreation.

figure will almost certainly be much higher. A dramatic increase in these numbers is likely as more facilities are provided – the use of artificial snow may lengthen the season – and as every year many more Scottish schoolchildren get professional ski instruction. Another development is the demand for Scottish estates and sporting properties. Many overseas buyers are attracted by the excellent facilities for hunting, shooting and fishing.

In England and Wales all the National Parks report

increasing pressures. The Friends of the Lake District Park reported in 1964 on the traffic there and referred to it as 'the potential destroyer of the Lake District'. In the Peak Park there are many measures in operation to meet the vast re-creational and tourist pressures from the nearby conurbations. It is the only Park with a full-time Director and it has a corps of voluntary wardens. The active management it receives and its intrinsic high quality won for it the first European Diploma, awarded in 1966 by the Council of Europe. The Snowdonia Park and the Gower Area of Outstanding Natural Beauty also report great pressures. And the south-west of England, with its two Parks and its beautiful coastline, has the greatest summer holiday pressure of all.

The development of a seaside resort at Towyn on Cardigan Bay is now taking place. Under consideration is the building of a holiday village for 6,000 people in the Pembrokeshire Coast National Park. These projects may make a useful contri-bution to more positive policies for coast and countryside, particularly those of concentrating facilities and people. The use of forests for open-air recreation has already been referred to in Chapter 3. The wide-ranging provisions of the National Trusts for England and Wales and for Scotland make a signi-ficant contribution. County councils are being encouraged to establish country parks for amenity and recreation, and a number have done so already.

But of all the phenomena produced by the population ex-plosion and technology, it is the private car which is likely to have the greatest and most pervasive effect on the landscape. There were 14 million motor vehicles in Britain in 1967. There are likely to be about 20 million in 1975, 24 million in 1980 and 37 million in 2010. On average, Britain's 1968 population of approximately 52 million had two days of leisure each week. In the year 2000 with 75 million people taking three days off each week (or perhaps four), the potential impact on coast and country will more than double. And all this will be further in-tensified by shorter working hours and the trend to more and longer holidays. The construction of a Channel tunnel or bridge could also vastly extend the influence of leisure and tourism here and on the Continent.

Traffic planning in the countryside is now being given the attention it merits. The West Riding County Council is studying access needs over a large area of Yorkshire and plans to develop new tourist routes and traffic and recreational facilities. The 'Countryside in 1970' Conference of November 1965 had a Study Group specially devoted to 'Traffic and its Impact on the Countryside'. In adopting the Study Group's Report the Conference recommended that appropriate bodies should take action now:

To deal with the problems of motorized access to, and the passage of traffic through, the countryside on a national and regional level as an integral part of town and country planning.

To press ahead with the channelling of through traffic on a national network of high-capacity highways; to provide intensive recreation areas near to large towns; to prepare local plans for access to the countryside in order to ensure that the motoring public can enjoy the countryside without spoiling it; and thus help to reduce the pressures of traffic over the countryside.

Many planners propose not only special facilities for motorists, but also motor-less zones and car-free countryside roads to enable fuller enjoyment of the countryside. The coast is probably the primary attraction for most people – for recreation, holidays and tourism. Its importance and the pressures upon it increase yearly. In the most favoured localities shortage and surfeit are common: a shortage of car parks, viewpoints, mooring berths and paths is allied to a surfeit of seasonal congestion, conflict and urban unsightliness. Fuller details on the coast are given in Chapter 12.

Whether they go to the coast or stay inland, the greatest number of active recreationists need water on which to boat, canoe, dive, sail, swim or water-ski. Even more enjoy viewing the 'waterscape'. And this is universal. The Rockefeller Report showed clearly that water is the focal point of much active recreation. Water which is suitable for sports is, surprisingly, in short supply. Although there are altogether 600,000 acres of water in Britain, only about 200,000 acres of lakes, rivers, reservoirs, canals and Broads are in England and Wales; and not all of this is available for access or managed in a way which allows for recreation. As shown in Chapter 9, many waterways in Britain could be made into excellent recreation areas, but to do this will cost initially £350,000 a year. This potential needs to be harnessed in a strategic plan that will make the waterways available to clubs and individuals under agreed conditions. The plan should be based on sound economics – most people can afford to pay for their leisure, although some public money could reasonably be invested to reflect the values to society of the activities fostered and of the land and water saved for other uses.

Inland waters are particularly valuable in this context as many of them lie within urban areas. The Report on Inland Waters and Recreation, outlined in Chapter 13, proposes a wide range of uses for reservoirs, canals, gravel pits and rivers. Often these are found in the cities and, if suitably managed, could meet local and short-term holiday needs. The Lee Valley Report, also noted in Chapter 13, put forward an outstanding scheme for the utilization of poor or derelict land and water within a conurbation. Such developments would provide more appropriately for specialized activities like underwater swimming and water ski-ing. They would also help to relieve the travel and traffic problems by reducing pressures on countryside and coast. In short, what does it cost not to use these resources? Certainly, without their exploitation there will be a real loss in the quality of the environment as the leisure boom and other demands on land and water intensify.

Other potential sources of water-based recreation are the reservoirs of river authorities and water undertakings, though, of course, safeguards are necessary to ensure that the quality and quantity of water is not affected. The Government are encouraging the authorities responsible for reservoirs to allow public access, and thus to help meet the increasing demand for boating, and other water sports. The Countryside Conference in 1965 advocated that all authorities should be required to identify recreational opportunities arising from their operations and, as far as practicable, to provide facilities for enjoying them.

What are the results of these pressures on water and key

stretches of countryside and coast, so often inadequately planned and managed in relation to them?

One of the most serious is the erosion which takes place simply because so many people visit places of beauty and other natural attractions. Even in 1958, before the great wave of mobility and leisure was fully under way, the National Trust for England and Wales reported that: 'a given area cannot properly support more than a given number of visitors without strict control.' The problems of coping with erosion by humans are great; the sheer physical trampling by walkers and picnickers can create lasting damage. But perhaps worst of all are the litter and refuse which mark the passage of humans and stress the need for higher standards of behaviour.

Litter anywhere is a difficult problem. It leads to insanitary and dangerous sites, pollutes water, poisons domestic animals and wild life, and invariably reduces the aesthetic pleasures of the countryside. For example, in the New Forest over 1,000 tons of litter a year have to be removed by the Forestry Commission; on one day in March 1966, 500 volunteers from youth organizations in southern Sweden, working with local landowners, collected from 12 miles of coastline near Malmö over 700 tons of litter. This problem is primarily a task for the education and information services. There is no real substitute for self-discipline. This is not to deny that there is still a vast scope for improvement in facilities, notably in the provision of bins in lay-bys and modern sanitation at the larger and more frequently used stopping places. But it is neither practicable on financial and legal grounds, nor desirable on siting and aesthetic grounds, to spread litter-bins over the countryside. People must learn to take their refuse home with them, where it can be dealt with properly.

In sum, pollution arises from people and their cars; poorly situated and badly designed facilities disfigure the countryside; congestion causes conflict and disturbance to humans and wild life; farmland and cattle are interfered with and forests set ablaze; water catchments are eroded; oil pollutes reservoirs; and generally the special qualities of country and coast are replaced by the least desirable of urban characteristics. Gradually wear and tear are reducing the supply of land and water for recreation. Conflict between recreational users is frequent and on the increase. The absence of suitable space and facilities for youth to 'let off steam' obviously leads to discontent and helps to produce those near-riots which make headline news. Outdoor active recreation provides an outlet for instincts, drives and emotions, as well as having social and cultural values. How should these be focused? How can a clear relationship be established between conservation of resources and continuance of leisure pursuits?

In recent years numerous reports have stressed the main elements of the leisure boom. The political parties have produced detailed proposals covering broadly the same issues. The National Parks Commission was reconstituted in 1968 with wider responsibilities and powers to promote the enjoyment and conservation of countryside and coast. Similar tasks were given to the Countryside Commission for Scotland set up in 1968. Appendix 4 gives details. In 1966 the Conservative Political Centre published the report *A Better Country*. It advocated private-enterprise investment to meet many leisure needs, traffic planning for pleasure, toll roads and payment for entry into national parks. These measures would help to provide finance for the more effective management of the better landscapes. The Report also proposed national water parks, including one west of the Isle of Wight. Perhaps the most comprehensive survey of leisure in Britain is 'The Fourth Wave' – by Michael Dower for the Civic Trust – published in the *Architects' Journal* in 1965. Valuable papers have been published by Wye College in Kent (University of London) and other universities.

Many reports have appeared in continental Europe. Some countries have more experience of particular aspects than others; for example, it would probably repay detailed study to appraise how the land and water of Switzerland have withstood a severe impact of visitors twice-yearly without much noticeable loss of quality, except in a few localities. The Council of Europe is preparing codes of practice for tourists and recreationists. Once these can be applied in all countries and more personal responsibility developed, then Europe will be on the way to the 'civilization' of leisure.

Clearly there is no easy solution. Primarily it is vital to define the requirements of the various recreational activities and to relate them to existing resources. These will include strict zoning for specific pursuits and control over the times and frequency of use. Existing resources must be allocated and managed for specified categories of use. A distinction should be made, for example, between high-density areas such as the Lee Valley, where recreation will be the main consideration; general recreation areas, such as the Solent, New Forest and Windermere, where a balance will be kept between recreation and other uses like forestry and water conservation; and high-quality areas, in which scenic, scientific or other special interests would be given priority.

In some cases the values assignable to certain areas of popular interest have been assessed. These take account not only of those factors expressed in direct charges (the entry to a historic building or a fee to fish on a river) but also of the values which cannot so easily be translated into monetary terms. Burton and Wibberley (*op. cit.* on p. 79) have used the basis of the travel costs of visitors to Ashdown Forest and worked out the economic value of the area for recreation as opposed to its present uses. All these methods are in their infancy, but they have already revealed some of the things which must be considered if provision for recreation is to be soundly based.

Coupled with wiser use and management of existing resources must go the planned expansion and development of land and water for recreation. Too few people recognize that human needs can rarely be met the moment that they are felt and this applies no less to leisure activities. Hence planning for leisure must become an integral task of government at all levels, in close cooperation with bodies such as the C.C.P.R., B.T.A., the Welsh and Scottish boards for tourism and travel, the resort and area associations, and information centres in National Parks and coastal resorts. Demands must be anticipated, perhaps a decade or more ahead. The supply of areas suitable for recreation and tourism must then be reserved and development in them coordinated in relation to long-term objectives. In some localities recreation will have to be regarded as a dominant use of land and water in its own right. The management of green belts, common land and national parks, the reclamation of derelict land, the use of gravel pits, waterways and canals, the creation of new facilities on marginal land, the promotion of facilities in urban parks and schemes such as the Lee Valley, can all contribute to meeting the urgent demands for recreation and tourism. Cooperation between the Countryside Commissions and the Sports Council should help to define the social values of leisure and relate them to natural resources. However, to realize the full potential of areas for leisure activities and to avoid their erosion requires more than the provision of regional and country parks, recreational reserves, and coastline and water facilities. The pressures concentrated on such sites at peak times are too great to be sustained indefinitely with the increasing numbers of people. Thus measures such as the extension of the holiday and tourist season and the strengthening of publicity, information and counselling services are essential to guide people and traffic to particular attractions or recreations at particular times. The 'House Full' notice may have to go up on occasion! People must be helped to use their leisure more wisely to their own greater satisfaction and for the maintenance of quality in the environment. One of the conclusions of the report *Traffic in Towns* (the Buchanan report) may be applied only too easily to problems created by increased leisure activity: 'Unless the greatest care is exercised it will be easily within our ability to ruin this island by the end of the century.'

APPRAISAL : CHAPTERS 2–5

Agriculture is undergoing sweeping changes; forestry is being expanded and serves new uses. Urban development encroaches steadily on the good land; technological impacts on the countryside are visible everywhere. And overshadowing all is the leisure boom. Despite measures for conservation, the natural environment is in peril. The land is not yet fully recognized as a vital and finite resource. Many important areas of landscape, intrinsically a natural resource, are threatened.

Clear principles and policies are required – preventive, remedial, anticipatory and positive – in which trusteeship for the land must be the cardinal theme. In this, as in so many other cases, *laissez faire* equals *laissez détruire*.

National policies should ensure the maximum use of land in relation to its optimum value, based upon the capability of soil for multiple uses and other 'supply' factors. The best soils need to be conserved for cultivation and for future disposition. Land less suitable for cultivation should be managed and enhanced for such uses as forests and outdoor recreation according to its natural advantages and the part it can play in a unified landscape. Overall, more attention must be paid to improving the productivity of the land for all purposes. Even now, more than half the earth's population live on the land and obtain their living from the soil and the crops and animals it supports. Agricultural land must therefore be conserved for its own sake. It may also be necessary to assess the contribution which intensive agriculture will, in fact, be making to the renewal of natural resources. If the population explosion continues Britain and other importing countries may find their supplies of primary products diminishing rapidly by the end of this century.

Although urban development requires more land, the actual quantity is not so vital as the quality and location of the land taken and whether the development is designed in harmony with the natural environment. Obviously greater encouragement should be given to the use of degraded or low-quality land. Much more research into the impacts of technology and leisure is essential. Facilities for traffic and recreation are urgently required and must be integrated with other uses of land and water. Higher standards of awareness and respect for the rights of others are essential. These and many more measures still to be considered are needed if the optimal utilization of natural resources, on which all man's progress is based, is to be achieved.

In the long term all this is sound economics. But man is not solely an economic creature. His motivations are much wider and more complex and he responds to many other stimuli; ethics are inherent in most of his situations. He may well refuse to accept that the present pattern of land use and distribution is necessarily and automatically related to the wisest long-term use of natural resources. Whatever the basic approach, few today will question that the physical environment plays a major part in health, happiness, productivity and culture. With increasing recognition of these values, land acquires a new significance. For amenity and leisure, for solace and refreshment, for adventure and for the challenge of primitive living, land now has an even greater potential for the mass of the expanding population.

And yet it retains its pre-eminent values as a source of food, a place to live and work upon, and as a continual challenge to man in seeking an understanding of his place in the natural order.

CHAPTER 6

AIR

Away with Systems! Away with a corrupt world!
Let us breathe the air of the Enchanted island.
George Meredith, *The Ordeal of Richard Feverel*

WITHOUT air there can be no life. Without air of good quality there cannot be a healthy life. Air pollution is an old problem which has in this century assumed wide economic and social significance. Perhaps the first general realization of the new dangers came with the great London smog (smoke plus fog) of December 1952. For five days the capital was enveloped in a grey shroud. After days of spluttering, cursing and frustration, the costs were assessed: over 4,000 people had died and incalculable numbers had suffered a worsening of such ailments as bronchitis and heart disease.

An average person requires over thirty pounds of air a day or about six pints every minute, and he has to take it as it comes. He would not readily stand in sewage or drink dirty water. Yet daily the individual draws 26,000 breaths, between 18 and 22 each minute, many of which – if not all in some cases – are of filthy air. The lungs of town inhabitants are usually greyish in colour; those of country people are normally pale pink.

POLLUTION

. . . this most excellent canopy, the air, . . . why,
it appears no other thing to me but a foul and
pestilent congregation of vapours!
Shakespeare, *Hamlet*

One of the major problems in dealing with air pollution is to know fully what it is. Black smoke and exhaust fumes are easy to see; it is more difficult to identify many of the potentially dangerous gases being emitted today which may not be noticeable in normal atmospheric conditions.

Air is polluted in many ways. In his message to the United States Congress in February 1966, President Johnson recommended measures to 'clean the air that is today blighted by smoke and chemicals'. In the city of Pittsburg, U.S.A., over 7 million tons of coal dust are poured into the atmosphere every year. In Britain about 1½ million tons of grit and ash, 2 million tons of smoke and 5 million tons of sulphur gases are discharged into the air annually. The Report of the Beaver Committee* stated that this atmospheric pollution cost Britain in 1954 more than £250 million, or £5 per head, each year. Current estimates put the cost at over £350 million a year.

Perhaps the classic case of air pollution today is that of Los Angeles. Over 70 per cent of the total space in the city is devoted to the car (twice the average for other American cities). Over 3 million vehicles crowd into the conurbation daily, releasing 2,000 tons of exhaust fumes and 450 tons of nitric acid. These often coagulate into smoke and fumes so dense that the wondrous Californian sun is just not visible. Even worse, perhaps, is the air of New York, whose skyscrapers trap traffic fumes and which is also polluted by sulphur dioxide from industries. But it would be misleading to blame all air pollution on industry and motor vehicles. In some areas by far the greatest source is the open fire in the home – in fact, it accounts for about 75 per cent of the air pollution in many cities.

Effects

What does it mean to be on the receiving end of this pollution? The dramatic suffocation of the London smog of 1952 is not, perhaps, so serious in the long term as the slower, daily poisoning of the human frame which insidiously lowers the quality of living for so many people. Pollution causes people suffering from bronchitis and other respiratory diseases to lose countless working days each year. Generally, the health and well-being of all individuals who breathe polluted air is affected; worse still, many are losing the taste for good air, and so may never notice that yet another prime element of a high-quality environment is debased or about to disappear.

The effects on clothes and buildings are almost equally

* Committee on Air Pollution, Cmd 9322.

serious. Laundry bills soar fantastically in the areas of heavy industry, and wear on clothes is high; a little-known minor phenomenon is that where the sulphuric acid content in the air is high it causes stockings to ladder. Anyone can see that the paintwork of buildings is badly affected, but not many people appreciate how much air pollution corrodes brickwork and metal too. Many of Europe's antiquities – buildings, pictures and statues – are being destroyed by air pollution, particularly from cars, in cities from Oxford to Athens. Workers in industries which produce a lot of air pollution often require special protective measures and most governments have inspectors to check on these and to reduce the pollution.

Air pollution has direct and indirect effects on plants and animals. Plants play a vital role in the 'natural balance' of life. Those containing chlorophyll take in carbon dioxide from the atmosphere and give off oxygen. Using water and carbon dioxide they convert the energy of light into chemical energy (photosynthesis) and manufacture organic substances (sugars). Being fixed by their roots, they are very susceptible to environmental factors; a reduction in their light supply because of air pollution can be serious and result in a slower growth and reduced yield. It is virtually impossible at present to calculate the real and long-term effect on plant growth of the loss of effective sunshine, but the Beaver Committee in 1954 estimated that the damage in Britain to agricultural crops alone was then £10 million a year. In some parts of Britain there is an annual deposit of over 125 tons of polluting matter per square mile; this contains substances such as ammonia, chlorine and sulphur dioxide, all of which are lethal to plant life. The layers of filth prevent photosynthesis and stop up the tiny holes (stomata or foliar pores) on and under the leaves through which the plants transpire. Many plants exposed to this treatment wither or die.

Animals derive their food from plants either directly, or indirectly by feeding on herbivorous animals. They are, therefore, quickly affected by any deterioration in the quantity and quality of their food source. Air pollution may choke the capillary respiratory passages in animals. Some of the cattle present at an agricultural show in London during the 1952 smog had to be destroyed; examination showed them to be afflicted with respiratory ailments and heart disease. The central nervous system of man and animals is responsive to even small changes in the intake of oxygen from the atmosphere but, unfortunately, not enough is known about the detailed effects in this way of air pollution. It is, however, known that ultraviolet light is excluded by smoke and this clearly has an adverse effect upon all life.

Insects, particularly bees, and mammals mainly dependent on insects for their food supply, have suffered heavy casualties in many places because of specific industrial pollutants. Fundamental changes have arisen in the populations of some species as they have adapted to the changes in their environment caused by air pollution. One of the most striking cases is that of the industrial melanism of the peppered moth in certain parts of Britain and continental Europe. Two forms of this insect exist, one light and one dark. The dark species was very rare a century ago and is still uncommon in rural areas but it is today by far the more common in industrial areas. Here pollution has killed off the lichens on trees and the dark form of the moth is nearly invisible on the dark trunks. Birds thus prey more easily on the lighter variety, and have almost exterminated it in certain localities. In the countryside, the advantage is with the light form as they are similar in colour to the pale, mottled lichens.

Less noticeable changes have probably taken place, or may be developing in other species, but usually the process is a slow one. Apart from their obvious direct relationships to man, plants and animals often serve as indicators of the effects which changes in the environment are likely to have on man himself. Rainfall in areas of air pollution will pick up acids or oxides. Clearly this affects plant life; it also affects the soil and its minute flora and fauna. Large quantities of lime are regularly required in certain areas to alleviate the acidity caused by air pollution. Study of green belts near towns and of the uplands and forests near industrial areas would undoubtedly be profitable.

Our whole planet is being affected by the massive atmospheric pollution now taking place. A vast quantity of carbon

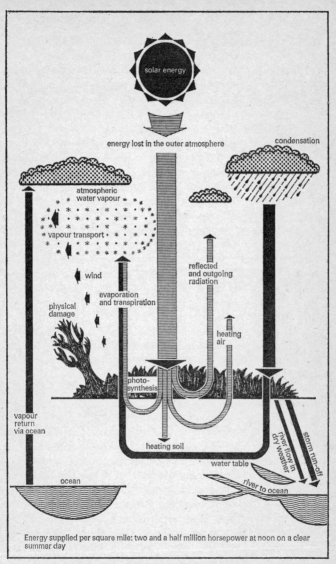

Energy supplied per square mile: two and a half million horsepower at noon on a clear summer day

11 Dynamics of the atmosphere (B. H. Grimes)

dioxide is being pumped into the atmosphere, and it looks as if plant life will use up a smaller and smaller proportion of it. The effect will probably be to create a blanket around the earth, one which will retain the heat. Such an overall rise could melt some of the polar ice-caps. Disasters such as the great North Sea flood of 1953 might then become frequent and widespread. A raising of the water level would probably result in the loss through inundation of low-lying lands and thus leave even fewer plants to deal with the carbon dioxide.

In view of all the effects of air pollution it is obviously of some importance to resolve or contain it if a healthy environment is to be achieved. The main lines of approach appear to be threefold. We must try to reduce or eliminate existing pollution, to prevent or minimize new pollution, and to control and limit the effects of all pollution which has to be accepted in the present state of technology. To achieve any success, action against the main pollutants is required on a wide variety of fronts – technological, planning, legislative and social.

Sources

First, there is pollution from the domestic fire, often the main offender. In recent years there has been some progress in setting up smokeless zones, such as those in Britain referred to in Chapter 7. Progress is affected by many factors; for example, the importance of the coal industry in the national economy, the availability of smokeless fuels, the expansion of central-heating schemes, particularly oil and gas, and district heating on new housing estates. Progress depends largely on a greater public and individual awareness and acceptance of responsibility for the domestic causes of air pollution.

As the engines of petrol-driven vehicles become more efficient and technical devices are developed to eliminate or re-use exhaust fumes individual cars will cause less pollution. In the United States from 1968 all new cars must take into account the need to control air pollution from exhaust fumes. Unfortunately, until every vehicle is virtually a non-pollutant, the vast increase in the number of petrol-driven vehicles on the roads is certain to increase the total air pollution from this source. In time, the better planning of cities and roads with modern traffic engineering should help to reduce its effects.

Industry has generally been responsive to technological progress and to control over air pollutants. Smoke consists of particles of unburnt carbonaceous substances left over by the incomplete combustion of fuel. This is, in effect, a measure of inefficiency; replacing the inefficient equipment often gives an improved industrial performance as well as reducing air pollution. Most of the main industries concerned, such as coal, electricity generation and chemicals, are carrying out research and technological studies to reduce pollution. Unfortunately, some major pollutants, such as sulphur dioxide from electricity power stations, oil refineries and chemical plants, cannot be controlled except at great expense. Considerable progress can be made by wise location of industry, by taking into account prevailing winds, local topography and relationship to populations. Design factors, such as shapes and heights of buildings, cooling towers and high chimneys (some are now 750 feet high) are also important in helping to disperse or reduce the local effects of air pollution.

Research

In Europe alone there are over sixty research stations studying air pollution. Most of the solutions to specific problems can usually be applied in many countries. One line of study which does not, however, seem to be adequately pursued concerns the effects of air pollution on wild life, on the micro-fauna and flora of the soil and on the ecology of the 'natural' environment as a whole.

One of the interesting developments of recent years is the study of 'air sheds'. These are zones, comparable to water catchments, which can be related to the general shape of the land. The air currents in such localities tend to come together and flow in such a way as to create a zone of distinct character. In some areas of consistent prevailing winds, there are well-defined air sheds, both in urban and rural territory. Unlike water in a catchment area, however, air in such a shed may on occasion reverse its flow and go upwards. Air sheds are also prone to 'vagrancy'. Despite these variables, a greater knowledge of air sheds, and how they can be altered, would contribute materially to environmental planning.

International

Air pollution recognizes no boundaries. This is strikingly shown by radioactive gases and dusts arising from nuclear bomb tests and nuclear power stations. These radioactive pollutants may stay in the upper atmosphere for months and fall out anywhere on earth. With their long life they can contaminate the land and impair the health of people thousands of miles from the source of pollution.

Appraisal

Pending developments on some of the lines indicated in this chapter, much more use should be made of the forecasting services of meteorological and climatological stations. Local broadcasting stations could provide a regular service relating the known local pollutants to current weather conditions. This would be especially valuable when inversions are expected (that is, when the air becomes warmer aloft than below) and thus there is a threat of fog. Housewives might also appreciate it! Such a service would develop a better public awareness of the dangers and problems of air pollution. To act in the ways suggested here will require not only that the public must become conscious of the dangers of air pollution but also that scientists find ways to assess the social cost and benefits of good air. It may be necessary, in order that future inhabitants can enjoy clean air, that more of the cost is borne by long-term central government funds. As air pollution varies enormously from place to place and can, indeed, be very local, it may also be necessary for the central government to allocate money so that local authorities can meet special local problems.

It is essential that local government authorities regard the quality of the air as one of their major responsibilities. Such authorities can usually contribute a great deal through their various committees for public health, housing and town and country planning. They can obviously plan zones for industries by relating them to climatic and other geographic factors. They can develop district heating schemes and low-density housing or high-density flats. In particular, they can plan their towns in relation to the traffic they must withstand. Air must be 'planned' if its quality is to be ensured.

Man is always interfering with nature, sometimes intentionally, sometimes accidentally or unconsciously. Air pollution is obviously not intended, but that does not make its effects any less serious and man should act consciously to control it. Air pollution may, in the long term, cause an imbalance in the environment which exceeds the interferences or controls deliberately imposed by man.

CHAPTER 7

AIR OVER BRITAIN

AIR pollution has been a problem in some localities for seven centuries, since coal began to replace wood. The first law to stop the smoke and smuts in medieval London was passed in 1273. Inevitably it failed. And despite the work of John Evelyn, who, in 1661, wrote his *Fumifugium, or the air and smoake of London dissipated, together with some Remedies humbly proposed*, air pollution continued to get worse.

The chief sources of pollution in Britain are industry, vehicles and domestic fires. The general effects of these have been dealt with in Chapter 6. But Britain's air pollution confers a peculiar distinction – bronchitis – known on the Continent as the 'English disease'. It kills off five times more Britons than road accidents do. The incidence of bronchitis in the towns is much more serious than in the countryside: the death rate from it in industrial Warrington is six times that in the seaside resort of Hastings.

INDUSTRIAL

The greatest impact on the quality of our air came with the Industrial Revolution. Vast clouds of smoke and noxious fumes poured over the country and led to descriptions such as that given in the report (1875–6) of the first Chief Alkali Inspector:

Is it not true that those coming into Widnes, even from very dark and gloomy skies, enter that town with a certain awe and horror and wonder if life can be sustained there. . . . Persons told me that when they went to take up their residence in Newcastle they looked from that great high-level bridge on to the Tyne and cried in a kind of despair at the banishment from the south-west, which if not always sunny, is at least always supplied with clean air.

Air pollution was probably at its most vicious when the heavy chemical industry expanded in the nineteenth century. The absence of any planning, inadequate technological knowledge and the 'hands-off' attitude of many industrialists led to whole localities being degraded by noxious fumes.

The worst offender was the factory producing soda. Following an official inquiry, the first Alkali Act was passed in 1863 and this laid the foundations for a control of industrial emissions as thorough as competitive international economics and technological progress then allowed. The 1863 Act and the codifying Act of 1906, on which the present system is mainly based, recognized that it is not always possible to eliminate all noxious emissions. The 1960 Act required gases to be rendered harmless and inoffensive before discharge into the atmosphere.

The improvements effected by the official Alkali Inspectorate (coupled with the recognition that smoke pin-pointed inefficient equipment) have led to great progress. Industrial smoke is now much less of a problem. Modern industrial extraction plant can remove over ninety-nine per cent of grit and dust. The Clean Air Act, 1956, allowed industrialists seven years to enable them, for example, to replace out-of-date plants. Now that this period has passed and more smokeless zones are being created, industrial smoke could become relatively insignificant.

The main industrial air pollutant is now sulphur dioxide. Huge quantities are emitted by chemical plants, oil refineries and power stations, in fact, wherever coal, coke or oil are burned. It combines with water vapour in the atmosphere to form droplets of sulphuric acid. This occurs not only under damp, rainy conditions but also wherever industrial plants discharge large quantities of steam into the atmosphere. And at present there is no solution wholly acceptable on technical and economic grounds.

One method, used at the London power stations of Battersea and Bankside, is to wash out the sulphur dioxide from the flue gas before emission. This, however, makes the smoke plume cold and wet; on days when the natural dispersive powers of the atmosphere are low, it sinks to ground level and can cause serious pollution. This method is also very expensive and gives rise to water pollution. Experiments are in progress in Britain, based on work in Germany, to develop a method for treating the flue gas with a dry absorbent of sulphur dioxide.

At present, the only practicable method is to disperse the sulphur-bearing gases as widely as possible and thus to minimize any concentration. This is done by discharging the flue gas at high velocity (nearly 50 m.p.h.) through a tall chimney (about 650 ft). The gases thus ejected usually rise to around 2,000 ft and spread over a large area. To disperse this sulphur dioxide

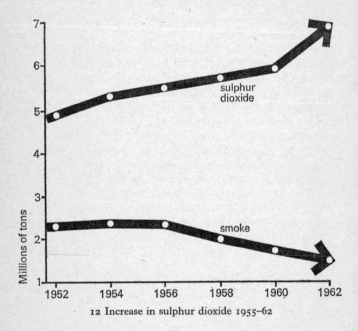

12 Increase in sulphur dioxide 1955–62

pollution the chimneys should be as high as possible. Their height, which may be controlled by local authorities, should be $2\frac{1}{2}$ times that of the nearest physical feature – building or landscape. It is, however, often impracticable to obey this rule if there are high and low buildings packed rather closely together in the same area, and it is in such instances that there is danger of the chimney from a low building causing pollution at the windows of an adjacent tower block of offices or flats.

In some areas there is also serious air pollution from the brick, lime, scrap metal and other 'outdoor' industries. This can be remedied or lessened by equipment such as wet sprayers, screens and filters, but it is sometimes difficult to get the industrialist to employ them. The 1956 Act requires proof that the neighbourhood affected by the pollution is inhabited. The processes of the alkali legislation may not apply. The nuisance provisions of the Public Health Act, 1936, require any abatement notice to specify the works to be done to remedy the nuisance. So progress is slow. The primary fault lies, of course, in the indifference of the public.

One of the most detailed studies of the effects of air pollution on a community and its environment in Britain is that of Haverton Hill (near Billingham, County Durham) by Peter Gregory. What was started after the First World War as a 'garden city' settlement has, through the impact of subsequent industrially created air pollution, become an area with an 'atmosphere of dereliction'.

Every month upwards of 100 tons of grit and ash fall on the homes at Haverton Hill. The rain contains sulphuric acid. The author says that:

Haverton Hill is very probably the most heavily polluted settlement in the country. This pollution is in the form of dust and gases and affects the appearance of the area. Plant life is stunted and destroyed, metals and fabrics corrode rapidly, and there is usually an unpleasant smell.

The physical environment is flat, drab, treeless and dust-covered. When it is windy dust blows everywhere; when it is wet the hard-packed earth turns to 'glutinous mud'. Naturally, most residents have lost their pride in the area and many houses look neglected; additionally, between 1957 and 1962, the average annual cost of maintenance per house on one of the estates was significantly higher (20–33⅓ per cent) than for comparable properties in other districts. In 1951 the area was shown in the Durham County Development Plan as one where no further residential building was to take place. The existing residents resent their conditions and the author comments that:

It is probably because of this unpleasant environment that the estates suffer from a high level of population turnover.

This appears to result in a community from which those of higher social and economic status have moved.

The grave economic and social problems revealed in this study emphasize the influence of the physical environment on people. All development needs to be looked at thoroughly for unintended or side effects. Planning must be comprehensive if it is to succeed: the cost of failing to do this effectively is infinitely greater than that of any anticipatory and precautionary measures.

DOMESTIC

By far the worst offender in Britain is the domestic coal-burning fire. The majority of Britons live in small houses with small rooms heated by large coal fires and the bituminous coal they favour gives off a lot of smoke. Every 100 lb. of coal burned in an open domestic fire pours out $2\frac{1}{2}$ to 5 lb. of smoke; from a factory chimney the same amount gives only about 3 *ounces*. In 1963 domestic fires were estimated to be sending over a million tons of smoke and 100,000 tons of grit into the atmosphere.

The problem is both psychological – most people like the glow of the open fire – and, again, economic. Supplies of coke (now as dear as many grades of coal) and some of the treated smokeless coal fuels (usually dearer than coal) are not adequate in all areas. In the more prosperous south, many families use these smokeless fuels, gas and electricity, and many have central heating. This has, therefore, led to considerable progress here in reducing air pollution from domestic sources. Surveys of central London show that smoke pollution has dropped by 66 per cent since 1955. The smog of 1962 killed far fewer than the one of 1952.

In the North and Midlands, the preference for coal fires is still strong. This, the proximity to mining communities, which get large supplies, and a tradition of profligate use, combine to create serious air pollution.

The Clean Air Act, 1956, enables local authorities, with Ministerial approval, to declare smoke control areas or 'smokeless zones', in which the emission of any smoke from chimneys is an offence. About half of the necessary smokeless zones were in operation in the mid-sixties, but in more than a quarter of the areas designated for such zones local authorities had failed to take all the necessary action, and one in eight of the 324 'black areas' in England had no smoke control plans. Generally, industry has progressed more rapidly than domestic users, so that smoke emission is now about 25% from industry and 75% from homes.

The Clean Air legislation of 1968, therefore, increased Ministers' powers to promote action. It widened and strengthened the scope of the 1956 Act, particularly to deal specific sources of pollution which become more obvious with the gradual elimination of the 'smogs' and pollution of recent decades.

TRAFFIC

The Clean Air Act, 1956, does not apply to vehicles, which are controlled by regulations, generally regarded as inadequate, made under road traffic legislation. Pollution from motor vehicles is becoming the prime offender in many urban areas. Diesel engines, if properly maintained and operated, cause negligible pollution. Unfortunately, there are in Britain too many lorries emitting thick, black fumes and more stringent controls and enforcement are required. For example, Belgium, which insists on frequent tests, has a regulation enabling any policeman to order the driver of a vehicle with bad exhaust fumes to return it at once to his home garage for attention. Petrol engines are a most intractable problem. Their exhaust fumes contain a complex mixture of poisons, particularly carbon monoxide. Proper tuning and adjustment can halve the pollution but so far no wholly satisfactory and economic method of eliminating it has been found. Some solution is essential if the air of the countryside is not to be permanently endangered.

Appraisal

Britain is one of the countries most advanced in the study and prevention of air pollution. The Warren Spring Laboratory of the Ministry of Technology is carrying out a national survey of pollution, with daily measurements at some 1,100 sites in 450 towns and in rural areas. This survey will help to pinpoint where action is most urgently needed, promote good planning and give further data about effects on health. The Laboratory is also studying methods of preventing the emission of pollutants and of facilitating their dispersal in towns.

Dispersal can, however, never be a substitute for prevention according to the Chief (Alkali) Inspector for England and Wales in his 1966 Report. He attached high priority to tackling sulphur dioxide, grit and dust, internal-combustion engine exhausts and domestic emission. He stated that 'All the important trends of future growth in this country promise a steadily worsening position unless early action is taken'.

Much depends on the National Society for Clean Air – a powerful voluntary body which is working to abolish all forms of air pollution. The Society has achieved a great deal in the field of public education and has produced some excellent leaflets and reports on conference proceedings. There is now little excuse for any local authority which pleads ignorance or public apathy, and fails to put into effect the regulations at its disposal. Clearly, however, a greater integration of factors governing air pollution is needed at all levels of environmental planning and building design.

Above all, there is the major problem for the country of deciding how much it is prepared to pay and what standards the individual will observe in order to secure clean air. It is a complex problem to strike a balance in this case between the desire for clean air, which is technically realizable, and the cost of obtaining and maintaining it everywhere.

CHAPTER 8

WATER

Everything originated in the water,
Everything is sustained by water.

Goethe

WITHOUT water all life ceases. Man is two thirds water. The surface of the globe is seven tenths water. Yet men and animals still die of thirst, plants wither and deserts increase. Historically, water has determined the location of settlements and industry and the choice of routes. If anything, its influence in all these ways is even greater today. The 1960s will go down in history as years of great drought. Famine menaces the peoples of India and some African countries as crops fail without water and as populations increase. Much of the shortage is due to, or accentuated by, faulty management. Unless effective action is soon taken to conserve water and improve supplies in many countries, this century may be dominated by drought.

The mass of the peoples on this earth are profligate in their use of water, probably because so few pay its real worth. In some countries there is a proper respect for water, induced by its costs; for example, 1,000 gallons of water, after they have been purified of salt, cost a housewife in Kuwait 30s. 1,000 gallons of water in Britain might cost an average of 2s., but many families get all the water they need (average consumption 35–50 gallons per person per day) for a water rate of a few pounds yearly. Industry in Kuwait has to pay 12s. per 1,000 gallons but in Britain the cost is as low as one shilling in many areas. Vast sums are being spent on reservoirs and water distribution schemes in many countries, and their cost may ultimately lead to water being priced and treated as the vital natural resource it is. In fact, although so much of the earth's surface is water, 97 per cent of it is salt water. A third of the remainder is frozen in glaciers or polar ice-caps, and the minute amount left over is not evenly distributed – the temperate zones get most of it.

However, in many temperate zones the waste of water continues and rivers are polluted by the effluent from houses and industry. There are annual alternations of flood and drought, often in the same areas. This deplorable state of affairs is at last receiving some attention on the necessary scale, both in Europe and the U.S.A., mainly through the legitimate pressures arising from the vast increase in demand by agriculture and industry, and from the new range of values assumed by water as it becomes the focal point of outdoor recreation for the mass populations. In many areas the lakes and waterways now have a new significance since the development of hovercraft. They will become highways to places hitherto almost inaccessible.

SUPPLY

First, where does the water come from? Figure 13 illustrates the water or hydrological cycle. Water is evaporated by the sun, carried as vapour and clouds in the atmosphere, and condensed by temperature changes to fall as rain, hail, sleet or snow. The amount of water available changes little – only its form. The water coming out of a tap today may once have slaked the thirst of an ancient caveman or a prehistoric animal.

One of man's main objectives is to forecast and control the natural process so that ultimately the water can be directed to where it is most needed. Such power is a long way off. Effort is generally concentrated at present on conserving water and modifying its distribution and quality in order to get the right amount to the right place at the right time. Considerable resources are devoted to bringing water from remote upland valleys to industrial towns, to devising techniques for re-use of water by industry and to eliminating pollution.

One point of major importance is that the *total* available water in the cycle is not substantially affected by man's activities. Rainfall figures show that man's interference at various points in the flow of water on the ground affects a relatively small part of the whole water cycle. Even in a country such as Britain, the distribution of rainfall can vary greatly – from 200 in. per annum in the wet north-west to 20 in. per annum in the drier zone of East Anglia. An average annual precipita-

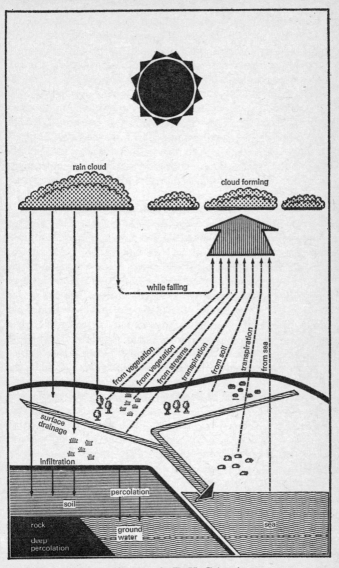

13 Water cycle (B. H. Grimes)

tion (rain and snow) of 30 in. is common and is the figure for Britain and the U.S.A. Of this, approximately 20 in. is returned to the atmosphere through evaporation and transpiration from plants. Perhaps at the most 3 in., and usually less than 2 in., of the water remaining is controlled and used by man for water supply.

Small variations in this ground flow, therefore, can have far-reaching effects. If the ground cover is altered so that it facilitates evaporation, or the water is drained very rapidly, then the consequential reduction in the yield of water available can be crucial. On the preceding figures, a reduction of about 2 in. is a loss of 20 per cent in the potential yield for water supply of an area.

At this point both surface water and ground (under-the-surface) water are being considered. Surface water has for long been measured and controlled in varying degree but until recently insufficient effort has gone into exploring and tapping ground water, which usually provides at least half the water required by vegetation and trees. Now there are prospects of utilizing the great underground lakes below the deserts of North Africa. In Britain, however, very large quantities are taken from underground aquifers and it is now proposed to develop underground pumping schemes to tap the vast supplies of water underneath the Thames Valley (see p. 123).

Another important feature of the water cycle is that the movement of water in untouched rivers and natural channels is generally slower than when man has interfered – for example, with engineering works. Left to nature, water usually percolates through numerous outlets in soils, bogs, mosses, fens and woodlands. These act as sponges, retaining water in wet seasons and releasing it in dry. They exercise a moderating effect on the flow of water and enable it to make its special and vital contribution to the life cycle and the renewal of natural resources. Where man has cleared the forests, denuded the mountains of vegetation, straightened and dredged river banks and beds and provided geometrical patterns of drainage channels, then the water cascades and rushes to reservoir or sea and cannot properly fulfil its life-giving role. Furthermore it can become an agency of destruction, carrying with it the

rich top-soil, leaving lower water tables (the level of the water
below the surface of the land), impoverishing agriculture,
silting-up reservoirs and flooding townships. Many floods of
this kind occur every year in most temperate countries. A
particularly interesting situation arising from a flood control
project is that of the Everglades of Florida described in
Chapter 12.

Some water authorities oppose the afforestation of their
catchment areas, contending that trees transpire more than
other types of vegetation and so planting them will result in a
loss of water. Often overlooked are the many other benefits
derived from tree cover, particularly a more stable ecology,
the retention of more water in the soil and tree roots and
possibilities of multi-purpose use. Unfortunately, this controversy cannot be settled by any reference to a nice, tidy
balance sheet. No one has been able to work out yet the exact
value of any woodland to a society nor, in particular, its role in
the water cycle. Much more research is required into the
effects of different forms of land use and management –
especially the multi-purpose use of catchment areas and gathering grounds – on the supply of water and on the implications
of such uses for the quality of the water.

At present no one knows enough about the long-term implications of draining for agricultural use ('improving') the
boggy uplands from which so much water derives. The functions of wetlands – marshes, estuaries, swamps, gravel pits and
other shallow waters – in the water cycle are insufficiently
understood, although more people are realizing that these
areas form part of the complex balance of a whole river basin.
Clearly, they must contribute to the maintenance of the water
table of adjoining land and perform a regulating function within the water cycle. One aspect of which there can be no doubt
is their role in providing food for wild life, and sport and
recreation for man.

Flood plains are another natural feature of considerable importance. These stretches of below-river or river-level land in
the lower reaches of rivers play a vital role in coping with
floods. This function has greatly increased in importance over
the past hundred years as overgrazing, deforestation and soil

erosion in upland areas have led to more severe flooding. Unfortunately, many urban developments encroach on flood plains, which are usually accessible and easy to build on. For this and many other reasons it is essential that land planners cooperate closely with river authorities.

DEMAND

It is expected that world water needs will have increased four-fold by A.D. 2000. First, direct consumption by man is increasing at a tremendous rate, not only because of the rising populations but because of the higher living standards to which water is the key. The purity and quality now expected of water are higher and its range of uses for hygiene and for sanitation increases daily. Authorities have to cope, too, with a quickly fluctuating demand; in Amsterdam, since 1964, the water authorities have had to assess the quantity of water required in their controlled rivers by the peaks of domestic water used when television programmes finish.

Despite the tremendous increase in the amount of water required for personal and family needs, these domestic uses take only about ten per cent of the water supply. The covering-up of much of the land surface by urban development means, however, that the rain in these areas is no longer absorbed by the ground but is washed away. Expensive sewers are, therefore, usually required to avoid flooding.

Agriculture and industry are the great consumers and account for roughly fifty-five and thirty-five per cent respectively of all water used. Where water can be made available for continuous irrigation of crops it is estimated that on suitable ground it can give rise to a ten-fold increase in yield. The development of large-scale long-distance canal and pipeline projects, as in Holland, Belgium and Israel, is leading to vast and increasing demands for water. In industry, particularly for hydro-electric power and for the rapidly expanding range of chemical products, there is an almost unquenchable thirst for more water. Prodigious quantities are used; for example, the water required to produce a ton of cement is 800 gallons, of coke 4,000, of paper about 60,000 and of artificial silk 150,000 gallons. It even requires 350 gallons of water to make a gallon of beer! Although industry everywhere is re-using many times over the water from its processes, it is often expensive to re-move impurities before re-use and to dispose of them and the polluted water.

Demand and shortages grow together. Water shortages are the product of many factors. They reflect society's failure to conserve and direct the rainfall to where it is needed. This is an indication of faulty attitudes and economic values. Too little money and effort has been expended on, for instance, research into new underground sources, the relationship of natural features in the water cycle and methods of removing salt from sea-water (desalination).

Long-term solutions to the shortage of water require more than reservoirs, dams and *ad hoc* schemes. Water must be studied and dealt with by teams of professionals, land managers, and many scientists – geologists and pedologists, climatologists and meteorologists, biologists and botanists. These studies must be based on a thorough understanding of the inter-relationship of natural forces, and a detailed know-ledge of the water cycle and where and how best to direct it for man's use. All concerned with the conservation and supply of water must appreciate the unity of the many natural features in river basins.

POLLUTION

Quality is obviously an important consideration for water authorities. For this reason, where they are unable to carry out full purification of drinking water supplies they quite properly object to animals grazing on reservoir gathering grounds and people indulging in recreational or other activities likely to lead to pollution. As the area of controlled water-gathering grounds in Britain covers about 425,000 acres, it is obvious that every effort should be made to improve technological and social means of eliminating pollution. In practice, ground water may remain polluted for many years. In its slow passage through numerous outlets it is less susceptible to natural 'flushing' whereas a river carries most pollutants out to sea relatively quickly.

A major effort is, however, needed to reduce and, in time, perhaps, to eliminate the heavy pollution of lakes and rivers which has such disastrous and far-reaching effects. Many rivers are mere open sewers, loaded with the refuse and filth of town and industries. The water is poisonous to aquatic flora and fauna and the result is desolation. Once salmon were caught in rivers such as the Rhine and the Tees. On Lake Erie in the U.S.A., six of thirty-two public recreation and swimming areas had been closed by 1965 because the water was unsafe for human beings. The blue pike catch in the lake had fallen from 20 million lb. in 1937 to 7,000 lb. in 1960. The capacity of a lake or river to cleanse itself disappears with the loss of its natural organisms. Rivers should be treated as living, inter-locking systems of dissolved nutrients and elements and of plants and animals. Kept in better health, they would be able to withstand some pollution. In effect, they would 'digest' it and provide healthy water. But this natural balance of rivers has been destroyed over much of the globe.

Many rivers are the major sources of supply for drinking water in towns. Although filtration and chlorination have reached high technical standards, they are not able to keep pace with many of the new discharges into rivers. For example, it is unlikely that the treatment processes now in use can cope adequately with all the many fertilizers and pesticides which leach through the soil on agricultural land into ditches, streams, and rivers and lakes.

The Hague Water Supply uses an ingenious method for reducing pollution from river water required for urban pur-poses. Between 1949 and 1955 an enormous project was com-pleted to bring water from the River Lek (the Rhine) to the Hague (Holland). The heavily polluted river water has to be cleansed of much silt and organic matter before it can be pumped through the pipeline to the city. To make the water drinkable it is fed into sand-dunes nearby from which the main water supply has been obtained since 1874. The natural filtration effected by the sand-dunes gives a much-improved and better tasting water. The scheme replenishes the under-ground reserve of water, an additional safeguard when the river water is too polluted to be pumped through the pipeline or when part of the project breaks down. In addition, small lakes have been created and these have led to considerable changes in the flora and fauna of the dunes, parts of which are used for public recreation.

The cost of eliminating pollution entirely from rivers would be prohibitive at present in most countries. It should, however, be possible to reduce pollution considerably and to prevent the development of obvious new sources. Pollution can also ruin the use of water for outdoor recreation. It should be possible to collect more revenue from some of these recreation areas, and some of this money could then be spent on diminishing pollution. Cleaner water is not only necessary for public health but also for industry, which has to have good-quality water for many processes. But much more research is essential into all aspects of the supply of and demand for water. Standards of tolerances must be established for varying uses. Financially feasible technological aids are required to prevent or reduce pollution, both at its source and in the rivers, and to help calculate the true 'carrying capacity' of individual rivers and lakes. A further major problem in many countries is that pollution is often difficult to trace. It frequently originates long distances away from its impact, often outside the area of the authority which has to take action. This problem of assessing the social costs and benefits of securing clean water is, therefore, usually closely related to the structure of local government.

CONFLICT

Shortage, surfeit and pollution of water are major issues facing society. In many localities all three occur with disastrous and costly frequency. Inevitably, authorities will have to limit the individual's freedom to waste, mis-use or pollute water. These limitations are essential if posterity is to have pure water. Water has always been a source of conflict. In Britain a great body of common law has been built up from case after case dealing with individual and commercial rights. Legislation abounds in every country on the rights and obligations of riparian owners and the uses of wells and surface waters, and it will be an exceedingly difficult operation to relate these traditional principles to the measures necessary for the full development of river-basin resources.

The conflicts are spreading. Take, for example, the very beautiful Semois Valley of the Ardennes in Belgium. Plans were going ahead during 1966-7* to flood this valley in order to provide extra water for Holland. In England, the city of Manchester and thirty-one authorities in the north-west succeeded in 1967 in getting powers to obtain more water from the Lake District National Park. In such cases great opposition has developed, not only from farmers and villagers but also from tourist and amenity organizations. In the U.S.A. the major cities, such as Los Angeles and New York, face a critical situation over their water supplies. In recent New York mayoral elections, notably in 1965, the water-supply problem, accentuated by severe drought in the summer, has vied with that of pure air as a major electoral issue.

Scientists, members of the professions, public servants, voluntary bodies and industrialists contend in private and public, with members of every group on opposite sides. All profess that the common good is best served by their own use of the available water. With the increasing recreational use of water, conflict becomes more personal and cuts vertically through all strata of society. An angler on the bank needs a small space and quiet, a fisherman in a rowing boat may require half an acre, but a water-skier requires fifty acres and his speed-boat may create a pollution. There are many adjustments to be made between all users if the full potential of water for recreation is to be realized.

POLICIES

Clearly a national policy is essential for all aspects of the conservation, supply and use of water. It should be part of the strategy for developing the environment at all levels. Far-sighted, imaginative planning is required. What specific lines of approach should be pursued to get sound long-term policies for water?

* Strong public opposition led to the adoption of other schemes.

Rivers should be regulated for optimal use as a whole; for example, the re-use of water *en route* to the sea is very important. Subject to this principle, water abstraction should normally be as near the mouth of the river as salinity allows. The piping of water from upland reservoirs is an ecologically unsound practice. It prevents the use of the natural channels of streams and rivers, and it stops the water from fulfilling many useful functions. The maintenance of flood plains must be given priority; in watersheds soil conservation practices – such as terracing, contour ploughing, multiple small-scale damming and vegetation planting – must become part of the normal management of the land; and water-drainage schemes should be based on multiple-use possibilities and conservation principles. More utilization of underground supplies must be achieved and new techniques of storage – for instance, treating or covering the water in reservoirs with chemicals to reduce evaporation – should be explored.

Obviously the technological requirements to achieve desalination and better purification should be regarded as major priorities. Government authorities are spending about £11 million a year on research and development in the U.S.A., and about £1½ million in Britain. Private enterprise is also devoting much research effort into water for industry. Few people have yet realized the flexibility in the location of industry which could result from cheap water from the sea. This may also have a profound influence on the world economy, as at present many areas with reserves of energy – for example, oil – are short of water. With these two major resources and a rapidly expanding population, some countries could change their status within decades.

To secure and maintain high-quality water requires an expensive outlay of skill and other scarce resources. In order to bring home to the individual its real worth, charges for water – for consumption and recreation – may have to be more direct. It may be necessary to devise systems for domestic as well as industrial consumers which differentiate between different qualities of water so that, for example, people stop cheerfully using the same tap for drinking, washing and cleaning the car! If new sources are not soon available in many countries, it may become necessary to instal water meters everywhere, as well as devices which automatically regulate the supply. Systems for re-use of, say, domestic water could be mass-produced for installation in new houses. Strict financial and other penalties will be necessary to prevent misuse and pollution of water.

To carry out these policies a central authority is needed which can maintain a continuous survey of available water resources and develop potential supplies. Such an authority would initiate the necessary scientific and technological research; it would establish broad priorities between domestic, agricultural, industrial, transport, recreational and other uses and ensure that its strategy is implemented. A specific task for the central authority is to develop the teams of scientists and professionals necessary for this work and to ensure that there are sufficient trained personnel for all levels of the water industry.

Regional development plans should embody measures for the conservation and use of water. There should be close co-operation between the central organization, the regional governments, their supporting authorities and the river authorities. Ideally, the best geographic and administrative unit for water conservation, supply and pollution control, is the river drainage basin, that is the whole territory drained by the river and its tributaries. But this will rarely coincide with the areas of local authorities, hence the need for coordination at regional level, and close cooperation at local level.

INTERNATIONAL

Under the pressure of increasingly acute water shortages, and with a high level of international cooperation, arrangements in most countries are being rapidly overhauled. Many changes have been made in Europe. Britain now has a system as advanced as any in the world, and other countries are adopting similar measures. In the U.S.A. a top-level Water Resources Council has been set up to guide national activity, with River Basin Commissions to plan the use and development of water resources. Powers were taken in the conservation legislation of 1966 to cleanse the vast river systems and lakes of the U.S.A.

and then to maintain them at much higher standards. In particular, the U.S.A. is pioneering conservation measures to establish a national system of 'wild rivers'.

Water is an important subject of international cooperation. Since 1860 over forty European conventions have been concluded. One of the most essential, and long overdue, was that of March 1963 to protect the Rhine against pollution. It is not surprising, therefore, that there are numerous organizations active in undertaking research, seeking knowledge and formulating agreements for general observance. One major project is the International Hydrological Decade, organized by Unesco. Some fifty-nine countries are cooperating in a long-term programme of research which began in 1965 and will last for at least ten years. The issues being studied include the balance of water at all points of the water cycle; the influence of man on water supplies; and technical research on erosion and the composition of water.

The increasing prospect that large-scale desalination will be required to augment world water supplies is yet another reason for preventing oil pollution of the seas. Fortunately, an International Convention for the Prevention of Pollution of the Sea by Oil was signed in 1954. Its coverage was extended in 1962 and its rules are now observed by most countries. The convention stimulated the major oil companies to devise new techniques for minimizing pollution from tankers and pipelines, but recent oil spillages and incidents show that the problem is not yet under control.

This emerged dramatically in March 1967, when the giant tanker, *Torrey Canyon*, ran aground ten miles south-west of Land's End, England. In a short time over 30,000 tons of oil had poured into the sea; a similar amount gushed out as the tanker broke up a week later. Ten days after the *Torrey Canyon* had run aground the broken pieces of the ship were bombed and the remainder of its cargo of 118,000 tons of oil set ablaze.

The immediate impact of the oil was severe. Many beaches in the south-west of England, and later in France, were contaminated. Sea-birds and other marine-based wild life and the sensitive aquatic flora and fauna were drastically hit and, in some areas, wiped out. Experience in localities which suffer from oil spillage shows that some effects persist for years.

The further development of massive oil tankers, to carry perhaps half a million tons of oil, with the ever-present possibility of wrecking, pin-points how technology outstrips man's capacity to comprehend and to provide for all its implications. An urgent review of the International Convention was started to take full account of the lessons of this disaster. In Britain an official chain of specialist units to deal with oil on beaches was initiated in 1968.

Following a major review of freshwater pollution in 1965, the Council of Europe has prepared general principles for the conservation, supply and use of water which all member countries are recommended to adopt. In 1968 the Council published a 'Water Charter', to put over the ideas which every citizen must be helped to understand and to act upon.

Appraisal

Policies for the conservation, supply and wise use of water are required at all levels – international, national and regional – with effective measures for their implementation. Particularly at regional level, these must be closely integrated with the needs of farmers, industrialists, householders and sportsmen.

Water must be studied and dealt with as a precious natural resource. This requires a systematic inventory of known supplies, research into ways to use them or to develop other alternatives, and action to prevent pollution.

People should be educated and informed about the importance of water and the need for its wise use. Without such an awareness, it will be difficult to deal with the many complex problems involved in, for example, guaranteeing minimum flows of river water at certain places and times; in retaining surface water and regulating water-courses; in protecting some areas and allowing others to be used; and in constructing estuarine barrages. Above all, perhaps, people should know the causes of the floods that seasonally affect them and the droughts that imperil their industries and disrupt their daily routines.

CHAPTER 9

WATER IN BRITAIN

A RAPIDLY increasing demand for water and new pressures on all sources have led to great changes since 1945. These are intended to conserve and to make better use of the vast quantity of rain falling on Britain every year. Some estimates give this as an average of 5,000 tons on every square mile every day. First, however, what are the main features of supply and demand?

A glance at the average school atlas gives the facts. Rainfall varies from 200 in. annually in the north-west of Scotland – much of upland Britain has over 80 in. – to about 20 in. in the south-east of England. The drier areas contain a large proportion of the population and industry; in contrast, most of the areas of greatest rainfall are thinly populated. So that although there is plenty of water over the country as a whole, it is not in sufficient quantity at the right place and at the right time. This uneven distribution affects all water policies and is a prime factor in the floods and shortages which have so troubled England and Wales in recent years.

There are many other awkward factors. Much of the evaporation takes place in the summer months, when there is usually less rain; in the south-east evaporation may exceed rainfall. With such a variation in the availability of water, storage is essential. There are, of course, lakes and man-made surface reservoirs, which help to cope with peak wet season flows and floods, and large areas of natural underground storage which help to replenish rivers in dry weather. The information available suggests that in England and Wales the total quantity of water flowing overground and in underground strata in a dry year is equivalent to a daily average of about 16,000 million gallons (m.g.d.).

Industrial and domestic users are the two major consumers of water in Britain, taking respectively about 300,000 and 600,000 million gallons each year. It is thought that if water can be made available cheaply, agriculture would readily use another 50,000 million gallons a year by 1980. The Water Resources Board (see below) have estimated that in A.D. 2000 the total demand for water might be of the order of 10,000 m.g.d. and thus approach 'the usable daily flow in a dry year'. But it is necessary to make an allowance for the considerable re-use of water for industrial and domestic purposes. The general prospect is, therefore, that if it uses water carefully and reduces pollution, the country should have enough for many decades. The need, then, is for effective national policies and measures to conserve this water and to distribute it to the areas of greatest demand.

ORGANIZATION

Britain's organization is now, perhaps, the most advanced and comprehensive in the world. The Water Resources Act, 1963, governs the conservation and utilization of water resources in England and Wales. It established a central Water Resources Board and twenty-nine River Authorities. The Rivers (Prevention of Pollution) (Scotland) Act, 1965, seeks to bring the position there broadly into line with that in England and Wales. It provided for River Purification Boards, but these do not have quite the same range of functions, in particular for water conservation, as River Authorities.

The Water Resources Board functions as a national planning authority for water. Its members are chosen for their special competence in this field and it is financed from central government funds. The Board advises the Minister of Housing and Local Government and the Secretary of State for Wales on the strategic planning of water resources and on management and control. It maintains close liaison with the River Authorities and gives guidance on the exercise of their water conservation functions.

The River Authorities are responsible for the basins of the major river systems. Each has wide powers for controlling rivers and water resources and for land drainage, prevention of pollution and control of fisheries; these include the making of by-laws. These latter powers were developed over the years

by the Catchment Boards, effective from 1930 until superseded in 1948 by the River Boards, which in turn were replaced by the River Authorities. Some of these powers go back
to 1876 but they have, of course, been codified and extended
since, notably in 1951. The water-resources functions were
conferred on the Authorities by the 1963 Act, together with
other new powers, one of the most important enabling them to
control the use of water in rivers. With certain exceptions,
water may not be abstracted from or impounded in lakes and
rivers, or abstracted from underground strata, without a
licence from an authority. Rights and uses existing before 1
April 1965 were licensed as 'of right' on application to the
River Authorities.

The River Authorities are required to determine the minimum acceptable flows needed in rivers to safeguard all
interests in them. They must forecast future demands for
water and try to ensure that adequate resources are available.
This is most important work, as action in one area may substantially affect the values and uses of land and water many
miles away. The membership of a River Authority includes
nominees from the major local authorities within its area and
representatives of a wide range of interests, including public
water supply, land drainage, agriculture and fisheries. It obtains its income from precepts on the local authorities, contributions from the internal drainage boards in its area (these
handle local drainage works), government grants, rechargeable
works and, in due course, charges for abstraction licences.

A final link in the water-supply chain is the Water Undertaking. There are now about 500 in Britain; some are public
authorities, others are statutory companies. Much depends on
their responsiveness to the River Authorities and on their
capacity to plan ahead on the scale required. The water industry employs 40,000 people and claims, justifiably, that no
other country can match Britain either in the extent of water
piped to householders or in the provision of reliable and
constant supplies.

An important task of the Water Resources Board is to
identify and promote any research necessary. It can call on
many organizations. The Natural Environment Research

Council has a unit engaged in hydrological research; one of its components – The Nature Conservancy – carries out experiments on the water cycle on national nature reserves. The Water Pollution Research Laboratory of the Ministry of Technology at Stevenage has, since 1927, undertaken extensive research into the effects of surface water pollution, the disposal of sewage and industrial effluent, and many other issues, including the 'polishing' of effluent so that it can be re-used by industry. Other important organizations contributing in related fields include the Meteorological Office, the Water Research Association, universities, the Forestry Commission and some industries.

POLICIES

The Water Resources Board has already stated its view that the most appropriate way to convey water is through the natural river system. It sees no case at the present time for a national network of mains or national water grid to redistribute water. Such a system would divert water from rivers and be very expensive to construct and maintain. The Board favours the further development of upland storage reservoirs in the north and west, coupled with the transfer of water in river channels, and the controlled use of ground water storage. At the outset rivers and reservoirs should be planned for the fullest multiple use and, in particular, reservoirs should be harmonized within the landscape.

Proposals are being studied for the transfer of water from the wet areas to those where the supply is inadequate. Schemes are being looked at for pumping water from the Severn over the Cotswolds to the upper reaches of the Thames, and for similar transfers from the Eden to the Tyne and the Ribble to the Aire. At Clywedog, the highest dam in Britain conserves one of Wales' primary resources – 11,000 million gallons of water – plays a major part in controlling flows in the Severn and meets some of Birmingham's massive demands for water.

The Thames Conservancy (one of the twenty-nine River Authorities) plans to tap a vast natural reservoir beneath the Downs at the western end of the Thames Valley. Here there is

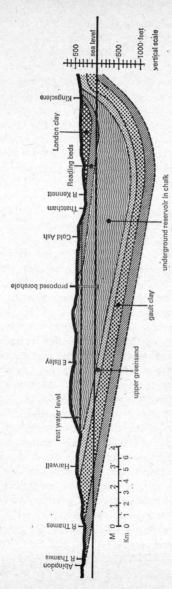

14 Proposed borehole into an underground reservoir in the Thames Valley (Thames Conservancy)

a great bed of chalk and below it lies a thick layer of clay which prevents the rainwater from draining away. It is estimated that the water thus stored, replenished annually by winter rains, amounts to 500,000 million gallons. In 1966 the Thames was officially referred to as the 'lifeline' of the southeast, so important has its water become for so many purposes.

In recent years numerous proposals for estuarine barrages have fired the public imagination. Barrages already under investigation include those for Morecambe Bay and the Solway Firth. Perhaps the proposal on the grandest scale is that for the Wash, which would, it is claimed, not only provide 620 million gallons per day for water supplies but also help to stop flooding from the sea, improve land and water communications and prevent seepage of salt into the ground. Another proposal is to harness the great tidal bore of the Severn by a barrage; this project could create a 200-square-mile reservoir in the estuary as well as much hydro-electric power. It is a notable feature of barrage schemes that multiple values are claimed for them, particularly in the Solway, and it will be essential to deal with their economics on this basis and not solely as a water resource.

Desalination is being actively pursued and in this Britain leads the world. In fact, British companies currently produce most of the distillation plant on the world market. The United Kingdom Atomic Energy Authority, with government backing, is carrying out experiments to link nuclear power with desalination. One study has suggested that a 1,200-megawatt advanced gas-cooled reactor linked to desalination plant could provide 24 million gallons of water daily at about 4s. per 1,000 gallons. The problem is to obtain an economic relationship between the production of nuclear power and water. To British industrialists, water is the one major resource they can get more cheaply than many of their foreign competitors can. It will, therefore, be necessary to bring the cost of production of desalinated water into line with that from conventional methods – as low as 1s. per 1,000 gallons in some areas – before it can play a major role in Britain's water supplies.

Problems

The Water Resources Board considers that the major problem
areas are south-east England; south-west England; Tees-side;
South Wales and the West Midlands: in other words, the
areas of great population and industry. Action for the south-
east has already been mentioned. For the north-west,
measures are being taken to abstract water from Ullswater and
Windermere in the Lake District, mainly for the Manchester
conurbation, but these are likely to cope only with the needs of
the next decade. For South Wales, a comprehensive plan is
being prepared for the fullest utilization of the rivers Usk and
Towy in the interests of all the local authorities.

All water problems are complex, whether on a large scale,
as for Tees-side, or a relatively small scale, as in Broadland.
On the Broads one of the major needs of the growing resident
and holiday population is an adequate supply of water for
domestic and industrial purposes. The farmers are also demanding more water for spray irrigation. But any lowering of
the existing dry-weather flow of the rivers through increased
abstraction would not only lower the level of the water table
of the Broads and the unreclaimed fenland but would allow
saline water to penetrate farther into the freshwater system. As
well as prejudicing freshwater supplies, this would also affect
the whole character of the area.

It is, however, the problems of how to supply enough
water to the great concentration of population and industry at
Tees-side which have sustained most interest in Britain from
1964 to 1967. They involve almost all the policy and operational factors discussed here and in the last chapter. In late
1965 the Tees Valley and Cleveland Water Board decided to
seek Parliamentary approval for its plans to construct a
reservoir at Cow Green. The Board hoped this would provide
for the growing demand for water in their area and, in particular, for the extra twenty-three million gallons of water a day
required by 1969–70 to meet the needs of industrial development, notably by I.C.I.

The increasing need for water at Tees-side came into
prominence in 1956, when the Board had first considered Cow

Green as a site for a reservoir. It was then advised that there were serious geological difficulties and later sought a site at Dine Holm, five miles downstream. This other site was abandoned following opposition by the Nature Conservancy. Instead, a reservoir was built at Balderhead which was expected to meet the water demand for many years, but before it was completed in 1965 the Board had already resumed its quest for further supplies.

The Cow Green site lies within an outstanding 'scientific area', defined as 'an integral part of our proposals for the study and utilization of the scientific resources of this country' (see Chapter 16). Part of this area is the Upper Teesdale National Nature Reserve and another part was proposed for inclusion in it; most of the remainder was designated a Site of Special Scientific Interest. Much that is significant to science in the area would be destroyed by the reservoir and the value of the whole national series of scientific sites, of which it is an integral part, would be prejudiced. The National Parks Commission also opposed the proposed reservoir at Cow Green because of its intrusion into a wilderness area.

In the previous eighteen months, the Board had explored nine other sites but, from its point of view, there were substantial objections to each of them. As the body statutorily responsible for safeguarding the scientific values of the area, the Natural Environment Research Council made observations on the choice of Cow Green. It accepted that a reservoir was necessary to tap the upper waters of the River Tees and suggested a site higher up the river which would produce nearly the quantity of water required by the Board. This site would flood some of the Moor House National Nature Reserve and affect the experimental work there but the Council was prepared to accept this if the site at Cow Green could be saved.

The Board could not accept this alternative site, as a reservoir there would take two years longer to construct and thus the water would not be available in time. It would also cost over £3 million more. One further major factor was that the Water Resources Board reported that the Cow Green site was the only one which could meet the demand in time and was a logical step in the development of the resources of the River

Tees catchment. The Water Board did not, therefore, agree to
the alternative site, and went ahead with its Private Bill. This
was considered in great detail in Parliament and became law
in 1967.

Throughout the period 1964–6, the parties involved had
held a generally civilized dialogue in an effort to find mutually
acceptable solutions. In the end, the immediacy of their own
specific responsibilities drove them into formal opposition in
Parliament. The Board pointed out that the jobs of 50,000
workers would be imperilled if there was a water shortage between 1969 and 1971. The Research Council together with the
voluntary scientific and naturalist organizations stressed that,
once gone, the Cow Green site was lost for ever to science.
They contended that it should be possible to devise some
means of averting the threat of water shortage in 1969–71 so
that the less objectionable site could be developed. This case
illustrates, yet again, the complexity of land and water problems and the need for anticipatory, strategic planning, with
positive integration at regional level.

The nineteenth century left Britain with some of the most
heavily polluted rivers in the world. But since 1951, the new
measures, particularly the controls over new discharges, have
led to an improvement in the quality of the rivers. The capacity
of rivers for self-purification means that, if pollution can be
limited, the water can be re-used many times during its
passage downstream, until perhaps the infiltration of salt
water makes this no longer practicable. Legislation requires
pre-treatment of effluent before discharge and the River
Authorities are enforcing the prescribed standards. This
should reduce pollution and, as the technical problems are
overcome, lead to further improvement in the quality of rivers.

In recent years floods in the Severn Basin and the West
Country have become seasonal and involve great waste of
water and damage. Clearly, the new organization under the
1963 Act will provide storage reservoirs and control river
flows but much greater public support is required to ensure
that all the necessary measures are fully implemented. National
Parks lie mainly in the areas of high rainfall. The inevitable
need to site some water-storage reservoirs in them will further

intensify recreational demand. As the motorway system is extended and mobility and leisure increase the Parks will be subject to increasing pressure, much of which will be concentrated in the drier months. The problems involved are considerable and call for the greatest regional cooperation between the River Authorities and the local authorities and other bodies concerned.

RECREATION

More than ever before, water is now the focal point for much outdoor recreation. Recognition of this fact led to the inclusion in the Water Resources Act, 1963, of permissive powers to enable River Authorities to provide for the recreational use of their waterways. The Institution of Water Engineers published in 1963 a booklet *Recreational Use of Waterworks*, which suggests arrangements and standards for clubs and organizations. The Water Undertakings, who are rightly concerned with the purity of water, must be encouraged to accept that modern purification techniques enable them to permit certain recreations on their reservoirs, once they can be assured of the cooperation of responsible clubs.

Perhaps most important of all for recreation is the policy of the British Waterways Board, which is responsible for about 2,000 miles of inland waterways. In an interim report – *The Future of the Waterways* – published in December 1963, towards the end of its first year of office, the Board referred to their potential as a network for pleasure cruising. The report also gave details of the extensive recreational use – for example, angling and rowing – which the waterways had for years provided. About three quarters of the waterways are available for fishing and the Board hires out pleasure boats and cruisers. Many canals are important for science and education; some have considerable amenity value and are of great significance in the landscape.

But in the report *The Facts about the Waterways*, published in December 1965, the Board makes the point that

in hard reality the field open to discussion on 'amenity' grounds of pleasure boating and leisure use lies between (*a*) a rock-

bottom starting point not of zero but of £600,000 a year; and
(b) a figure for using most of the non-commercial system as it
is for pleasure boating, which is some £300,000–350,000 a year
higher. The true room for manoeuvre (subsidy, use of volunteer
monies and the like) lies in that latter range. The £600,000 is not
optional!

In 1967 the Government decided * that the social importance
of these waterways for recreation and amenity justified the cost.
The Board will receive a Government grant to develop over
1,400 miles of this 'priceless asset' as pleasure cruiseways for
boats and for angling, canoeing and other interests. Legislation
to give effect to these proposals was introduced in 1968 (see
Appendix 4).

Many voluntary bodies such as the Central Council of
Physical Recreation, the anglers' associations, the county
Naturalists' Trusts and many navigation and local authorities
are active in acquiring interests in, and managing, stretches of
water. The Sports Council and its network of very active
regional councils are seeking means (with the central Ministries
concerned) of encouraging voluntary and local action. But the
legal and financial issues are inevitably complex, and practical
problems in reconciling the various legitimate interests – pure
water supply, navigation, drainage, recreation and so on – are
great. Apart from the inherent conflict, many water-based
recreations are potentially dangerous so that the authorities
and clubs must pay special regard to safety precautions. Despite these caveats, it is clear that there is widespread acceptance of the recreational values of water. With the new powers
and techniques, and a readiness by individuals to accept high
standards of behaviour and responsibility, it should be possible
within a decade to provide for recreation within the planned
re-shaping of all the nation's water resources.

Appraisal

A century after the Richmond Committee of 1865–7 advocated a policy of national control of water supplies, it seems
that Britain now has everything – the organization and powers,
the policies and the research, and, above all, the rainfall. An

* Cmnd 3401 British Waterways: Recreation and Amenity. H.M.S.O.

outstanding requirement is for much greater integration of water policies and projects within regional planning as a whole. This calls for the closest cooperation between planning authorities and river authorities, and with bodies such as the Gas Council and Gas Boards, whose plans for the large-scale storage of gas in natural underground reservoirs have implications for water supply.

But there is still one critical weakness – the ignorance and indifference of the public. Much waste and pollution could be eliminated if there was higher regard for water as a natural resource. Much conflict could be avoided if people understood more about water's limited capacity to sustain certain uses and of the incompatibility of some activities. And people need to know more about the significance of water for all aspects of the communal environment.

In Britain today there is now no reason why rivers should not be managed on a comprehensive basis. This should be done with full regard for their natural unity and their great potential for multiple use, and with the aim of conserving and enhancing their quality for posterity.

CHAPTER 10

WILD LIFE

From Nature's chain, whatever link you strike,
Tenth, or ten thousandth, breaks the chain alike.
Alexander Pope, *Essay on Man*

LAND, air and water are obviously necessary to man – but is wild life? Wild life may, in one sense, be regarded as a measure of biological equilibrium, and is essential in the inter-relationships between all life on earth. Its reactions provide information vital to man's control of his environment and for science and education; it is economically significant in food production, sport and recreation; and it is a deep-rooted factor both in man's atavistic impulses and in his civilization.

BIOLOGICAL

First, then, to the fundamental biological inter-relationships on which all the rest are based. Plant life is the primary source of food for all animal life and is itself substantially modified by the activity of animals. The existence of both is governed by the soil and rocks upon which they live (and which, in turn, they affect) and by the climatic and other physical factors influencing the whole of the natural environment. Sunlight, air and water are necessary for soils to produce vegetation. Plant cover is needed to protect soils from erosion by wind and water and to retain water in and under the land. Animal life is essential to the growth of many plants – for example, for pollination and by preying on pests which destroy plants. Animals help to renew the soil by converting plants into excremental matter, and their own bodies turn into splendid compost when they die.

These inter-relationships are in a continuous state of change, so that although at any one point in time there may be a 'balance of nature' this phrase is misleading if 'balance' is thought of as static and not dynamic. Wild life is an integral part of the constant interplay between the many forces of the

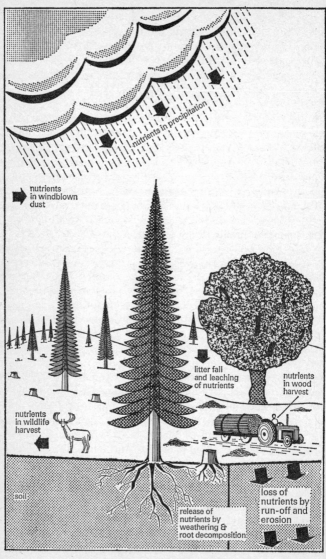

15 The nutrient cycle (B. H. Grimes)

environment, and both the competition and cooperation of animals and plants contribute to keeping equilibrium. As science learns more about wild life, it reveals greater scope for man's control, illumines the penalties for inaction and highlights man's responsibilities. Often the people most concerned with management need re-educating. For example, scientists have shown that the average density of grouse on different moors depends on the quality of the soil and vegetation and its annual variations are affected by the growth of the heather. Far more effort should be concentrated on moor maintenance and burning rather than on the all-too-common destruction of predators. Investigations into the habits of shags and black-headed gulls have shown that, contrary to the belief of many fishermen, the birds do not feed significantly on commercial or marketable fish. Bounties for the reduction of pests have been studied in recent years and it seems that, generally, they are a most inefficient and ineffective form of control. Those awarded in the past for killing grey squirrels and common seals, and the subsidies for pigeon shoots, have usually led to the killing of no more of the population than would have died anyway from other causes. But to convince the average person involved is often a more difficult task than to get at the facts.

Many problems in agriculture and afforestation arise through over-simplification of the habitat, particularly by monoculture. Conditions are created which are favourable to a few species – for example, wood-pigeons in conifer forests – which become a nuisance to the forester and farmer. Some pests can threaten whole crops; for example, the grey squirrel imperils hardwood trees. One difficulty is that few birds or mammals are completely beneficial or harmful all the year round. So much depends on a wide range of changing factors – alternative food supplies, competition from other species, seasonal variations. Too often the wrong action is taken because predators and pests are confused. The definition of either is, of course, subjective and given from the point of view of man: many animals are both. Grey squirrels, coypu, pigeons, starlings are some examples of pests whose numbers must usually be rigorously kept down; foxes, badgers, and some crows, are examples of predators whose activities are usually helpful to man. Most birds and some mammals do little harm to agriculture and forests – and many, by keeping down pests, do good. Suitable management may obviate the need for direct pest control which is often very expensive. When action is needed it should be selective; the crops should be protected at the vulnerable time, that is when the pest is likely to be operative, and measures be directed against the pest when it is most susceptible in its seasonal cycle. It is unlikely that, without spending far more than society can afford, any pest can be wholly eliminated.

A classic and recent illustration of an existing 'balance' being disturbed occurred when myxomatosis killed millions of rabbits. The disease became virulent in Britain in 1953 and within a few years many beautiful chalk downlands in southern England were imperilled by scrub and gorse. Some of the rare and botanically more interesting plants could not survive in competition with the tough species previously kept down by the rabbit. In Holland, scrub cover grew so high that pheasants died out in many areas as their food supply dwindled; pheasant-rearing has now been re-established with imported birds and rabbits have again achieved some equilibrium. On the other hand – more important on economic grounds – the production of agricultural crops, freed from the depredations of the rabbit, gained considerably. A large effort is, however, now required to reduce the numbers of myxomatosis-resistant rabbits which have survived during recent years. This case illustrates how animal populations can remain stable for many years and then have their 'balance' radically altered, with far-reaching effects. Changes can affect any type of animal. Look at what has happened to the elephants in the Tsavo National Park in Kenya. In this, the world's largest game reserve, there may now be 10,000 more elephants than the available supply of food and living-space can sustain. Investigations suggest that the present over-population and habitat change were initiated some ten years ago by the sudden elimination of human predation, which was then accounting for some 2,000 elephants a year.

With the rapid interchange of ideas, peoples and materials all over the world today, there is a mingling of natural organisms which would have taken nature thousands of years to achieve.

In some cases, animals, plants and minute organisms are moving across continental barriers and oceans which they would probably never have crossed without man's intervention. These changes give rise to increasing strain in some localities. Where a species of plant or animal finds favourable conditions it can spread rapidly in the absence of the restraints in its original habitat. This is well illustrated by the great spread of the water hyacinth (*Eichhornia crassipes*) which came originally from South America. In some places on the Nile it has thrown a 'blanket' across the river on which people can walk.

Wild life is also a source of gene pools. A species may have inestimable value to science as the product of a unique line of evolutionary selection. Even the common potato – so basic to the average diet – benefits from the product of research now being carried out into species of wild potatoes. Both wild plants and animals may provide much needed strains for cross-breeding to strengthen certain cultivated plants and domestic cattle. But if man is to obtain the maximum benefit in profit and pleasure from plants and animals he must not act in ignorance. All too frequently he applies his technology without an adequate understanding of its cumulative and side effects.

ECONOMIC

Clearly there is a close inter-relationship between biological considerations and the economic justifications for exploiting wild life for food and sport. The economic factors are more obvious as in many parts of the world local populations still depend on wild life for their main supply of protein. The food potential of wild life has not, however, been fully developed in most cases, although some animals, like the whale and the bison, have been so over-exploited that they are in danger of being exterminated altogether. The management of wild life to give a sustained yield, whether for food or sport, is not yet adequately based on scientific knowledge, except for a few species in limited areas.

The wild life of the oceans is obviously going to be increasingly important for food and to some extent for sport too. Measures for 'farming' fish instead of just hunting them, for making flour from fish and for cultivating fisheries on sea and inland, should, in time, make a substantial contribution to the world's food and recreational needs. But the popularly imagined boundless wild-life resources of the oceans present problems of even greater complexity than do those on land.

There are the same basic relationships of plants and animals within the food chain – the algae (phytoplankton) are food for the tiny animals (zooplankton) on which larger fish feed, and so on up the scale. There are many cross-patterns of feeding and predation – for example, whales (the largest mammals) live mainly on plankton, and many of the largest fish feed on the smallest and are themselves prey for smaller fish. What is different is that the organic matter from living and dead plants or animals – so vital to renewal of fertility – falls towards the bottom in the seas, whereas it remains in the top-soil on land and is thus readily available to plants. The shallower zones off the coasts are generally high fertility areas, but in the deeper seas the fertility of the upper water is maintained by the major convection currents (shown on any school atlas). These currents inevitably lead to an uneven distribution of fertility and therefore affect the location and uses of some fisheries. Some accessible areas offer very poor catches but, for example, the Humboldt current produces rich fertile waters within easy distance of Peru. These support vast quantities of fish, notably the anchovies which provide the country's major industry of fish meal. Inevitably, the great shoals of fish attract sea birds, in fact, the largest populations in the world, and their excrement (guano) gives rise to Peru's big fertilizer industry.

Another factor is that certain fish are not yet wanted commercially. They may be thought of as inferior, or an economic use may not have been found for them. Overall, only a small part of the food required in the world is obtained from fish but this proportion is likely to change rapidly as science discovers better ways of abstracting protein from the seas. Britain is one of many countries carrying out officially backed experiments to find the best conditions for producing and harvesting large quantities of fish. The most intractable problems will probably be the result of people's attitudes and legal controversies. The fisheries of the seas have long been the subject of great conflict between nations. There are marked trends towards over-fishing in the more accessible fishing grounds. The failure of whalers to observe scientifically assessed limits threatens to wipe out many kinds of whales,* including the blue whale, the largest animal ever to exist on this planet. Legal battles over offshore fishing rights often continue for years. Competition between fishermen is fierce and often disregards the agreed limits and seasons set by international conventions. All these problems need urgent top-level attention if the oceans' resources are to make a contribution to feeding the world's hungry millions.

Few fishing enthusiasts go out to sea for their sport in comparison with the enormous numbers who try their luck in rivers or inland waters. But more and more people are taking up fishing of all kinds and they are spending more and more money. In the U.S.A. approximately one in four men and one in ten women fish for sport. In 1963 approximately 30 million fishing and 14 million hunting licences, costing about 125 million dollars, were issued by the States. In Britain about four million rod licences are issued each year and the main associations of fishermen are very powerful. Enormous services have been developed to provide fishing tackle, boats, tourist facilities and accommodation. When river-fishing rights come up for sale they are eagerly bought by associations, whose members are often urban sportsmen. In Britain, £54,000 was paid a few years ago for a mile of fishing on the River Wye. Some farmers would find that the financial return from marginal land flooded and set aside for fishing – for brown trout perhaps – could exceed that from sheep-farming. Leasing caravan sites and selling eggs, milk and similar produce to fishermen could provide a lucrative secondary income.

On land, African wild life presents some of the best possibilities for food production. Many species have acquired resistance to the diseases which prevent domestic cattle from being grazed over the four million square miles of the great savannahs. They have developed living and feeding habits which enable them to withstand the uncertainty of water supplies there. A striking balance exists between wild animals and plants: the giraffe browse on the trees and tall bushes, the

* See the reports of the International Whaling Commission.

large impala deer feed on the bushes within their reach and the small deer and other animals such as buffalo and hippopotamus feed on the grass cover. The introduction of domestic cattle has often destroyed this equilibrium without offering any long-term prospect of an equal or better one. It therefore makes good sense to farm and crop these wild animals for food. Unfortunately, African traditions – such as reckoning wealth in terms of cattle – have prevented much development on these lines. As a result, the farming of domestic cattle is leading in many places to erosion, loss of water, and a reduction in the numbers of wild animals as their habitats dwindle and are impoverished. There are, of course, many areas where conditions would support both wild and domestic animals.

Sir Julian Huxley has summed up the African position in four words: 'Profit, Protein, Pride and Prestige'.

Julius Nyerere, President of Tanzania, has said in *The ARUSHA Manifesto* (1961):

The survival of our wild life is a matter of grave concern to all of us in Africa. These wild creatures and the wild places they inhabit are not only important as a source of wonder and inspiration but are an integral part of our natural resources and of our future livelihood and well-being.

But it is not only in Africa that there is scope for farming wild animals. The kind of experiment which can be profitable has been shown by Russia; in 1900, the numbers of the beautiful Saiga bulbous-nosed antelope were down to an estimated 1,000. Following conservation measures since 1919, the population now runs into several millions and can be farmed for food. Research and management show that on land wild life could supply us with far more food than it does at the moment. And areas where wild life was 'farmed' could become enormously valuable for recreation. This is particularly promising for Africa, for many parts of Britain, such as the Scottish Highlands, and for poorer farming districts in many countries. Additionally, it is possible to provide for much wild life on agricultural land. The provision of hedges, windbreaks and ponds and the retention of some wetlands would encourage birds and mammals whose economic value for sport, and perhaps for food, may outweigh their disadvantages to agriculture.

Although wild life has always been, and still is, an important source of food and clothing, its greatest economic and social value in western countries is undoubtedly to sport. Fishing has already been referred to and the shooting of wildfowl and the hunting of game are increasingly important. As the car gives increased mobility to more people, the pleasures of the few are being avidly adopted by the masses. The field sports – hunting, shooting and fishing – are booming everywhere. Somehow we must try to conserve adequate stocks from which to take a reasonable 'harvest'. Here sporting and conservation interests should coincide. Proper management and research could produce better habitats and food supplies for wild life, an increased understanding of how to maintain a balanced and healthy stock, plus 'controlled over-population' so that sportsmen could do the task normally left to natural selection.

Another need is to establish and enforce a code of sporting behaviour to take account of humanitarian considerations and man's wider responsibilities for wild life. To enforce such a code is more difficult. The main associations concerned have high standards but many non-members do not know them and do not always behave sensibly.

SOCIAL AND AESTHETIC

To many people the overwhelming importance of wild life lies in its aesthetic and social values. This is revealed in the art of cavemen of 20,000 years ago and their modern descendants – the television advertisers. Many totems, taboos and rituals of tribes and nations relate to wild life and it provides numerous rallying symbols, from the U.S.A. Eagle and the Elephant of the Republican party to the Russian Bear. Selected national birds personify protectionist movements, and a host of private societies in many countries identify their symbols of loyalty with animals and plants.

Yet today many of the wild plants, birds and other animals immortalized in art are threatened. Sculpture, painting, poetry and literature, music and many other facets of a healthy society and a full individual life would be gravely impoverished if cut off from an awareness of the animals and plants which have inspired and enriched so much of man's heritage. At one time philistines might have argued that as few people ever have the opportunity or make the effort to see the golden eagle in Scotland, the great herds of deer in Africa or the teeming wild life of the Amazon forests, the survival of these species was of no importance. But television has changed this. Its wild-life programmes attract tremendous audiences to whom rare animals and plants are now meaningful as part of their culture. And colour television will strengthen this attitude.

It is increasingly recognized that the mental health of urban man needs the refreshment and stimulus of the countryside and the joy of its wild life. Many ascribe spiritual values to a right relationship between man and nature. Undoubtedly there are ethical and moral considerations in this relationship. Man has more and more responsibility for the fate of wild life. Who would wish to be personally responsible for the complete elimination of a particular animal or plant which has, perhaps, been on earth for millennia? Who would deny posterity the opportunity of seeing a wide range of life forms because man is careless or fails to make the effort to save them? Yet in the past fifty years over forty species of animals and birds of great interest have become extinct and many others are in danger of joining them. Once gone, they are gone for ever.

But conservation often necessitates culling – selective killing. The population of a species protected by man from its natural enemies and adverse environmental conditions cannot increase indefinitely without affecting its food supply and the requirements of fellow creatures within its web of relationships. So man is forced all the time to make decisions – to choose which way he will manage wild life and which individual he will select within any species. He must act positively for all the biological, economic, aesthetic, ethical, humanitarian and social reasons already given.

CONSERVATION

Modern conservation is a dynamic, evolving concept of co-partnership between man and nature. It requires the strict management of each resource – land, air, water and wild life – to ensure optimum value and continuity of supply. Conservation of wild life cannot be separated from resource management whether for food supply, forestry, sport or any of the other basic needs of man. The more that man applies his intelligence to the use of natural resources the more he will obtain satisfaction and long-term returns.

Action on many of the points of management made in the chapters on land, air and water will benefit wild life. Proper land and water management will prevent over-grazing, erosion, waste and pollution. Application of ecological principles will enable engineering projects – dams, land reclamation, motorways – to be more in harmony with the landscape and the needs of wild life. Intelligent use of pesticides and the increasing range of alternatives should increase food production without leading to infertile soil or unnecessary casualties in wild life.

But more and urgent action is required for effective conservation. Positive measures to ensure supplies of food, water and space for wild life are essential. Threatened species need special consideration. Nature reserves and scientific sites must be set aside as laboratories for research. They must also serve as open-air museums – to retain representative samples of habitats and flora and fauna – and as the centres for advanced education in a wide range of subjects. These national sites must be supported by local ones so that the supply of particular species can be maintained for sport, research, and education in schools. The habitats chosen should be large enough to be self-supporting. Ecological 'islands' – the old 'pocket-handkerchief' reserves – are unlikely to remain viable for long. Larger birds and mammals would die out and in time a community of plants and animals quite different from that intended for conservation would be left. Positive management is required to keep down pests and to prevent animals or plants from saturating and destroying their own habitats. Special regard must be paid to the power of human erosion on sites used for education and public visiting. Even the most considerate and well-behaved visitors if they arrive in large numbers can destroy an area.

In addition to legislative measures, such as those controlling close seasons and protected species, codes of behaviour are needed for all users of the countryside. A spell as a voluntary warden in the countryside could be accepted as a regular duty by citizens; continuous programmes of information and education should be maintained by the appropriate authorities and by the voluntary bodies concerned. Greater use should be made of urban parks for educational work and for the study of wild life. For example, the wide scope for bird-watching in the great cities has, as yet, hardly been noticed by the schools. If more understanding and education can be encouraged nearer the urban hearth, there is a better prospect for rural conservation. In time, better attitudes to the use of natural resources, especially wild life, should emerge. The higher standards of behaviour sought, and the active contribution which has to be made to achieve them, will probably help man himself to get into better relationship with his fellows.

In nineteen hundred years the world has lost 107 mammals and close on 100 kinds of birds. The extinction of plants and the lesser animals is not known but probably vastly exceeds that of birds and mammals. Nearly 70 per cent of these losses have occurred in the past century and mostly through the activity of man. Here and there throughout the world, on every continent and on many of the remotest islands, a host of other species, more than 1,000 strong, faces the imminence of complete and final passage from the world's fauna. Extinction has been an essential companion of evolution since the beginning of time, and there is no reason to believe that the process is complete. Nevertheless, it is an ideal of conservation that no creature should pass from the face of the earth through the instrumentality of man. If we would pose as the masters of creation, to prevent extermination of a large and obvious form of life stands as a challenge to our ingenuity and our competence.*

The U.S.A. Secretary of the Interior declared in January

* Dr Ian McTaggart Cowan, *Nature*, 18 December 1965, p. 1145.

1966 that America was 'still losing the overall battle to save America's endangered species of fish and wild life from extinction'. He went on to say that 'What we allow to happen to rare and endangered species of wild life may become our own destiny too.'

Measures to save nearly 300 species of mammals and over 300 species of birds, reported as being in danger of extinction, were reviewed by the International Union for Conservation of Nature and Natural Resources at its triennial conference in 1966 at Lucerne.

Thus wild life is now rightly one of man's main preoccupations: to see and enjoy, to hunt and fish for sport, to remove or destroy because of crop damage, to understand and to manage – in some way most people have an interest in wild life. The claims of wild life on land and water and the resources directed to its conservation are considerable and must, therefore, be justified in relation to man's criteria. Although this is the view put forward here, there are those who believe that wild life, in the grand scheme of things, has its own right of existence, perhaps, ultimately, independent of man.

CHAPTER II

WILD LIFE IN BRITAIN

CONSIDERABLE variations in the basic ingredients of climate and rock have combined to give Britain a wide range of plants and animals. For example, vegetation in the wetter parts of the country is usually lusher and, because of the milder winters, its growing period is longer than in the drier and more continental climate of the east. The type and distribution of soils are largely determined by the geology of Britain, the oldest rock deposits being in the north and west and the youngest in the south and east. The distribution of plants and animals broadly reflects these factors and some species are so directly related to them as to be 'indicators' of a whole complex of local climatic and soil conditions.

But man's long and intensive occupation of the land has led to substantial changes in the populations and, in some cases, distribution of plants and animals. These have been further affected by man's controlling species in the interests of agriculture, forestry and game, and by his deliberate introductions. Man has brought into Britain several new species, such as the pheasant and red-legged partridge, and has made substantial reductions in the numbers of game predators – for example, the golden eagle, the pine marten and kite. Rabbits were one of the most significant introductions – carried here by the Normans who tried to farm them in warrens for their fur and meat. In this century coypu (known commercially as nutria) and mink were brought in for fur-farming, but as the demand dwindled they were allowed to become feral and this has created serious problems. The spread of towns has also dislodged some plants and animals from their habitats and yet has given rise to even further variety of species as adaptation and evolution continue. Many mammals, insects and plants brought in by man develop into pests. But some introductions remain popular – like the larch and many of the other trees in Britain.

1 'Garden of Hell': brown
coal strip mines in
Czechoslovakia

2 'New Prairies': treeless
and hedgeless Downs,
Wiltshire
3 Primroses beneath hazel
coppice, Somerset

4 Snowdonia, viewed from Bethesda, North Wales

5 Climbing instruction at the Plas y Brenin National Recreation Centre
6 Peak District National Park, Grindsbrook and Edale Valley

7 Industrial smoke. Scunthorpe, 1951

8 Wilderness in England : the river Tees at Cauldron Snout, Durham and Westmorland
9 Stabilization of sand dunes by planted marram grass at Braunton Burrows National Nature Reserve, Devon

10 Camargue, France

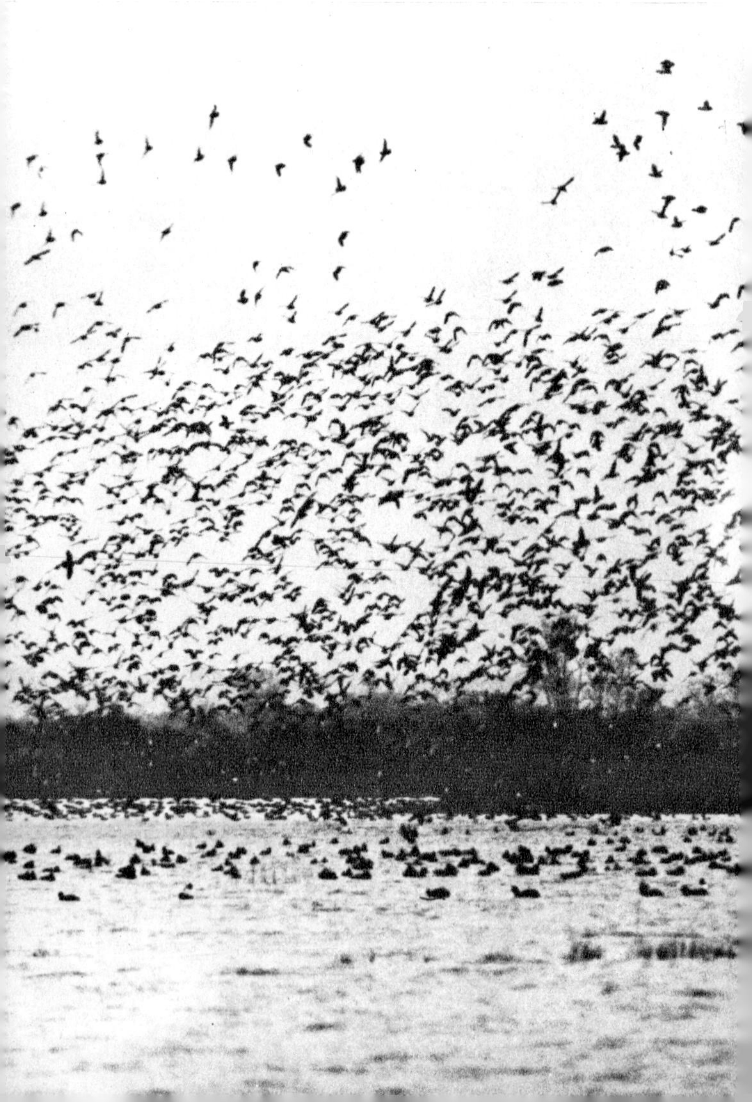

11 Coastline at Coombe Martin, Devon

12 Relic from the Industrial
Revolution: the White Rock
Copper Works, Lower Swansea
Valley, 1720–1930
13 Home and factory,
Haverton Hill, 1963

PLANTS

Plants may be divided into those which are seed-bearing and those which are not. In the former – the so-called higher plants – there is a further division between the conifers which carry their seeds on the cones and the flowering plants whose seeds are in the centre of the flower.

There are about 1,500 native flowering plants and about 600 introductions. The grasses, which include the cereals, provide most of the ground cover for much of the 'natural' countryside and are essential to the production of meat and dairy products. Grasslands are largely man-made and the grasses themselves are the end-product of years of intensive cultivation by man. Few other British plants are important for food, despite the seasonal enjoyment of blackberries, bilberries and nuts. They are, however, valuable reservoirs of genes and help to maintain and improve the stock of cultivated plants. Within the category of seed-bearing plants come trees and shrubs. Among the commonest, excluding the plantations of introduced conifers, are oak and ash. Trees are a major element in our landscape and serve as gene reservoirs in a similar way to grasses.

The lower plants – the seedless category – are found here in great numbers and variety. They include the fungi, such as mushrooms and toadstools; the algae, which live in water and vary from single-celled minute plants to large seaweeds; and lichens, mosses and liverworts. These plants are of minor importance for food, but may be much more significant to scientists and land managers in relation to controlling the impact of moulds, rusts and other lower plants on agricultural crops.

ANIMALS

Here the divisions are well known – the vertebrates (animals with backbones) such as birds, mammals, reptiles, fishes; and the invertebrates, the many insects, snails and other creatures without a backbone.

Nearly 200 species of birds breed in Britain of which about three quarters are resident throughout the year. Regular winter visitors or passage migrants number about fifty species. In addition, there are over 200 irregular or scarce visitors. Birds are important for both food and sport. Grouse, pheasants and partridge are economically valuable; wild duck and geese, waders and pigeons are important to sportsmen, as well as providing a useful 'one for the pot'. At the peak of a good season there may be over one million wildfowl in Britain, of which about half are mallard. Many birds exercise significant control over mammal and insect pests, although some are pests themselves. Those that are the most nuisance include the wood pigeon and, in some counties, the fruit-eating bullfinch. Birds are also a great subject for study by scientists and naturalists and provide a unique insight into ecological factors. The changes in agriculture and forestry referred to in Chapters 2 and 3 are likely to lead to many changes in the numbers of some birds in Britain. Hedgerow birds will tend to diminish, wood pigeons seem destined to increase and the new forests should support an increasing variety of woodland birds. There may also be some more 'natural' changes, like the recent colonization by the collared dove.

The country is not rich in species of mammals, having about 60, of which 14 are introductions. About 30 types of whale and seal frequent or visit the seas near by. Certain mammals – deer, hares, rabbits – have been important for food in the past but are today more significant for scientific study and sport. Some mammals – foxes, otters, badgers – control the numbers of certain other species.

Britain has around 30 species of freshwater fish and about 50 marine, with about 20 – such as the eel – which live in both rivers and sea. They are increasingly important for sporting and economic interests. Recent experiments include those of the Central Electricity Generating Board which is breeding Chinese carp in the warm water produced by some power stations in order to control a weed which clogs their outflows. Generally, introductions are being widely practised and may need more supervision; other examples include the restocking of beds with oysters from Spain.

Of native species, Britain can claim only six reptiles – three lizards and three snakes – and six amphibians – a frog, two toads and three newts. The adder is Britain's one poisonous reptile and is hardly dangerous or numerous enough to justify the persecution it gets in some localities. The primary value of this group of animals is for scientific study.

There are many species of invertebrates in considerable numbers in Britain. For example, it has been estimated that in Sussex there may be about one million spiders to the acre. But all too often invertebrates are eliminated by man in the interests of agriculture and horticulture without adequate regard to their role in the ecological web. Many of them perform vital activities in the breaking-up and re-use of vegetation; others, such as bees, are useful for pollination. Apart from the honey-bee and some crustacea – for example, crab, lobster and shrimp – these animals are not important themselves for human food, but they often have a direct impact on food production. Research increasingly reveals the significance of invertebrates as indicators of specific conditions of land and water; in this way they may lead to a deeper knowledge of management requirements.

HABITATS

By now the inter-relationship of plant, animal and habitat requires no further emphasis. The main types of habitat are obviously land and water and also waterside, which includes fens, marshes and dunes. In every town there are large areas of open space – parks, ornamental gardens, house gardens, playing fields, reservoirs, gravel pits and sewage farms – which support much wild life.

There are many distinctive land habitats – the moorland and uplands, the downs and wolds, the lowland heaths. Although the use of herbicides has largely eliminated the buttercup from the meadow and the poppy from the cornfield, grasslands still contain numerous plants and farmland supports a wide range of birds and insects.

Most woodlands have a rich carpet of plants and small soil animals, and a profusion of insects and numerous species of birds. Every woodland contains a series of major habitats (ground, herb and shrub, and canopy), and minor ones (rides, dead trees, mosses). An understanding of the intimate relationships of plants and animals in these habitats is vital if the maximum biological productivity is to be obtained from forests.

Hedgerows have long been considered one of Britain's tourist attractions. Ecologically, their mixture of strips of wood-

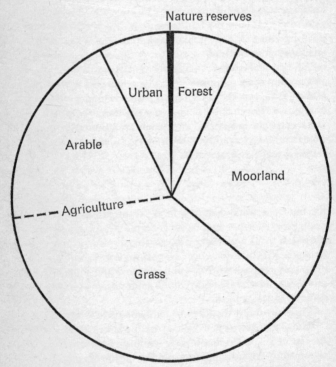

16 Habitats for wild life in Britain (Dr N. W. Moore). This diagram gives only an approximation of the relative areas of land use; in particular, it exaggerates the proportion for nature reserves. Nevertheless, it shows what a small fraction of the land in Great Britain is set aside as nature reserves. Wild life must therefore be conserved as fully as possible in farmland, gardens and forests

land, stone walls and grass verges is rich in plants and animals, often no longer found on the fields adjoining. Although this man-made environment is relatively recent, perhaps 300 years old on its present scale, it has shown great resilience in the face of changes in land tenure and modern technology and it harbours many plants and animals important as part of a food chain or for pollination. The Merthyr Report (1953) stressed the importance to a balanced countryside of hedgerows and farm timber, issues raised again in Parliament in 1968.

Inland waterside habitats have particular qualities which enable them to support a distinctive range of plants and animals. Mammals include otters, voles and, in Broadland, coypu; plants include a whole series of interesting species; birds, the kingfisher and moorhen. Seaside habitats – cliffs, dunes, beaches, salt marshes – are equally rich and provide great contrasts in species. All these habitats are very vulnerable* to man's contamination and to modern technological management. The great variety of fresh and salt water habitats in Britain is a major resource for education and science; it is well utilized by the Field Studies Council and some other bodies, but inadequately exploited by the basic educational system. Wetlands are a key sector in the physical environment and merit special attention; detailed examples are given in Chapter 12.

CONSERVATION

What are the policies and measures which Britain has taken to conserve these important natural resources of plants, animals and habitats?

Initially the basic aims were preservation and protection. We have records from the time of the Norman kings of measures to preserve game animals and, later, to maintain woodlands, such as the New Forest. Most relevant legislation was primarily intended to safeguard an interest in wild life, such as a sporting right, or to prevent damage to property by wild life. There are in force today numerous statutes dealing with licences, burning of territory, close seasons, and poaching, as well as methods relating to game and freshwater fish, but

* See *Torrey Canyon*, p. 117.

they hardly take account of the wider considerations touched on in the last chapter.

Probably the legislation which has most reflected the increasing public interest in wild life has been that for birds. An Act of 1869 to protect sea-birds was followed by a more comprehensive measure in 1880 and numerous specific Acts and local Orders culminating in the Protection of Birds Act, 1954. This repealed fifteen previous Acts and greatly simplified the law. It laid down the general principle that, with certain exceptions, any wild bird, its nest and its eggs are protected. The exceptions are to allow for the legitimate interests of agriculture, sport, research and education. Offences against certain rare birds are punishable by special penalties.

The development of a more humanitarian approach to animals was seen in the Cruelty to Animals Act, 1876. This laid down that 'no person shall perform on any living animal any experiment calculated to give pain except subject to the restrictions of this Act'. In effect, this meant that the experiment must be in the interests of science, or for saving life or alleviating suffering. It had to be carried out under anaesthetic and the person undertaking the experiment had to be officially licensed. An Act in 1954 enforces compulsory use of anaesthetics, save for very minor exceptions.

The Grey Seals Protection Acts of 1914 and 1932 are very important. The latter provides for close seasons from 1 September to 31 December. The population of grey seals in British waters was believed to be in danger of extinction in 1914, with some naturalists estimating their number as low as 500. It has increased to an estimated 36,000 in 1963. There has been controversy since 1963 over the decision to vary the close seasons in order to cull a certain number of grey seal pups each year. Perhaps what is really significant about this problem is that it brought about the first widespread discussion in Britain of some of the ideas underlying modern nature conservation and led to a Conservation of Seals Bill in 1968.

Legislation to conserve and control red deer in Scotland – the Deer (Scotland) Act, 1959 – followed a widespread outcry against the cruelties and destruction arising from poaching. The Act prescribes measures to prevent poaching, provides for

close seasons for red deer and other species, and appointed a
Red Deer Commission to further the conservation and control
of this attractive animal. An Order in 1966 laid down close
seasons for roe, fallow and sika deer in Scotland. The Deer
Act, 1963, provides for close seasons for red, fallow, roe and
sika deer in England and Wales. It prohibits the killing and
taking of deer by certain weapons and devices, and introduces
a 'curfew' for deer-killing (between the expiration of the first
hour after sunset and the commencement of the last hour before sunrise).

Although advocated in 1947 in the famous report (Cmd 7122)
of the Wild Life Conservation Special Committee, *Conservation of Nature in England and Wales*, there is as yet no 'comprehensive Wild Life Protection Bill* for Great Britain as a
whole'. Undoubtedly the most important conservation legislation is the National Parks and Access to the Countryside Act,
1949, which set up the National Parks Commission and the
Nature Conservancy, and the Countryside Acts of 1967 (for
Scotland) and 1968 (see Chapter 16 and Appendix 4). Today,
the measures carried through by these two bodies make a significant contribution to the conservation of the landscape and wild
life of Britain. Other national bodies active in conservation are
the National Trusts and the Forestry Commission, which own
many important reserves and sites. Local authorities also have
powers which could be used more fully.

As so often in Britain, the voluntary movement pioneered
good, practical measures. Pre-eminent is the Royal Society for
the Protection of Birds. Since its establishment in 1889 it has
created and managed bird sanctuaries and reserves and played
a leading part in promoting legislation and education about
birds. The Society for the Promotion of Nature Reserves,
founded in 1912, also does much valuable work. During the
Second World War it fostered a Nature Reserves Investigation
Committee which provided the basic list of reserves and sites
proposed in Cmd 7122. In the 1950s the Society played an
important part in the development of the county Naturalists'
Trusts which now cover all England and Wales, and it supports a number of Trusts' nature reserves. In 1958 the Council

* A Wild Plants Protection Bill was promoted in 1968.

for Nature was established. It acts as the national voice for over 400 national and local societies and has a membership of around 100,000. It promoted National Nature Weeks in 1963 and 1966 and has been one of the sponsors of the Conferences in 1963 and 1965 on 'The Countryside in 1970'. There are over 60 national natural-history bodies affiliated to the Council for Nature and many of them are active in conservation. Particularly prominent are the Botanical Society of the British Isles and the Royal Entomological Society. The Wildfowl Trust (of Slimbridge) is another voluntary initiative of great significance. It is also essential to take account of the great contribution of the amenity and landscape societies, particularly the Councils for the Preservation of Rural England and Protection of Rural Wales and their associated bodies. Without their work much of the countryside would have been despoiled and many important habitats lost.

Undoubtedly the public is now very interested in the fate of wild life. This derives from two broad and interacting causes; first, the increasing numbers enjoying motoring for pleasure, outdoor recreation and field sports; and secondly, the great growth in knowledge about wild life and its significance to man which has been fostered by television and the voluntary bodies. Many people now contribute, through membership of angling societies, to the maintenance of clean rivers and lakes and to the development of artificial ponds for fishing. Others support wildfowling clubs which through their national body (Wildfowlers' Association of Great Britain and Ireland) promote research and conservation and the creation of breeding and feeding grounds for wildfowl. Many more are following the traditional field sports of game shooting and fox-hunting.

Most people in Britain show some interest in wild life and landscape features. But, ironically enough, this is not always an advantage – as disturbed nests, eroded paths and every littered beach can testify. This interest also leads to conflict – for example, over blood sports or the measures necessary in some areas to restrict access in order to conserve plants and animals. How, for example, can areas of quiet and solitude be ensured for those who wish to enjoy them? How can the concept of 'wild rivers' be fulfilled if they are all to be used for recreation?

The teaching system and the public information services must obviously undertake a much more positive role in environmental education. Many educational activities can be combined with active conservation; for example, the management of a local site or green belt, the reclamation of tips and gravel pits, and the formulation of standards of behaviour. Bird study is particularly profitable and this can easily be placed on a near-professional basis by membership of a natural-history society or county trust. Information services should relate measures for the conservation of wild life to man's interests and should show their contribution to a high-quality environment.

Appraisal

In the past, change has not been so rapid and there has been time for plants and animals to find an equilibrium with man. Much of man's cultivation of field and forest was compatible with the retention of many animals and plants. It has, in fact, given Britain a much-treasured landscape in which the profusion and variety of plants and animals is part of the 'natural' heritage. But today there is little time for wild life to adjust to man's new technologies on the farm and in the countryside generally; and above all to the numbers of man himself.

Fortunately, as the threats mount, man has become more aware of the importance of plants and animals and in inevitable reaction to his own powers of destruction has developed special measures to conserve wild life. But these cannot be enough. The great part of land and water is managed primarily for economic reasons. If landscape and wild life are to be maintained and enhanced, then the nation must state this to be part of its policy for the farmlands. And farmers and landowners must be helped and encouraged to fulfil this policy.

CHAPTER 12

UNITIES

THE features described here and in Chapter 13 have been
chosen for special consideration because together they embody
almost every aspect of the discussions on land, air, water and
wild life. They show how dependent on man are countryside
and coast; how little of the landscape is wholly natural; and
how vulnerable it is to the new pressures arising from the
population explosion. They also show how large is the scope
for man's creative powers and how desperate is the need for a
more responsible and comprehensive approach to environmental problems.

WETLANDS

Wetlands are usually defined as areas of marsh and water less
than twenty feet deep (six metres). They include lakes, lagoons,
gravel pits, rivers, swamps and estuaries, which serve as
natural water reservoirs. To the scientist, they are a valuable
and scarce resource which maintains a wide range of animal and
plant life. To teachers, students and amateur naturalists, they
offer unlimited scope for study and pleasure. To the sportsman, they offer fishing, shooting and sailing. Following the
boom in these sports, more and more of these areas are being
commercially exploited. Wetlands are also frequently the subject of limited single-purpose projects, such as drainage and
flood control. For these reasons, they are disappearing faster
than most other ecological systems. The following three case
studies have, therefore, been chosen from different countries
in order to illustrate some of the values of wetlands and the
problems and needs common to them all.

The Everglades National Park, Florida, U.S.A.

The Everglades lie on the south-western tip of the peninsula
of Florida. Short distances away on the east coast are Miami
and Palm Beach, on the west lies the Gulf of Mexico, and to

17 The Everglades, Florida, U.S.A.

the north Lake Okeechobee – one of the largest freshwater lakes in the U.S.A.

The Glades – as they are commonly known – extend roughly 100 miles north to south and are about 60 miles wide. Perhaps four centuries ago much of the area was covered by a large, shallow lake, fed by a slow-moving river beginning at Lake Okeechobee. This gave rise to swamps and small islands and conditions uniquely suited to rare plants, to many birds (among them egrets, ibis, herons, storks), and to alligators, otters, panthers and snakes. This spectacular habitat was dedicated in perpetuity by President Truman as recently as 1947. Surrounded by water – dependent for existence on water – the Everglades National Park is recurringly threatened with disaster from man-made drought. Why and how did this situation arise?

In 1947 South Florida was severely affected by a hurricane and floods. The following year Congress sanctioned a major flood-control project. This has removed, and gets rid of each year, so much water that now shortage prevails. Today, the flood-control aspects are not, perhaps, the most significant. The drainage carried out under the project has increased land productivity and the richness of the reclaimed land, known locally as 'muckland', has led to the area becoming one of the greatest centres of market-garden produce in the U.S.A. New developments along the attractive coasts of Florida also demand more water. Large reservoirs have, therefore, been created to the north of the Park and thus further affect the water available. The policy of the flood-control authorities was not to restore water supplies to the Glades until all human needs were met.

The effects of these activities and a below-average rainfall in recent years have reduced the area of the Glades, led to large stretches drying up and had a drastic impact on the wild life. And this need not be. Before the flood season starts, large quantities of water are released to the sea from Lake Okeechobee to lower its level. An old waterway – the Miami Canal – could transfer water from the Lake to the Park. Numerous other possibilities exist if science can be allied to engineering and if research into the ecology of the area can be stimulated.

But the probable economic consequences are also far-reaching and should be set against the income from the reclaimed land and flood-control project. The Park attracts nearly a million tourists a year; loss of this income could be serious. Its waters are the nurseries of the shrimps on which a multi-million-dollar fishing industry is based and they are the spawning grounds of the snook and tarpon and other fish in an area world-famous for its fish-sport.

The choice is not, however, between man and wild life, nor between agriculture and fishing, nor even between food and sport. It is primarily between long-term scientific planning of the area's total resources and the aims of some limited sectional projects.

Broadland, East Anglia, England

The Broads of Norfolk and East Suffolk, long-famous for their beauty and wild life, are shallow lakes formed by the flooding of peat excavations during medieval times. Interconnected by waterways and marshy valleys, they form one of the most unusual wetland areas in Europe. There are over 40 Broads, covering about 1,700 acres of open water, and approximately 90 miles of navigable channels.

The Broads provide the richest and most varied freshwater habitat in Britain. They are valuable fisheries and are important for duck and other wildfowl. Birds found there include the marsh harrier, great crested grebe and bittern; and plants such as the water soldier and marsh sow thistle are abundant. The surrounding marshes have been developed for grazing and tend to be dull and flat. But the view on and from the water – the 'waterscape' – and the great diversity of birds and plants make Broadland fascinating to visitors.

During this century the traditional crafts based on marshland produce, like thatching and the cultivation of forage and litter for horses, virtually ceased. In consequence, the marshes were no longer managed. Scrub grew in the open fens and dykes silted up. Many broads moved through these natural processes and became overgrown with vegetation. Concurrent with these natural changes there has been a tremendous increase, particularly over the last two decades, in direct human pressures on Broadland. The rapid expansion of the area as a national holiday and recreational centre has led to considerable wear and tear – pollution of waterways, litter, erosion of banks and noise.

Until recent years the holiday-maker on the Broads favoured the sailing boat. Many came simply for the quiet and repose, others to take pleasure in its unique natural history, some to fish. Today the majority require motor-driven craft, with all the comforts and shore-based facilities of urban man. To meet these demands the important and expanding holiday industry provides numerous boatyards and other facilities. Much of the pressure falls on the northern rivers owing to their easier access. Scenically and scientifically this northern part is the most important and the most vulnerable.

Outdoor recreational activities – angling, canoeing, dinghy sailing and racing – have become very popular. Recent appraisals show that there has been a three-fold increase in holiday and recreational activities in Broadland in the past two decades. Inevitably, conflict tends to arise when these coincide in time and space. And the trends point to an even more rapid increase in the next twenty years.

Additionally, the waterways of Broadland are important for domestic water uses, agriculture, industry, drainage and sewerage, and for navigation. These demands, too, will certainly increase.

The *Report on Broadland* published by the Nature Conservancy in 1965 proposed a strategic plan. Its main long-term proposals were for new Broads and waterways, developed to spread existing and future pressures and to facilitate zoning in space and time of the many activities in the area. It led to the setting-up in 1966 of a consortium of the Norfolk County Council and the River and Navigation Authorities to co-ordinate relevant policies and action. Within two years the data had been assembled and a master plan was in preparation. Much depends on the speed with which it can be implemented, for Broadland is an outstanding illustration of the pervasive and rapid impact of the leisure explosion on the delicate ecological balance found in wetlands.

The Camargue, South France

The Camargue, in the valley of the Rhône, is one of the most famous wetlands in Europe. It is a major link in the migration routes of Europe's birds and is a wild-life habitat of great importance, especially renowned for the rose flamingo. 20,000 or more of these beautiful birds are in the area during the spring and usually over 1,000 winter there. Resident and migrant birds number hundreds of species.

After the Second World War the production of rice for food was increased in the delta. It now covers an area of over 50,000 acres. The economy of the area is partly dependent on the rice crop and a large seasonal labour force (mainly from Spain) has been built up. Drainage channels have been developed for the rice fields and much of the irrigation water from them is drained into the lakes and marshes, raising the water level and lowering the salinity through washing salt out to the sea. Many marshes can no longer dry out fully in summer and this changes progressively the very special wild life, which is adapted to seasonal drought and varying salinity, into more normal communities of average European freshwater marshes. The habitat of the 'flamingo has been reduced to a fringe of lakes along the seashore and the salt pan, covering more than 25,000 acres. These birds have so far maintained their numbers, but had no breeding success during the last few years.

Part of the area has been a nature reserve since 1928 under the National Society for the Protection of Nature and Acclimatization. The Government has designated the Camargue as a regional park. This covers a much larger area than the reserve and will be zoned for agriculture, forestry and wild life. Conservationists all over Europe are eager to safeguard this unique and vital part of the European heritage, the importance of which was formally recognized in 1966 when it was awarded the European Diploma of the Council of Europe.

Appraisal

The Everglades situation arises when one environmental problem is tackled without adequate consideration of others. Broadland reveals the vulnerability of natural phenomena and their limited capacity for self-renewal. It points to the importance of planning, managing and enhancing the supply of resources and of reconciling these with the demands made on them. The Camargue is an example of the unintended effects of man's activities. No one wishes to eliminate this marvellous habitat, yet this could well happen if it is not regarded as a unit or if people fail to realize its importance to the whole of Europe.

These cases reveal the great economic, scientific and aesthetic wealth of wetlands, which are an essential part of the ecology of river basins and serve in many unique ways to meet man's needs.

COAST

Few of the natural features of the landscape are treasured more than the coastline. This widespread interest is a relatively recent phenomenon and reflects the dominant function of the coastline today as a place for leisure and recreation. These values are becoming world-wide; the problems arising from them are common to most Western countries, and the solutions being adopted vary little in principle.

Until the nineteenth century, limited parts of most coasts served mainly to support fishing harbours, seaports and naval bases. Only a few spas had been developed for the use of the leisured upper classes. Water – salt or fresh – was not very popular. During the Industrial Revolution the coast assumed greater importance in most Western countries for both industrial and urban development, particularly near the major estuaries. And although many excrescences blighted parts of the landscape and some beautiful sites were polluted beyond repair, remarkably little was lost. The great changes began with the large-scale sprawl of suburbs and seaside resorts during the inter-war years. After 1945 new pressures developed, many of them the result of increased leisure time. The coastline offers not only access to water but amenity, adventure, educational and scientific interest, with a sense of space and, in many places, even solitude.

But society is not yet sufficiently concerned. Suburbia-by-sea doubles its size to meet the demands for holiday, recreation and retirement. Caravans, chalets, huts and camps clutter the coastline; cars, with and without essential parking and other facilities, dominate the routes and views, and control people's mentality and activities; and all too often the rubbish visitors leave behind them contaminates the environment. This is not all. Industry still requires sites for power stations, ports and refinery centres. Developers of various kinds extract minerals from coasts, build sea walls, create barrages and continually make demands on this limited natural resource. New inventions like the hovercraft, and new sources of power like the gas from the North Sea, will lead to additional pressures on the coast. Service departments claim assault beaches, cliff climbs and testing grounds for weapons and equipment.

Most of these pressures are increasing every year. In many Western countries the development of the coast is taking place at a much greater rate than development inland. In Scandinavia the last major unspoilt coastline of Europe is already threatened. In Mediterranean countries the inevitable demands and purchasing power of tourism have created long stretches of beach camps and recreational facilities. In the U.S.A., the east and west coasts are being built up and wilderness is disappearing fast.

The effects of all this on the ecology of the coast are fairly obvious. Some habitats for plants and animals are eliminated; in others, the pressures force out certain species and may create conditions favourable to pests. Geological features are often obliterated or marred by excavations, while in some places mineral extraction and ill-considered development lead to coastal erosion. The beaches of many large estuaries are besmirched with sewage and other pollutants.* Temperature changes in the water near power stations may alter the interrelationships of flora and fauna. Barrages obviously alter the scenery and river flows and affect the ecology of large areas. Crowds disturb wild life and disfigure the coastline. Motor boats can cause pollution; riding and ski-ing on some sand dunes jeopardize their stability; and aquatic sports in some areas are a new hazard to vegetation and fauna.

* See *Torrey Canyon*, p. 117.

Policies

What is being done and what must still be done to maintain and enhance this scarce and finite resource? How can the increasing and competing claims be harmonized? What policies are required to leave some unspoilt coastline for future generations?

The first requirement is for a synoptic view of the coast as a whole, as a unique resource, whose landscape and natural features, including wild life, merit special consideration. A second is that no development or exploitation of the coast should be permitted if it can be accommodated suitably inland, unless its long-term importance outweighs the complete loss of the resource it displaces. A third facet which policy-makers must consider is that of concentration: for example, holiday camps in suitable localities which provide for the gregarious obviously relieve pressures elsewhere. A fourth requirement is that planning control for the coast should be in depth. The nearer activity is to the coast the greater the potential loss of the resource, and social cost–benefit analysis should be weighted accordingly. It is absurd to try to conserve the coast by safeguarding just those areas which are within a few hundred yards or metres of the beach. Coupled with these considerations, there should be a continuing policy of clearance and enhancement. Modern technologies make it possible for us to undo many of the results of past abuses. Many sites can be redeveloped to meet new needs – for example, outdoor recreation – and thus relieve pressures on unspoilt areas. Positive action should be taken to create facilities for the use and enjoyment of the coast in a manner which does not reduce its quality.

The two main measures adopted to implement policies in most countries are planning and related controls, plus acquiring land or substantial and effective rights in it. Planning authorities must know what is happening to their coastline and be able to assess the needs of agriculture and industry, residence and recreation, and education and science. Perhaps most urgently needed is research, not only into the capacity of the coast to withstand the mounting pressures but also into the trends and motives of the human population using it. The information so gathered must be reflected quickly in planning, management and development policies at all levels. The planning authority should ensure that all sections of the community are fully catered for. In particular, there must be adequate provision for vehicle routes to the coast; well-sited and designed terminal facilities for the motorist; and, without endangering the interests of landowners, effective access by foot for further use and enjoyment. The limited number of people skilled in planning and landscaping should be encouraged to work on major projects and selected areas so that they can make the maximum long-term contribution to the natural beauty of the coastal landscape.

In certain key areas, planning and controls must be reinforced by complete ownership which, in some cases, is the only fully effective long-term safeguard. This is necessary not only to ensure that the tremendous cash returns from tourism and recreation do not outbid the long-term public interest but also to provide the positive management required in the more vulnerable sites of amenity and scientific interest. Here, staff must devote much of their time to guiding and informing the public, as well as to the specific measures aimed at maintaining and enhancing local resources.

In many countries the main weaknesses are lack of public support for measures to safeguard the coastline, and the poor environmental education of those undertaking development of various kinds. The public, somehow, should be educated not only to contribute more directly to the cost of planning and maintaining the coast as an important part of their natural environment but also to support the limitations on their activities necessary in their own long-term interest.

England and Wales

Many of the most accessible stretches of the 2,600 miles of coastline in England and Wales have been under great pressure in the past few decades. Despite the safeguards and care of one of the most advanced planning systems in the world, the Minister responsible (Housing and Local Government) decided in September 1963 that the coastline merited special study and control. Maritime planning authorities were asked to make a special study of their coastal areas in consultation with the National Parks Commission, and, for scientific advice, the Nature Conservancy.

Then in January 1966, in view of the mounting concern about the coastline, a circular was issued based on the premise that 'the need for effective action to safeguard unspoilt stretches of the coast is urgent'. The Minister called for all maritime planning authorities to submit to him within six months a clear statement of policy for their coastal areas in standard cartographic form. A further step was then undertaken by the National Parks Commission. This body, anticipating its re-creation as a Commission with wider responsibilities for coast and countryside, organized during 1966 and 1967 a series of regional conferences of planning authorities and other bodies, which should result in much better regional coordination and, perhaps, a national plan for the coast. In this, the essentials appear to be the identification of the users' demands – by the B.T.A., Sports Councils, C.C.P.R., local authorities and so on – and the specification of those areas which must be conserved for one or more reasons. The Commission, the Nature Conservancy, local authorities and voluntary bodies have been involved and a major report will be issued in 1969.

In 1965 the National Trust launched 'Enterprise Neptune' to raise £2 million pounds so that it could acquire or place under protective covenant as much as possible of the best unspoilt coastline. The Government itself contributed £250,000 to the project. Many county councils are acquiring coastal sites as open spaces or for other special purposes, and numerous voluntary bodies, including county Naturalists' Trusts, are actively promoting measures to safeguard coastal sites of special importance. All these activities have greatly enhanced public awareness of the value of the coastline. If the current impetus can be maintained and a firmer basis of knowledge can be provided soon, then this essential natural resource should be secured for the use and enjoyment of the far larger population of the next century.

CHAPTER 13

UNITIES IN BRITAIN

ENGLAND is short of 'suitable' land. It is the most densely populated country in the world. Why, then, should so much land be wasted? Why should so much of all that is essential to a modern population be eroded away? And what land and water resources can be reappraised and dealt with in the modern manner to meet our needs? For a short discussion of these questions, three main features have been chosen – conurbation projects, open country and common land.

CONURBATION PROJECTS

The cases briefly described below illustrate the interdependence and interpenetration of town and country and of conservation and development. They cover three of the most densely populated and heavily used areas of England and Wales and show both man's capacity for destruction and his powers for creating new resources.

Lower Swansea Valley

Less than a mile from the lively town centre of Swansea lies the valley of the river Tawe, dead and derelict, a 'lunar landscape'. Over 1,200 barren acres bear witness to the depredation of nineteenth-century industry. Once it was a centre for copper and zinc smelting; now nothing is worked and almost nothing is grown in the Valley wastelands.

In 1961 the Nuffield Foundation provided money for an investigation, known as the Lower Swansea Valley Project. Its aim has been to study the physical, social and economic causes and effects of this dereliction and to suggest means of rehabilitation. A team based on University College, Swansea, working with many local organizations, has surveyed the area and evaluated the possible lines of action. In some of the practical experiments in the Valley several sites were cleared, considerable mounds of earth were shifted and trees planted. In the first year, out of about 80,000 young trees planted, over 1,000 were destroyed by local children. The forester in charge then undertook an intensive tour of nearby schools, explaining the project, talking about conservation and getting children to plant trees. Subsequently few of the 120,000 trees planted were lost through vandalism.

The Project has already established principles and developed techniques which could be applied in other areas. Unfortunately, they are costly, and visible results are slow to appear. The legal problems arising from multiple ownership are considerable, not only for getting action now but also in determining the allocation of future benefits. Rehabilitating this area involves the cooperation of several national bodies, such as British Railways, which has lines and land in the Valley; the Forestry Commission; and the Natural Environment Research Council. Locally, the county borough of Swansea, numerous private organizations and many societies are concerned. The issues extend far beyond the Valley. For example, reclaiming part of the site for light industry would affect employment in neighbouring valleys where coal-mining is on the decline. Its use for recreation could relieve pressures on unspoilt countryside. The Project illustrates how necessary it is for regional government to comprehend all the primary factors and to inject some dynamism (probably through the efforts of a consortium of public and private bodies) into removing obstacles which prevent better environments being created in areas like the Lower Swansea Valley. A formal report on the Project was published in spring 1967.

Lee Valley Regional Park

In 1961 representatives from many local authorities inspected this area and decided that it could and should be improved. By April 1963 they had formed a consortium and the Civic Trust was invited to make a broad appraisal of the Valley's potential. In July 1964 the Trust published its Report and by late 1966 an Act, supported by fifteen local authorities and other bodies, had been passed and a special Authority for the Park set up. What inspired such progress and what is the grand conception

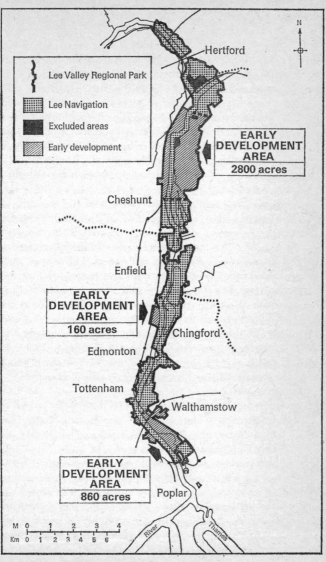

Lee Valley Regional Park

- Lee Valley Regional Park
- Lee Navigation
- Excluded areas
- Early development

N

Hertford

EARLY
DEVELOPMENT
AREA
2800 acres

Cheshunt

Enfield

EARLY
DEVELOPMENT
AREA
160 acres

Chingford

Edmonton

Tottenham

Walthamstow

EARLY
DEVELOPMENT
AREA
860 acres

Poplar

River Thames

M 0 1 2 3 4
Km 0 1 2 3 4 5 6

18 Lee Valley Regional Park

that fired the imagination of so many diverse organizations and people?

The Lee – second river to the Thames in London – starts at Luton sewage works. In its 58-mile journey to join the Thames near Blackwall it passes through the rural land and suburbs of Hertfordshire and the built-up areas of Essex, before becoming in its last twenty miles what the Report calls 'London's kitchen garden, its well, its privy and its workshop'. Certainly, far too much is being asked of the river and as a result it has lost its capacity for self-renewal. What was once Izaak Walton's idyllic river has become 'an ignoble stream'.

Within the river valley there lie large and small areas of land, some derelict and disfigured, some used for playing-fields and sailing lakes. The Trust identified sixteen separate sites within the total length of the Valley, each of which could become a park. Their area comes to 6,000 acres, most of which is unused. This compares with 8,800 acres of existing public open space in the former administrative county of London. The area of open water in the Lee Valley is 2,493 acres and exceeds that of the open water on the Norfolk Broads. The Trust's Report imaginatively proposed that these sixteen sites should be planned as a whole and developed for outdoor recreation and enjoyment as a linear park. This would unify city and country, and give the space and facilities for a fuller life to many of London's millions. By summer 1968, the Park Authority had prepared a draft Master Plan and started consultations.

Inland Waters and Recreation of the West Midlands

At the request of the Central Council for Physical Recreation (C.C.P.R.) in 1961, the Physical Education Department of Birmingham University initiated a survey of inland waters in the midland counties of Warwickshire, Worcestershire, Staffordshire, Shropshire and Herefordshire. They make up an area where most activities, facilities and trends can be found. The recreations surveyed were angling, bird-watching, canoeing, hydro-planing, cruising (in motor-boats), rowing, sailing, swimming (including underwater) and water ski-ing. The waters covered were reservoirs (waterworks and canal feeders), 'wet' or flooded gravel pits, canals, rivers and the few lakes in this area. Information was obtained both from individual sportsmen, their clubs and governing bodies, and from the 'controllers' of the waters surveyed – the landowners, the canal and water undertakers and river boards (now river authorities).

The Report of the Survey (published in 1964) estimates that there are in the area about 200,000 anglers, 6,000 hirers of pleasure cruisers each year, 3,000 members of sailing clubs, 2,000 of rowing and 750 of canoeing clubs. It showed 'conclusively that interest and participation in recreation on inland waters have increased very substantially in recent years' and that this trend would be even more pronounced if more suitable waters were available. The Report discussed the use of existing waters and mentioned the resentment some people feel because many waterworks reservoirs are out of bounds to the public. It considered that 'organized access is the only type of access' for these reservoirs and this was 'best achieved through the medium of a club'. Canal feeder reservoirs are particularly useful for recreation; twenty-five of the twenty-nine in the area were used for some activity, fishing and sailing predominating, and the Report argued that more of these should be set aside elsewhere for recreation. The Report referred to the efforts of the Sand and Gravel Association to promote recreational activities on wet pits and suggested that perhaps the best solution would be for local authorities to purchase and develop some of them.

The surveyors were 'pleasantly surprised at the small amount of reported conflict' between the followers of the various sports but said that all activities were to some extent 'guilty of a failure to appreciate the needs and interests of other users'. They advocated a code of behaviour for water users and the C.C.P.R., following cooperation with the many other bodies concerned, published one in August 1966. The Report stressed the need for 'a clear statement at governmental level of national policy about water-based recreation'. This would give guidance to the British Waterways Board, the River Authorities, the Water Undertakings and other water controllers. It is significant that 'The Countryside in 1970' Conference of

November 1965 recommended that planning, navigation, water and river authorities should 'meet as far as is practicable and with the least harm to the countryside, recreational needs on coastal and inland waters'. The Birmingham University Report emphasized the importance of central policy to the planned development of water-based recreation at regional level, for which it favoured a Regional Development Council. To some extent, the Sports Council and its regional councils should meet this need.

The Report shows how urgent are the demands for facilities for outdoor recreation; the importance of these issues in national life; the wide scope for action with existing resources in most areas; and the great need for central encouragement of regional and local initiative. Clearly much can be achieved on the lines indicated by the Report and in its own words this 'could make a significant contribution to the quality of life in an urban society'.

Appraisal

Dereliction of the type ruining the Lower Swansea Valley can be found in all the old centres of the Industrial Revolution. It can be tackled and cleared away; Lancashire, Staffordshire and some other progressive authorities already have successes to their credit. Neglect and misuse of resources, like that in the Lee Valley, can be found on some stretches of most rivers, such as the River Trent. The general pattern for action has now been formulated and could readily be adopted; Newcastle already has its own master-plan for the Tyne. The West Midland Survey reveals how old eyesores can be made into new playgrounds. It is already being acted upon but much more civic and individual action is required everywhere. These projects reflect urban man's growing distaste for the squalor of his surroundings, and his dissatisfaction with the present provisions for his aesthetic and leisure needs. Certainly they all show how large is the scope for creative action, and how determined are some people and authorities to break through the fumblings and inertia arising from past and present failures.

OPEN COUNTRY

Most people today are content with being able to enjoy a view from or near to their cars or to roam short distances in pleasant surroundings. A more active few penetrate into the wilderness of mountain or moorland or ramble over unspoiled coast. To nearly all the public, such features as grasslands and heath seem a natural part of the landscape and have unity as open country. But their naturalness and unity are only in the mind of the user.

Grasslands

The chalk and limestone grasslands of England are of special importance as attractive open spaces for the urban dweller. Few appreciate that they are an artefact – a man-made creation – and that their continuance depends upon management. Fewer still appreciate that such grasslands may be eliminated within a few years.

The development of chalk grasslands probably began after the forest clearances of Neolithic times. This interaction of man and nature is revealed by archaeological features, the barrows and camps from the Neolithic, Bronze and Iron Ages and the outlines of 'Celtic fields'. The intensive agricultural use of the cleared sites gave rise to erosion of the poorer forest soils, until lower crop yields led to fresh lands being sought. Cultivation of the valleys in Saxon times probably eased the pressure on the chalk lands and these, in time, became grasslands. For centuries, they were grazed by sheep and rabbits, particularly between the eighteen- and nineteen-thirties, and they have come to be regarded by most people as part of the natural landscape.

During the inter-war years, when the land was cheap, many thousands of acres were afforested. Subsequently, economic changes in agriculture led to the ploughing-up of grasslands and their intensive cultivation with fertilizers and modern machinery. With the great reduction in the rabbit population and the decline in sheep-rearing, in many areas grasslands have tended to pass to scrub and coarse vegetation. This can become impenetrable to walkers and disfigure or ruin the amenity of grassland. The number of plant species diminishes rapidly, and animal life changes; for example, many of the more interesting insects disappear.

To maintain these grasslands requires a new administrative approach. Many County Councils now have Countryside Committees which seek to acquire and maintain open spaces for public enjoyment; the Nature Conservancy and county Naturalists' Trusts also have rights over numerous grasslands. But these activities touch only part of the whole pattern of grasslands; much more action is required, nationally and locally. The policy measures must be complemented by new techniques in management, basically intended to have the same effect as grazing where this is no longer practicable. Experiments are being carried out with chemicals and with new equipment. Fresh systems are proposed to enable these lands to be incorporated on an economic basis within modern farms. The public must be prepared to pay for the administration and management necessary. And they must recognize that these grasslands offer an excellent opportunity for leaving some choice to posterity in the use of land.

Heathlands

The lowland heathlands of southern England provide some of the most popular open spaces; many are also commons. They extend from the Brecklands of Norfolk and Suffolk to the heaths of the South Lizard in Cornwall. To the untrained eye heaths tend to appear a uniform mixture of heather and gorse. In fact, they harbour a great variety of animals and plants and are of considerable significance to educationalists and scientists. For example, the Dorset heaths are the habitat of the Dartford warbler and two uncommon reptiles, the smooth snake and the sand lizard. The vegetation includes pine heath, stretches of thicket, valley bogs and grassland, as well as heathland. To maintain them as heaths requires grazing and burning, without which they would revert to woodland.

One of the most valuable studies of recent years is that on Dorset heaths by Dr N. W. Moore. Like the chalk grasslands, the Dorset heaths illustrate the influence of man on nature.

Human pressures have greatly reduced them over the past 150 years. Their area has dwindled from 75,000 acres in 1811 to 25,000 acres in 1960. It is now broken up into small pieces which give little sense of open country and have a poor chance of survival outside nature reserves. The reduction in the size inevitably impoverishes the animal and plant life.

These changes, which appear to be typical of those in other heathlands, arise from the developments in agriculture discussed in Chapter 3. Afforestation, tourism and its popularity with prospective home-owners exert great pressure on lowland England. Heathland sites are also favoured for building because they are a source of gravel and sand for constructional purposes. It seems unlikely that, unless strong measures are taken, the little heathland that still survives will escape the developer for long. Parts of the areas most important to science are included in national nature reserves and require positive management to maintain their scientific and educational values. But unless the public actively support measures for conservation, it is probable that heathlands will cease to exist on any scale outside nature reserves by the year 2000.

Moorland and Mountain

As noted in Chapter 3, much of the land surface of Britain is moor and mountain; in the Scottish Highlands alone there are several million acres. Since the Ice Age, the quality of their soils has deteriorated and bogs and peat mosses have tended to oust woodlands and grasslands. Man's activities have greatly influenced the pace and direction of change. Reduction of the original woodland cover began in Neolithic times and was intensified in the Middle Ages by Norse settlers in upland areas such as the Lake District. They cleared the valley woods, drained the swamps and opened up areas to sheep-farming and other economic development which, in succeeding centuries, gave rise to the treasured 'romantic' upland landscape.

The soil is usually too poor and infertile to be cultivated without heavy doses of manure and fertilizers, notably lime, which reduces its acidity. Much of the vegetation is heather. In those areas which are under management, this is usually burned every seven to fifteen years. Remnants of woodland and grassland on the steeper slopes testify that woodlands once extended up to 2,000 ft. The erosion of upland peat continues, and bogs and mosses are common in the poorly drained areas. These conditions and the climate have led to the range of animal inhabitants being relatively small. They include, however, some very interesting and uncommon species, such as the wild cat (only found in the Scottish Highlands), the pine marten and polecat, and the golden eagle and peregrine.

Burning, draining and grazing are still man's main activities, with afforestation increasing in importance. Woods remove less from the soil than grazing animals, which make a continuing demand on soil fertility. Hence grazing, including overgrazing by deer, without intensive management as pioneered by Sir George Stapledon, may totally exhaust the soil here and leave 'wet deserts'. Afforestation can help to pre-

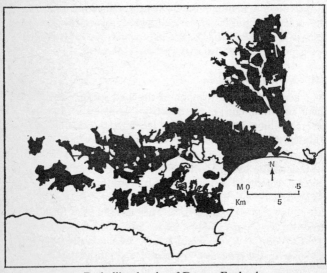

19 Dwindling heaths of Dorset, England.
a The heathlands of east Dorset and of Hampshire west of the River Avon in 1811. Based on the first edition of the Ordnance Survey. The Black Down outlier south-west of Dorchester is not shown for spacing reasons

vent leaching and soil erosion, and wisely chosen trees can, in
time, restore the quality of the soil. The creation of new woodlands has led to an increase in wild life and in some areas even
to plagues of voles. Some birds and mammals have returned to
areas which they have not frequented for many years. Clearly,
afforestation changes the landscape; in the south-west of England there has been conflict for many years over its effects on
the moors. To compensate for the loss of open country, forests
should be managed for their total biological productivity and
planted with landscape values in mind.

There are, of course, other qualities in these upland areas.
Many have important reserves of minerals; clay in the south-
west; limestone in the Pennines; peat, valuable for fertilizers,
and constructional rock in many localities. But above all,
they hold that most vital resource – water. The peat-covered

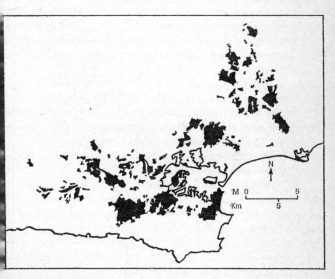

b The heathlands of east Dorset and of Hampshire west of the River
Avon in 1960. Based on the third edition of the Ordnance Survey and
on observations by Dr N. W. Moore (Crown Copyright reserved.
Reproduced by permission of the *Journal of Ecology*)

moorlands act as 'sponge-reservoirs' but ignorant management has often led to a loss of water-holding capacity, hence the too-frequent floods. In some areas, however, if man is to retain the present condition of the land, he must find a way to achieve a result similar to that once obtained from land uses which have now been abandoned.

Jostling for importance with water supply is, of course, man's demand for quiet and wilderness, tourism, adventure and challenge. How can all these values be balanced and harmonized? In some cases upland reservoirs can provide for outdoor recreation and be blended into the landscape, but this is not always possible. The National Parks Commission opposed the reservoir at Cow Green (see p. 126) because of its intrusion into a wilderness and the threat to the waterfalls at Cauldron Snout and High Force – two outstanding natural features. Some pursuits – for example, shooting and rambling – are not easily reconciled with different land uses and with each other. The climber is, perhaps, luckier, since his terrain is least susceptible to change, although in Snowdonia clubs have had to issue specific advice to prevent wear and tear on favoured climbs.

Appraisal

Most open country is largely the product of man and nature interacting over the centuries. The treasured wildness is in part artificial. And it is decreasing.

Particularly hard-pressed are the lowland heaths and grass-lands near the great centres of population. Threatened, too, are the wilderness areas. A strategic plan for open country is required to ensure that heathlands, grasslands, moors and mountains are planned as part of an integrated system and to take full account of regional and country parks and multi-purpose areas. Special regard should be given to areas such as the Scottish Highlands, which are significant on a European scale.

Undoubtedly this open country is of great importance to man. It will be recognized as a vital element in his pattern of life as his needs for space become better understood. But the open country changes inexorably and will not remain open without positive management. This requires the application of proper social cost–benefit analysis. Above all, the public must be educated to understand, respect and enjoy the values of open country. The more these are appreciated, the more likely it is that money and measures will be available to continue and enhance these features of the landscape.

COMMONS

The common lands and village greens of England and Wales cover about one and a half million acres, and are a major part of the uncommitted land in the country. They include woodlands and scrub, marsh and moorland, grass, pasture and arable land, and they sustain a wide variety of activities. Common lands are unique because of their links with past forms of land ownership, customs and uses, and because of people's attitudes to them. Yet, contrary to popular belief, commons are not publicly owned; the general public do not usually have legal rights of access over them, although under the Law of Property Act, 1925, they have a statutory right of access to *urban* commons for fresh air and exercise. Often records of ownership have been lost in antiquity and even those possessing rights over commons – for example, to graze cattle, to fish, to cut wood or extract peat and minerals – may no longer exercise them. Perhaps the major uses of commons today are for sheep-grazing in the north and west and for amenity and recreation in the south and east.

From 1955 to 1958, a Royal Commission on Common Land made a thorough review of commons and their report is a fascinating document of considerable social and historical interest. The Commission reported that many commons were neglected and no effective organization or management existed for them. They recommended that, subject to certain conditions, the public should have right of access for fresh air and exercise to *all* commons. One of the major proposals made by the Commission was that claims to ownership of, and to rights over, common land should be registered. This is to be implemented through the Commons Registration Act, 1965, under which registration of common land (and town and village greens) in England and Wales should be completed by 1 January 1970, after which unregistered rights will be lost. Many voluntary bodies, led by the Commons, Footpaths and Open Spaces Preservation Society, are concerting measures over registration. An official explanatory booklet is obtainable from council offices and post offices.

A second major recommendation by the Commission was that local committees should be set up to manage registered land; this will require further legislation. To give guidance on management the Nuffield Foundation and the University of Cambridge in 1961 provided resources for a survey by a specially qualified team. A preliminary paper was submitted in November 1965 to 'The Countryside in 1970' Conference and a comprehensive report * was published in 1967. It included proposals for voluntary management schemes by local commoners, landowners and local authorities; it classified commons on the basis of their physical and historical qualities; suggested principles for codes of practice relating to most uses and activities; and indicated the powers required by local management committees.

One of the most imaginative recent schemes is that sponsored jointly by the Freemen and City Council of Newcastle upon Tyne. In February 1966 they announced the winning designs (first prize £2,000) in a national competition (the first in Britain for sixteen years) for a landscape master-plan for the Town Moor. This is a site of about 1,000 acres in the heart of the city. It is mainly open grassland used for cattle grazing by the Freemen and is owned by the Council. Although surrounded by built-up areas, it has distinct character and beauty and a wild and open aspect. The scheme, on which work has started, provides a major open space for Newcastle and Tyneside and will function as a regional focal point for a wide range of activities. Playing-fields, golf-course, sailing facilities, car parks, cattle grazing areas, 100 acres of nature reserve and many other features are blended in this multi-purpose project, which, like that for the Lee Valley, demonstrates how important are the principles of unity, comprehensiveness and quality.

* Full report published in May, 1967: *Commons and Village Greens*, by Denman, Roberts and Smith; Leonard Hill Books, 1967.

In the 1970s the public is obviously destined to become closely involved in attempts to improve the quality of the environment. Because their management will affect so many people, the way in which problems are tackled on common lands will obviously receive the most publicity. Their management must, therefore, embody the very best of modern thought and practice and should seek to enhance their biological capital. What happens to common lands will change not only part of the physical environment but also a number of social patterns. Imaginatively handled, the management of these commons could become a matter of pride to every citizen and so patterns of cooperation and communal action of wide-ranging application could be developed.

CHAPTER 14

PEOPLE IN BRITAIN'S COUNTRYSIDE

THE emphasis so far has been on what is happening to land, air, water and wild life. But in this chapter the spotlight is focused on the dominant animal, the greatest predator of all – man. As already shown, it is not the amount of land man is likely to take for housing, industry and other urban uses that matters so much as where he builds and the uses to which he puts the rest of the rural landscape. These include agriculture and forestry, recreation and tourism, and the technological requirements for moving power and people.

And it is in terms of people that these uses must first be studied. What are the motives for the various activities? What are the needs of the different settlements? What do the trends suggest? These and many more questions must be answered if a true picture is to be obtained of the implications of total population growth and if the main directions of change are to be detected and guided, where necessary, to socially desirable patterns. A generally acceptable quality of environment cannot be created by dreaming at a desk or on sectional and arbitrary lines. The planner must identify and understand the factors of human ecology involved; in particular, the mainsprings of an individual or group response to fresh physical situations.

One of the problems in studying the needs of rural communities is to understand the real feelings of the rural dweller. It is all too easy for the townsman to place superficial interpretations on many actions but if he does so, then it will not be possible to plan successfully for the needs of the communities. To understand rural sociology it is necessary to share the experience of country-dwellers and to participate in community life. It is with these considerations in mind that a few of the major factors and trends now influencing rural life are to be assessed.

SENTIMENT

Sentiment about land is still very important. It includes the legitimate pride in heritage of a landed family, the feelings of those who make a creed of agricultural conservation, and the attachment of some workers to the land. There is much sentiment in the attitude of many townspeople – the portraits of village life on radio and television often reveal this – but frequently their feeling descends into sentimentality. Some people believe that the really lasting and worthwhile values are to be found only on the land – often underestimating the great cultural, social and economic achievements of the towns. But increasingly the sentiment arises from an understanding of how important natural things are to man, of the refreshment of mind and body which country and coast can offer, and of how towns can benefit from being set in a well-managed countryside. Sentiment is a real factor in determining the pattern and type of many rural settlements and it must be understood and evaluated if social needs are to be met.

Sentiment makes quite a number of owners disregard immediate gain as they provide for posterity by planting hardwood trees, and spend time and loving care on their property. Some still retain the approach, common to eighteenth-century landowners, of regarding their estates as settled on their families for ever and this is conducive to long-term aims in management. Others, however, find this no longer possible. Many workers could easily obtain jobs in towns, where their pay packets would be bigger and conditions easier, but they stay where they are because of the deep satisfaction they find in their work and the relationships they share within their local community. More and more people save so that when they retire they can move to coastal areas and to the south and west of England. And as mobility and personal affluence increase, more commute long distances from homes in the country to their places of work.

Economic Factors

Most landowners have to manage their estates primarily on a commercial basis. Normally they have to farm the land to pay expenses or provide themselves with a living. Only in a few cases as yet has the income from other sources – for example, recreation – been great enough to provide an equal, or higher, return. Economic pressures are clearly effecting fundamental changes in the rural population. For example, since 1946 the numbers and types of machines in use on British farms have increased enormously. This and the many other changes described in Chapter 3 demand a different type of manager and worker, one more closely akin to his urban counterpart and with a new approach to the land. Urban criteria start to prevail.

Many other changes follow from the overall fall in the 'true' rural population and in the manpower available for managing the countryside. One is the decrease in the numbers of 'length-men', who used to maintain roadside verges. Now County Surveyors have to employ chemicals or flail-machines, both of which tend to reduce the amenity of country roads. Many agricultural workers had a wide range of skills but the opera-tion of machinery was not one of them. The older type of craftsman, like the hedger, is being ousted by the skilled technician, who can run a complex and valuable piece of machinery without supervision and do essential running re-pairs. The tasks around the farm are more highly organized and mechanized, and the farmer cannot allow casual and un-trained labour to use his expensive equipment, fertilizers and pesticides. These changes, and increased mobility, are leading to the growth of a new class of specialized agricultural workers who drive in their cars to their work or are ferried there in transport provided by the farmer.

Other developments include the emergence of new rural industries. Now that electricity can be obtained in almost any district, firms can set up self-contained factories wherever it seems convenient to do so. Much of this small-scale industrial development is sponsored or helped by the Council for Small Industries in Rural Areas, notably in trades requiring few resources other than skill and enterprise; for example, plastics and precision engineering. These tend, however, to fit within existing settlements and to some extent offset the decline of trades traditionally associated with agriculture.

In many upland areas and on poor land in some agricultural districts afforestation has also led to changes. In a few areas it has eliminated the shepherds but in others it has arrested the decline in population and in some instances already reversed the trend. Afforestation needs skilled and vigorous labour, not only for the work in the forests but also for the ancillary industries it fosters, such as pulp mills and chip-board factories. The foresters are highly professional, with a sense of dedication; some were brought up and educated in towns. The forest workers receive special training and develop considerable skills; to use them efficiently requires continuity of employment and the facilities of well-organized villages.

POPULATION MOVEMENT

In Britain, as in almost every other country, there is a general drift of population from the countryside into the towns. There are, however, few clear-cut situations and many cross-currents of activity, some complementary and some opposing. In this context, it was authoritatively reported in March 1966 that over a million people had moved into rural districts since 1951. The effects of re-shaping transport systems, of stimulating rural industries, creating forestry-based villages, developing 'overspill' areas, and of the migrations to retirement havens and dormitories – all these tend to overlap. Problems arise where settlements are of one type; they also arise where incompatible types are thrown together. Some settlements are expanding too fast and social services have not kept pace; others are declining to a point where they are no longer viable communities.

Over the country as a whole the rural population is still declining, and the total is even lower if one excludes the immediate dormitories of the expanding towns. The number of agricultural workers was 976,000 in 1946; it had dropped to 551,000 by 1965. If, as some already assume, south-east

England must be regarded as potentially a large urban area with parkland, then the true rural population must be thought of as declining every time anyone moves from another part of Britain to the south-east or to the towns. The 1961 Census showed losses of ten per cent to be widespread. The main 'exporting' areas were the west – Wales, Devon and Cornwall – the north-east and north-west of England, the great agricultural areas of eastern England, and the Highlands and Islands of Scotland. The main 'importing' area was the south-east with its favoured climate and easy access to London. Most retired people and commuters are to be found here.

Details of the growth and movement of Britain's population between 1951 and 1961 were given in maps published by the Ordnance Survey in 1966. These show the rapid growth of populations on the outskirts of most towns and a decline in numbers in the centres, the speed of development along the south coast and rural depopulation.

Another important factor affecting people in the countryside is the interaction of the new towns and cities projected for the next two decades. Much will depend on their siting and planning and special account must be given to the urban–rural relationships.

What is lacking everywhere is reliable information on which to base the provision of the costly apparatus of modern civilization. In this context one of the key features is education. Undoubtedly the inadequacy of school facilities has contributed to rural depopulation in many areas. What are the relevant standards? Some assert that below a population of 2,000, or an infant school of 50 pupils and 2 teachers, a community is no longer viable. How valid are such assertions? Until information to answer such questions is sought systematically and acted upon, the situation can only deteriorate.

EXPECTATIONS

Most people who live in the country now demand social facilities and amenities comparable to those found in towns. New types of rural dwellers and different patterns of settlements require a fresh approach in education and planning. But an even stronger demand for changes in the countryside comes from people who do not live there except during their holidays, who do not work there for more than short periods or who go there only for recreation. These are mainly the town people – the 85 per cent of Britain's population who live on 10 per cent of the land. With their new mobility and free time over forty million people pour on to the countryside, not evenly spread on all the rest of the land but on to the choicest pieces of coast and country. As many of the new rural populations of retired people and commuters choose to live in such spots the result is increasingly unsatisfactory for everyone. In sum, this problem is one of too many people in a few select localities, often concentrated together in too short a time.

These town-dwellers expect the countryside to include hardwood trees, hedgerows, green and golden fields, shady nooks, commons on which to play and picnic, and all the variety and detail which makes Britain's landscape so attractive. Very few of them realize that the landscape is largely man-made and requires considerable planning and management. And they are not yet ready to pay the economic price for their use and enjoyment of the countryside. Tourism is the biggest earner of American dollars; outdoor recreation is big business. But neither contributes much directly to paying for the view and few of those who receive the direct benefit of visitors in a locality are involved in the management of local natural resources. Yet land must be managed to meet the new scale of these modern activities and they, in turn, must somehow be made to subscribe towards the cost of maintaining and creating an attractive landscape.

Outdoor Recreation and Mobility

The scale of these activities and their impact on land and water has been outlined in Chapter 5. Seasonal and peak congestions not only make heavy wear and tear on the natural environment inevitable but also cause new strains on people and demand many extra workers at these periods. Existing arrangements are not adequate, nor are they geared to such a situation. Inevitably this will give rise to further migrations as the popular places become overrun. These changes are taking place at a time when the impact of leisure activities on the countryside requires more creative management and more sophisticated use of the land. A new race of managers and technicians may be required to manage the landscape for amenity and recreation. All these factors must be carefully and continuously assessed and measures taken to prevent their adverse effects, otherwise they may disrupt existing settlements and the lives of the people in them.

Users and Students

Many urban people now work in the countryside to carry out technological tasks there; for example, to select a route for a power cable, a pipeline, a road or a site for a kiosk. They must seek for their task the site or route which is technically the best and often have to modify their proposals to meet other claims, such as those of science and amenity. These people, too, must be educated to see the countryside as an entity and to understand what they can do to maintain and enhance its qualities.

Finally, in this brief survey of people in the countryside, it is essential to mention the increasing number of teachers and children, scientists and students who make use of it. These come for short periods, usually to areas of special interest. Their numbers are increasing but as their objective is primarily the pursuit of knowledge and understanding, they may be expected to create fewer problems than other visitors. Their activities lead, however, to the growth of centres in remote and beautiful spots and stimulate further pressures on the countryside. An Outdoor Studies Code published in 1968 should help to alleviate these problems.

No note on people in the countryside would be complete without a reference to the work of the many bodies directly concerned with it. Some have 'grass roots', such as the National Federation of Women's Institutes, the parish councils, the churches and chapels, but they have, of course, acquired national status and have been influenced by urban as well as rural thinking. There are bodies with specific aims, such as the Council for Small Industries, the Rural Community Councils, the county Naturalists' Trusts and many others. Any attempt to plan for the countryside must take account of these bodies; their participation and support are indispensable. In effect, they are part of the essential process of adult education in a modern democracy.

Appraisal

All the many developments touched on here call for the utmost care if harmoniously balanced rural communities are to be developed. Conflicts have already emerged in many areas. Coastal resorts dependent on holiday-makers find their peace and profit shattered by gangs of urban hooligans. Some areas, such as Cornwall, object to being deprived of industry just so that they may retain their character for tourism and retirement. They object to being dependent on the seasonal resources of the tourist and the slender revenues of the retired. Although many people of urban background now reside in rural areas, these are not likely to provide manpower for the management of the landscape. The fall in population of rural settlements and the changes in its composition give rise to further problems, as in smaller communities it becomes difficult to cater properly for those who do wish to stay on. More facts are required about the people who live in, work on, use or enjoy the countryside. In particular, society must know the purposes for which it requires rural settlements, and take into account their capacity to remain viable as the population soars during the next half-century.

If cohesive rural communities are not to be obliterated and if great waste and erosion are to be avoided, these problems cannot be left to the 'invisible hand' of Adam Smith. Much more talent and effort should be deployed to solving them.

The Development Commissioners cogently argued the case for a positive policy for the countryside, particularly on social and economic grounds, in their 1966 Report *Aspects of Rural Development*. They press for 'the formulation now of a policy for the planned development of regions subject to, or threatened with, rural depopulation' and favour the planning and selection of 'trigger' areas for vigorous action.

These issues would be difficult enough to cope with even if the process of adjustment to the increasing pressures of population could be gradual, but time for correcting mistakes is just not available.

CHAPTER 15

POPULATION

There is an accumulative cruelty in a number of
men, though none in particular are ill-natured.
                                        Lord Halifax

FIRST, what is the extent of the population explosion? Is the
rate of change great enough to warrant so much debate and so
much gloom?

SCALE

Table 5 contrasts the phenomenal growth of recent years with
that of man's earlier history. The 1960s had, on average, 4 births
and 2 deaths each second. One calculation based on the current
rate of increase suggests that within 260 years there could be
400,000 million people – that is, there would be as many per
acre all over the world as we now find in Greater London. It

TABLE 5
Growth of World Population

Millions	Year (approx.)	Years taken to increase world population by 1,000 million
1,000	1830	200,000
2,000	1930	100
3,000	1960	30
4,000	1975 (forecast)	15

has also been calculated that, by the year 2400, for each
individual on earth there will be about one square yard of land.
The overall impact of these numbers on resources and living
standards has already been discussed; clearly they would
eliminate most of those things which today are thought to
make up a 'quality' environment. And not enough thought

TABLE 6
Population (*in millions*)

Area	1960	1970	1980	1990	2000
SOUTH ASIA					
Medium variant	858	1,090	1,366	1,677	2,023
Continued recent					
trends	858	1,092	1,418	1,898	2,598
EAST ASIA *					
Medium variant	793	910	1,038	1,163	1,284
Continued recent					
trends	793	941	1,139	1,419	1,803
EUROPE †					
Medium variant	425	454	479	504	527
Continued recent					
trends	425	460	496	533	571
AFRICA					
Medium variant	273	346	449	587	768
Continued recent					
trends	273	348	458	620	860
SOVIET UNION					
Medium variant	214	246	278	316	353
Continued recent					
trends	214	253	295	345	402
LATIN AMERICA					
Medium variant	212	282	374	488	624
Continued recent					
trends	212	284	387	537	756
NORTHERN AMERICA ‡					
Medium variant	199	227	262	306	354
Continued recent					
trends	199	230	272	325	388
OCEANIA §					
Medium variant	15·7	18·7	22·6	27·0	31·9
Continued recent					
trends	15·7	18·4	22·0	26·7	32·5
WORLD TOTAL					
Medium variant	2,990	3,574	4,269	5,068	5,965
Continued recent					
trends	2,990	3,626	4,487	5,704	7,410

* Includes Mainland China, Japan, Mongolia, Korea and China (Taiwan).
† Outside the Soviet Union and Turkey.   ‡ Includes also Hawaii.
§ Not including Hawaii.
Based on United Nations Provisional Report on World Population Prospects in 1963 (Doc. ST/SOA/SER.R.7). Medium variant is the more plausible 'medium' projection which allows for changes in the most recent trends.

has yet been given to the effects on world cultures and patterns of power of the increasing disparities between races and continents.

The world population in 1964 was estimated at over 3,220 million. Table 6 shows there is a firm prospect of this figure being doubled by A.D. 2000 and Table 7 shows the current

TABLE 7

Current Rates of Increase of Population

Region	Mid-1964 population (in millions)	Percentage annual rate of increase (1960–3)
Latin America	237	2·8
Africa	304	2·5
South Asia	943	2·4
Oceania	17	2·2
East Asia	840	1·4
Northern America	211	1·6
U.S.S.R.	228	1·6
Europe	440	0·9

rates of growth. Latin America leads in rate of increase, followed closely by Africa and Asia. The developing countries in these continents will account for about seven eighths of the anticipated increase, although the wealthy, sophisticated U.S.A. will have a population of almost 400 million, and the U.S.S.R. should exceed this number. Death-rates everywhere continue to decline and the developing countries maintain high fertility.

Table 8 compares the population of Europe, still the most densely populated continent, with that of the rest of the world. Before 1939 the net reproduction rate in Europe was declining. Europe faced serious problems. Since 1945 the rate and the total population have increased, but yet Table 8 reveals that the *proportion* of Europeans is rapidly going down. In Britain the population in 1700 was around seven million, and birth- and death-rates were high. The better diets following the agricultural revolution which began later that century and the improvement in hygiene, clothing and housing initiated about

TABLE 8

Comparison of Population
(*in millions*)

Year	Europe*	World	Percentage of world population in Europe
1900	320	1,550	20·6
1950	395	2,494	15·8
1970†	454	3,574	11·2
2000†	527	5,965	8·8
2000‡	571	7,410	7·7

* Excludes U.S.S.R.   † Medium variant trend.   ‡ Recent trends.

the mid nineteenth century, led to a phenomenal growth in population. The latter decades of the nineteenth century saw an increase of 4 million every year. The population is now 52 million despite a decline in the average size of families from 4·5 in 1900 to 3·1 in 1951. Total population change in Britain for 1951–64 is shown on page 311. If this trend continues the population in A.D. 2000 may well approach 75 million, although there has been a continuing slow decline in the birth rate since 1964.

Pessimists liken this population explosion to a cancerous growth – as life gone mad. Optimistic observers regard this century as providing an aberration in the normal balance of births and deaths and predict that, when all the developing countries have had their 'demographic revolution', numbers will return to normal – whatever that is! This view takes insufficient account of the fundamental changes noted above and the economic and social activity now taking place.

CAUSES AND IMPLICATIONS

What are the main causes of the population explosion? Primarily, it stems from 'death-control'. The birth-rate has risen recently (from 1945 onwards) in Western countries and has stayed high in Asia, Africa and South America, and the average length of life has increased, but these do not cause the great population explosion. For example, the birth-rate per

1,000 in the rapidly expanding population of Mauritius was 37 in 1900 but only 38 in 1964. Fertility is related to traditional values and social factors; mortality responds directly to scientific and technical advances.

It is the dramatic elimination, mainly since 1945, of the major killing and crippling diseases like malaria which has led to the great upsurge in population numbers. This process of control is itself accelerating. For example, a new product marketed in 1966 is intended to relieve sufferers from bilharziasis – a disease exceeded only by malaria in its impact on human life.

Europe really started the population explosion. It was the first continent to obtain from the application of science and industry more food and materials and better health and conditions for its peoples. As the factors which reduced its death-rate have spread across the globe, the populations of Africa, Asia and South America are now expanding. And, as in Europe during the seventeenth to nineteenth centuries, this gives rise to nationalist and expansionist trends. There are two vital differences, however, between the situation then and now: soon there will be no empty lands to emigrate to; also the latest weapons and the split between East and West make 'total' war possible. Population pressure is quite likely to become a major force in international affairs – to some extent it is already. It may even lead to more fearful, as yet undreamed of, polarizations of peoples, dwarfing even those of George Orwell's *1984* or Aldous Huxley's *Brave New World*. In fact, sheer weight of numbers could lead to a 'lemming-like' collapse of the structure of society.

The gap between the living standards of many nations – for example, between the U.S.A.'s and India's – can seriously prejudice human values. As the disparity between the population of India and its food supply remains and as North American farm surpluses – the only substantial ones – are used up, the situation may grow more menacing every day. It seems inevitable that food aid programmes will have to be linked to birth-control measures; for example, a mass issue of the intra-uterine coil device (I.U.D. or loop) could be made with every ton of grain.

The changing patterns of races must soon affect all the basic issues – living standards, social and political values, religions, governments and, of course, whether man lives at war or in peace. Clearly there can be no planning for the wise use of natural resources that is not founded upon the central issue of population control.

Many other vitally important and urgent facets of this expansion in numbers require attention. The genetic effects of keeping alive those with organic and other disabilities to pass on to their offspring can have a profound influence on man. In nature the weak and inefficient do not survive. An increase in the number of defective humans could debase everything; the sheer weight of numbers might lead to disregard for the individual and for the environment. Foolproof methods of birth-control are imminent. Sex-selection is on the way. The implications of these products of science and technology are enormous. How will individuals and states decide on the numbers and sexes to be born? If some nations rear more children, then sooner or later others will have to have less.

There is yet another significant aspect of the vast increases in populations everywhere, namely the 'age balance' of the population. For example, in Britain the censuses showed the number of 85-year-olds to be 224,000 in 1951 and 338,000 in 1961; the estimate for A.D. 2000 is 677,000. This is, of course inevitable as death-control measures spread (even though, because of the post-1945 'baby boom', the average age in some countries – for example, France – is currently lower than for many years). If, however, present high fertility rates continue, there will also be in the twenty-first century even more younger people. For example, the effect of both trends in Britain would probably be, overall, a younger population. As the proportion of young and old people in the population increases greater strain is placed on the middle age groups. The number of persons dependent on each member of the working population is rising. It might become necessary, at some future point, to cut, rather than prolong, the time spent in school or retirement. Essentially, the past two centuries have seen man's relative equilibrium and slow rate of increase transformed. Thus if man does not soon voluntarily control births he may be faced with possibilities repugnant on moral, social and religious grounds: for example, having to seek permission to have children or the use of eugenic and geriatric agents to determine the numbers and composition of the population. This may become the logical result of man's using the powers which have enabled him, so far, to flout natural processes.

CONTROL FACTORS

Population issues are all-pervasive. They penetrate into the mores of private and public life. Their sources lie deep in man's basic reproductive drives, and are modified by centuries of environmental conditioning. Interference with them touches every facet of society. But it is essential, at least for some decades, to limit population numbers by reducing the numbers born. What criteria should be adopted?

The adequacy of food and natural resources is obviously one criterion. But, historically and at the present time, food alone has not proved to be a strong limiting factor in the determination of the numbers of a family or nation. In the developing countries, food supplies have nearly always been inadequate – for example, near-famine conditions prevail in parts of India – yet this is not apparently controlling numbers. In the developed countries, the rapid gains in food and affluence are still too sharp in living memory for any bald assertion of Malthusian dangers of starvation from over-population to be effective. Besides, in these countries, it is often the unskilled and underfed who have the largest families, and are thereby sometimes the poorer.

The quantity of raw materials available has so far exercised little effect on total population numbers. While it may do so under the pressures of the vastly greater numbers of the next century, the situation may then be altogether too urgent on other counts. It may also be expected that man's inventiveness in respect of materials will lead to new sources of power and protein. But in any case it would be dangerously short-sighted to imagine that population issues could be resolved solely in terms of food and natural resources. What other criteria are there?

Clues may exist in the relationship of wild life to its habitats. Studies of wild life, and of rats under controlled conditions, have probed into patterns of behaviour and responses. They suggest that once numbers in a given area rise beyond a certain level social disorders and neuroses arise. Disturbances occur which may have their human parallels in the juvenile delinquency and mass frenzies of big cities. In the long term, an understanding of the numbers of fellow humans which people can tolerate in a given area seems vital to social harmony. Dr P. Leyhausen of the Max Planck Institute in Wuppertal believes that several countries have already exceeded communally healthy levels of 'density tolerance'. He states that*

. . . the danger of over-population does not rest solely on the need for food and shelter. It lies in whether the population will exceed the limits of human tolerance towards the presence of other humans. These limits have been set by evolutionary processes over millions of years.

Research into wild-life management has shown that where man has interfered to prevent the operation of natural forces, he must control and cull. This is essential to maintain a balance of numbers in relation to food supply and living space – in particular, the carrying capacity of the available land and water. Management also takes into account the biological productive capacity of the individual and group. It is interesting to note that the selective shooting of poorer-quality animals often leads to more breeding from the younger, stronger stock who thereby have relatively more food and space. And so culling must continue.

Man has altered many of the factors previously controlling his numbers but he has not altered the basic built-in instincts and drives characteristic of his species. While it may seriously mislead, in the present state of knowledge, to draw too many parallels between wild life and humans, yet it is still true that man is an animal and will tend to obey ecological principles. It seems that, as man's numbers and congestion increase, human society too may develop a 'pecking order' like that of

* *Discovery, 26, 1965.*

animals (each animal has a set place in the social pattern and cannot easily change it). Possibly a return to feudal and other hierarchical systems may emerge as man is increasingly crowded into limited areas. And the most serious consequence of all is that, unless there is a sudden recognition of these problems by the mass of people, it may soon be too late to avoid the use of drastic methods to deal with over-population.

Perhaps further criteria may be found in the principles behind positive family-planning. In this there is usually a direct relationship between numbers of children and the capacity of parents to bring them up in a healthy and happy home. The influence of the environment has been shown to be great. In Western countries it has governed entry to professions; in primitive societies it has determined the selection of leaders; and in most countries it has been starkly reflected in death-rates, with areas of squalor and poor natural conditions having rates well above those of more prosperous and equable regions. So, therefore, like sensible families, nations and the world must control their populations in relation to some standards, to some measurements of a high-quality environment.

Some standards are capable of objective assessment, at least in broad terms. Some may be related to the capacity of land and water to sustain the pressures upon them without detriment to their long-term supply. Others will probably always be, in part, subjective, but should increasingly be based on a scientific understanding of the major processes influencing population numbers. The difficulties in defining criteria and getting them adopted are great but must be resolved if quality is to be the touchstone. Any serious attempt to improve our environment will at once involve society in planning the use, management and development of its most pre-eminent resource – man himself. History shows that individuals can rarely be expected to think and act for posterity. Following the savage impact of the uncontrolled entrepreneur and worker on their environment in the nineteenth century, it was, historically, inevitable that legislation for the physical planning of towns should usher in the twentieth century in many countries. Probably legislation for the planning of populations in relation to their living space and other factors will initiate the twenty-first century. Already, some countries are striving to stop or limit the rapid growth of their populations, because it is clear that increases will mean a further lowering of living standards which are already hovering at subsistence level. Few would deny that, for the mass of the population of the world, the 'revolution in expectations' must have a hollow sound.

But even assuming that it would be possible to control or stabilize population numbers in thirty to forty years' time, there would still be great problems in relating them to resources, in meeting the expectations of the 'have-nots', in dealing with the aged and the defective, and in creating for all a healthy environment. In fact, the problems of the static or declining population might be greater in some respects than those of a population expanding roughly in relation to the increase in available resources and space. Static populations would have to face the task of making sure that the dynamic force of the younger members of society was focused where it could do the most good and of encouraging the proper levels of fecundity. The genetic effects of having an elderly population, as yet hardly studied, would be magnified in a static society. Without question, in any area the psychological effects of living in a declining nation, of accepting massive immigration, of facing vast structural changes in industry and commerce, and of having a high proportion of aged people could be far-reaching.

The personal issues are profound and inadequately understood. The urge to propagate is basic to human activity and is the greatest single problem planners will have to face. To ask some peoples to limit their children – for example, the Red Indians of North America – would be to invite individual misery in old age (as there would be few younger people to support the elders) and extinction as a tribe. To many of the fecund peoples of South America and India it would deny to them the only factor of significance in a relatively short and limited existence. Even in the richer countries, notably the U.S.A., trends are now confused, as some of the most educated and prosperous citizens go in for larger families.

It is not only the total numbers of people in relation to food and space – the 'capital' – but the level of recruitment of new members – the 'interest' – that is vital to society. Population growth is now the most important factor in determining society's demands. Any adjustment in its rate would have profound economic and social consequences, interacting upon and affecting all other bases of environmental planning.

POPULATIONS AND PLANNING

The world has seen little real attempt at population and resource planning. Efforts are being made to control certain major resources on an international scale, and physical planning, mainly of the urban areas, has been undertaken in most countries in the past fifty years. But there has so far been only a short period of relatively limited activity from which lessons can be drawn for the wider tasks ahead.

Despite the now obvious relationship of environmental capacity and population numbers, most physical planners have taken population and its growth as factors over which they do not exercise influence or have responsibility. They may make adjustments in the location of population – for example, overspill plans for a town or measures to check depopulation in rural or depressed areas – but they accept general trends. Although seventy per cent of the world's population still live in rural areas not enough is known about them and their needs and problems. Each year one to two per cent move into the cities and this is leading to a dramatic redistribution of population. At least it is known that most of the great urban concentrations, particularly in the developing countries, are suffering from 'intense physical congestion and social tension', and these issues are being studied. But in the long-term population numbers must be positively related to environmental capacity not only locally but nationally. Local action is now developing in Britain – for example, the aim over the next two decades is to arrest the unwanted growth, particularly in south-east England. Such steps are essential if later, more radical, developments are not to be jeopardized.

It is, however, clear by the criteria of common sense alone

that some countries are over-populated in relation to resources, that some areas in many countries are over-congested, and that in all countries many localities are being destroyed by the pressure of numbers. People and planners must therefore accept that in the long term there is a finite amount of habitable land and water on this earth. Land set aside at one time to meet requirements for, say, open space, amenity or outdoor recreation, will inevitably be needed for food production or constructional purposes within a few decades if population growth continues.

However ingenious the use of land for the basic needs of food, shelter and mobility, any land-use planning that ignores population control simply postpones the day of reckoning. Similarly, however important and desirable, advances in agriculture which make it possible to obtain more food per acre and developments in building which help to prevent land being wasted tend to obscure this ultimate limitation. By constant discovery and invention man has so far covered up the fact that the supply of natural resources, in particular of open land, may soon run out.

The citizens of the twenty-first century will have little room for manoeuvre. They will be faced with some very unpalatable decisions as the limits of population growth in relation to land supply are approached. Thus, to leave some choice for posterity, planners must now not only indicate fully the implications of population growth for the environment but they must also publicize how necessary it is to fight against the trends.

Population control cannot be formulated properly or translated effectively into a basis for action without full participation by citizens. Unfortunately, apathy and ignorance about environmental planning and population control are widespread. Yet if these objectives are to be served, all adults must be fully involved in their consideration, and the general aims of our communities must be appraised in all the forums of the nations and at all levels of society. Ignorance is at the root of many of society's problems. From their later years children should be educated to understand how important population control has become for each family, and to realize that the 'natural' environment can no longer survive without positive action by man to conserve it. They must realize that man himself cannot survive indefinitely on this earth, without an unacceptable debasing of standards, if he continues to multiply as he is now doing. Conservation begins with man. If man is to get a high-quality environment he must make a vastly greater effort to understand the criteria and standards required and to translate them into effective action.

But education and encouragement – the only processes acceptable in a democratic society – will take time. It is highly unlikely that, by A.D. 2000, any significant change could be made, since a large proportion of that year's population has been born already. Furthermore, the birth-rate still shows an upward trend which may well increase in view of the high proportion of young and fecund people in the world population today.

At the first European Population Conference – in Strasbourg, 1966, sponsored by the Council of Europe – M. Jean Bourgeois-Pichot said, 'Tomorrow death will be a social phenomenon for which we shall have to devise laws.'

Clearly, man has only a few decades in which to determine publicly acceptable standards, to get their implications understood and to initiate action on them, '. . . lest we become swamped in lost hordes of mini-citizens erupting, like bewildered human lemmings from more and more mega-cities.' *

Planners and conservationists have a critical role to play in this work. They can use their special knowledge and help formulate criteria, evaluate them in terms meaningful to the citizen and educate those in responsible positions.

* E. Max Nicholson, *Conservation and the Next Renaissance* (Horace M. Albright Conservation Lectureship, IV), Berkeley, University of California School of Forestry, 1964.

CHAPTER 16

PLANNING: FACTUAL

So far the term 'planning' has been used rather generally to indicate a comprehensive approach to the use and management of the 'natural' environment. In this and the next chapter the intention is to look more closely at 'formal' town and country planning. Its purpose is to create an improved environment – urban and rural, its emphasis has been, and still is, on 'town' rather than country. But modern planning aims to use wisely and to maintain the supply of all resources, including those of the rural areas. Most activities having an effect on the use or development of land, air, water and wild life are subject to some form of control. Few can be taken in isolation; they all interact in varying degree, hence, as environmental problems become more complex, the need for coordination becomes increasingly urgent.

Planning began in most countries in the nineteenth century with rules or prescriptions for building development directed mainly to achieving adequate sanitary and safety conditions. Much of its impetus stemmed from the realization that disease, fire and other disasters could be reduced or prevented by improving city design. But the supremacy in economic affairs of the dogma of *laissez faire*, the rapid development of great concentrations of industry and people and an era of social ferment inhibited any real progress. An Italian Act of 1865 was the first to include the term 'town planning' – ten years before either Germany or Sweden used it.

Britain's first Act was in 1909. For the following thirty years governments sought to plan, but with little success. Most of the laws and planning schemes were thwarted because local authorities found it too difficult or expensive to acquire land. Planning, as a whole, was largely negative, impotent to control the rapid expansion of industry and quite unable to deal with such features as the growth of London and the decline of South Wales. The history of the century to 1939 is well-documented and makes fascinating reading.

The plight of the depressed areas led to the setting-up of a Royal Commission to examine the distribution of industry and population. It reported in 1940 (the Barlow Report) and recommended the creation of a central authority, the redevelopment of congested urban areas, the dispersal of industry and population and the development of a reasonable balance of industrial activity throughout Britain. These proposals and the impact of urban encroachment on agricultural land led in 1941 to the Scott Committee on Land Utilization in Rural Areas. The Committee stressed the vital need to maintain good agricultural land, and attached great importance to maintaining rural amenities as part of the national heritage. It recommended the creation of national parks, nature reserves and access facilities to the countryside.

In 1942 the Uthwatt Committee examined Compensation and Betterment (betterment is the increase in the value of the land resulting from the efforts of the community). It also proposed the setting-up of a central planning authority and measures for state control of development, and advocated a drastic revision of the laws relating to compensation and betterment. The main arguments and facts given in this great trilogy of Reports were reproduced in numerous pamphlets and press articles. These deeply influenced the disciplined populace of the Second World War, whether in uniform or 'civvies', and helped to mould and inform public opinion ready for the vast and overdue social reconstruction which was to follow. The three Reports inspired many of the laws passed from 1943 onwards, and provided them with much of their practical content.

It was, in fact, the social climate of the Second World War which provided the spur to substantial advance. After much political and inter-departmental wrangling, the proposed central authority was set up in 1943. This Ministry of Town and Country Planning was able to capitalize on the wealth of ideas available and meet the spirit of the time. Its efforts culminated in the Town and Country Planning Acts of 1947. These measures have provided the administrative basis of the present planning system for over twenty years. Their main aims were:

1. To define by means of development plans the policies for the planning of each area.

2. To bring development generally under the control of a local planning authority or central government department.

3. To give further powers to public authorities to acquire and develop land for planning objectives and to extend the scope and scales of financial aid for these purposes.

4. To provide for special amenity issues, for example, buildings of historic or architectural merit, preservation of trees, the control of advertisements.

THE PLANNING SYSTEM

Under the system prior to the 1968 reforms (see Appendix 4), development plans have to be prepared by each local planning authority (county councils and county boroughs) and reviewed every five years. They are submitted for approval to the Minister of Housing and Local Government,* who holds a public inquiry into a plan if there are objections to it. The 1947 Act defined a 'development plan' as a plan 'indicating the manner in which the local planning authority propose that land in their area should be used'. These plans, which normally cover a period of about twenty years, include numerous maps, written statements and analyses, and frequently other related material. The written analysis, which describes and defines the major projects in the plan, is often a complex and bulky document.

In a county the map is drawn to a scale of one inch to the mile and is not very detailed. It may indicate certain areas which are to be the subject of town maps, but in rural counties large areas, usually agricultural land, are left 'white'. This shows that no change in use is anticipated within the period covered by the plan and that no proposals are being put forward for these 'white' areas. In county boroughs, two main maps are necessary: first, a town map, drawn to a scale of six inches to the mile, which shows in some detail the proposed zoning of land for housing, industry, open space, schools and

* In Scotland and, since 1966, in Wales, the Secretary of State.

other such primary uses; secondly, a programme map, which is, in effect, a timetable for carrying out the developments proposed in the plan. By 1961 development plans, approved in whole or part by the Minister, covered all England and Wales and almost all but the very remote areas of Scotland. Many of the five-yearly review plans have been dealt with and many others are going through the pipeline of preparation, submission, inquiry and approval.

In addition to the development plan and town maps, the local planning authority may prepare and submit for approval very detailed plans, at a scale of twenty-five inches to one mile, for those areas which, in their view, should be developed or redeveloped as a whole. Approval may also be sought for maps designating land for compulsory purchase by a governmental body (central or local) and for maps showing where new roads and streets are to be constructed.

Obviously, the development plan system is very comprehensive. It covers the whole of Britain and prescribes the main allocations of land use for most areas of population of over 10,000 people. Some counties have prepared detailed plans for small villages. Others have prepared plans, and are actively implementing them, to cater for 'overspill' population, that is, the people for whom accommodation and services at current standards cannot be found in the densely built-up boroughs. The second major feature of the development-plan system is that it is highly centralized. All the plans and subsidiary maps referred to have to be approved by the Minister. In October 1965 the Minister revised the procedure dealing with the reference to him of proposals involving substantial departure from development plans. Three classes were formulated: those for decision by the planning authority itself; those for local decision after advertisement, with the opportunity for the Minister to call them in; and the most important, to be referred to the Minister with full details. More systematic provision for advertisement was also introduced.

Development control is generally carried out on the basis of the development plan and the more detailed maps prepared under its provisions. Most developments – for example, the erection of houses, factories, cinemas – and most changes of

use – for example, houses to shops, open space to other uses –
require planning permission. Most agriculture and forestry
activities and ancillary developments – for example, certain
buildings – are outside planning control. The Ministry of
Agriculture, Fisheries and Food and the Forestry Commission
do, however, maintain close liaison with planning authorities,
especially in National Parks. Special procedures govern certain
forms of development, as noted later in this chapter. Generally, the control exercised is very pervasive, especially for urban
development.

County boroughs and county councils are the authorities
responsible for development control. In most counties there is
some delegation to district councils enabling them to handle
certain categories of planning application, usually on the advice
of an officer of the county council. Currently, all these authorities deal with about 440,000 planning applications each year.
About 82 per cent are approved. Applicants who are aggrieved
by a decision of a local planning authority to reject or modify
their proposals may appeal to the Minister, and there are
arrangements to enable objections to be heard at a public inquiry. Up to 1968 about $3\frac{1}{2}$ per cent of all applications were the
subject of appeal. The Minister received over 13,000 appeals in
England in 1965 and at February 1966 had 8,500 awaiting
determination. At that date the average time between receipt
and decision was 44 weeks for appeals dealt with by inquiry
and 32 for those settled on written representation.

Special amenity issues are dealt with by orders and 'tailored'
systems. Buildings of historic or architectural interest are the
subject of preservation orders; central ministries and local
authorities employ experts to advise on the selection and
maintenance of such properties. Local planning authorities
may prepare tree preservation orders, and the trees specified
cannot be felled except under penalty or with the consent of
the authority. Advertisements – for example, on buildings,
hoardings and so on – are rigorously controlled by the planning
authorities with guidance from the Ministry. Many other issues
are covered by special orders and procedures under supporting
Acts, like, for example, the Caravan Sites and Control of
Development Act, 1960.

Land may be acquired by county boroughs, district councils and, in some cases, county councils, by agreement or by compulsory purchase. These authorities may develop land or, if surplus to their needs, dispose of it. A financial system was set up by the 1947 Acts to resolve finally the problems of compensation and betterment. All development rights in land were taken over by the State, and before anyone could develop he had to pay a charge to do so – in effect, to buy the right to develop.* In practice, the system failed. The development charge was abolished in 1953, and the Central Land Board set up to administer it was disbanded. The system operating at the start of 1966 was based on legislation of 1959 and 1961. It provided for the landowner to receive the value he could expect to get for his land in a private sale in the open market if there were no proposal by any public authority to buy it. As most development requires planning permission, it was specified that, for assessment of compensation, permission would be granted for development or uses prescribed for the land in the development plan. The system was further affected by the Land Commission Act, 1967 (see page 256) and is again under review.

This massive framework of planning legislation was consolidated in the Town and Country Planning Act of 1962. The statutes, orders made under it, and the general instructions and explanatory notes, run into hundreds of pages. A major review of the future of development plans was completed in 1965 by the Planning Advisory Group (P.A.G.) of the Ministry of Housing and Local Government and formed the basis for many of the reforms introduced by the 1968 legislation (see Appendix 4). The features of the P.A.G. report relevant to this book are dealt with in the next chapter.

In addition to the town and country planning legislation, there are numerous measures relating to the physical environment, most of which bear directly upon planning policy. Although not all of this legislation is the responsibility of the central or local planning authorities, they have, nevertheless, to take full account of it and must often make special provisions to comply with it in development plans and town maps. These

---

* Any compulsory purchase of land by public authorities had to be at existing use value.

measures cover new towns and cities, the distribution of industry, communications, and the supply of power and raw materials.

DEVELOPMENT MEASURES

New Towns were officially recommended in the report of the Reith Committee in 1946. They were intended to be at a sufficient distance from London and other major cities to relieve their overcrowding of people and industry. The New Towns Act, 1946, enabled the Ministers to designate land as the site for a new town and to appoint a development corporation to lay out and develop it with capital advanced from public funds. Under the New Towns Act, 1959, a Commission was set up to take over and manage the property of the development corporations as they end their work of building the new towns; several have already been taken over. The Commission settles with the local authorities or statutory undertakers concerned the ownership and ultimate disposal of the assets of the corporation.

The Town Development Act, 1952, and a similar Act of 1957 applying to Scotland, were also intended to relieve congestion and over-population in the towns and cities. The Acts encourage schemes for town development in county districts and provide for cooperation by 'exporting' and 'importing' authorities, and for financial aid both from the authorities and the Ministry. Some of the more progressive authorities have already initiated considerable development.

Distribution of Industry Acts in 1945, 1950 and 1958 gave wide powers to the Board of Trade and the Treasury to secure a proper balance of industry throughout Britain. To this end, planning permission for a new industrial building or extension above a certain size could be granted only where the Board had issued a certificate of approval. The Board could build and let factories in prescribed areas, and the Treasury could grant and lend moneys to help industry to develop in 'development areas' or in places with high and persistent unemployment. The Board works very closely with the central and local planning authorities and is constantly under pressure to facilitate industrial development or expansion in the less prosperous

areas. These Acts were consolidated in the Local Employment
Act, 1960 (further amended in 1963), which gives special powers
to the Board of Trade to enable it to induce industrialists to
develop or expand in specified districts. These development
districts were replaced by the new and wider development
areas introduced by the Industrial Development Act of 1966
(see *Investment Incentives* Cmnd 2874). Manufacturing and
extractive industries in these areas (covering much of Britain
outside the South-East and Midland regions) can get investment grants for plant and machinery of forty per cent (twice
the national rate). These incentives are intended 'to give more
powerful encouragement to a better geographical distribution
of industrial growth' and to support the Government's regional
and national policies.

Obviously minerals can be worked only where they are
located and are accessible. They are clearly part of the wealth
of the nation, and the planning system must ensure their long-
term availability. The locations of most of the mineral reserves
of the country – sand and gravel, limestone, coal, china clay
and so on – are shown on development plans. Planning permission is required before mining can take place on new sites.
Special arrangements operate between mineral developers and
planning authorities to ensure that no unnecessary damage is
done to the countryside and that the land is reclaimed after use.

Technological developments, such as power stations, main
electricity lines, and gas and oil pipelines, are subject to special
procedures between the statutory undertakers and the planning authorities. The consent of the Minister of Power is also
required. Where scenic amenity is involved the Minister of
Housing and Local Government is consulted and often public
inquiries are held. No developments by the Crown, including
defence requirements of land, are subject to formal planning
control, but the local planning authority is usually consulted.
If agreement cannot be reached, the Minister of Housing and
Local Government arbitrates. Motorways and trunk roads are
subject to several Acts which empower the Minister of Transport to promote schemes to construct motorways and to extend
the national system of roads. These projects must be devised in
the light of national and local planning policies. The county

councils and county boroughs also have important powers for
the planning and construction of roads.

CONSERVATION MEASURES

> Conservation can be defined as the wise use of our
> natural environment: it is, in the final analysis, the
> highest form of national thrift – the prevention of
> waste and despoilment while preserving, improv-
> ing and renewing the quality and usefulness of all
> our resources.
>
> The late President John F. Kennedy:
> Message to Congress, 1962

A number of areas shown on development plans receive special
consideration within the planning system. They include
National Parks, Areas of Outstanding Natural Beauty, Areas
of Great Landscape, Scientific or Historic Value, Long-distance
Routes and national, local and forest Nature Reserves. These
provide for a wide range of interests – amenity, outdoor recreation, research, education and wild life. Most of them were the
primary responsibility of the National Parks Commission (in
England and Wales only) and the Nature Conservancy, the
two national bodies set up under the National Parks and Access
to the Countryside Act, 1949, which provides most of the
requisite powers. From June 1965 the Nature Conservancy
became a component of the Natural Environment Research
Council. The Conservancy undertakes broadly the same functions, but the formal responsibility rests with the Council.

By the Countryside Act, 1968, the National Parks Commission was reconstituted as a Countryside Commission, with
wider powers and responsibilities. It carries with it all the
functions under the 1949 Act and will promote public enjoyment of the countryside generally. The new Act provides for
the creation of Country Parks – for coast and country – to
provide leisure facilities and to relieve pressure on National
Parks and the countryside generally. The existing Exchequer
grants of seventy-five per cent towards the cost of preserving or
enhancing natural beauty and for facilities for its enjoyment in
National Parks and Areas of Outstanding Natural Beauty will
be extended to meet expenditure in the countryside on the

Legend:

- ■ National Parks
- ⌐⌐ (ON THE COAST)
- ▦ Areas of Outstanding Natural Beauty
- ⌐⌐⌐ (ON THE COAST)
- •••• Approved long-distance Footpaths and Bridleways
- ● National Nature Reserves
- ▲ Forest Nature Reserves
- ■ Local Nature Reserves

Shetlands

St Kilda

Inverpolly

Cairngorms

Northumberland

Northumberland Coast

Newcastle upon Tyne

Solway Coast

Lake District

Yorkshire Coast and N Yorks Moors Path

North Yorks Moors

Yorkshire Dales

Pennine Way

Forest of Bowland

Leeds

Manchester

Sheffield

Liverpool

Peak District

Lleyn

Cannock Chase

Snowdonia

Offa's Dyke Path

Birmingham

Shropshire Hills

Malvern Hills

Pembrokeshire Coast

Pembrokeshire Coast Path

Chilterns

London

Surrey Hills

Gower

Cardiff

Cotswolds

Brecon Beacons

Exmoor

Bristol

North Devon

Quantock Hills

Sussex Downs

SW Peninsula Coast Path

Dartmoor

East Hampshire

South Downs Way

Cornwall

East Devon

Isle of Wight

Dorset

Chichester Harbour

Plymouth

South Devon

SW Peninsula Coast Path

M 0   20   40   60   80   100
km 0   40   80   120   160

20 Statutory conservation in Britain (Crown Copyright)

measures propos' d in the new Acts. These include the maintaining of Coun try Parks, amenity tree planting, removal of
eyesores and the provision of facilities and access. A Countryside Commission for Scotland was established early in 1968.
The Commissions and local authorities are to have all necessary
powers not only for the conservation of the 'unique heritage of
scenic beauty' but also for the development of tourist and
recreational potential – see Appendix 4.

National Parks embrace extensive areas of beautiful and
relatively wild country in England and Wales. The ten parks
include the Lake District, the Peak District and Snowdonia.
Their characteristics are to be maintained for and enjoyed by
the nation. They were designated by the National Parks Commission, although Ministerial confirmation was required. Each
park is run by a Planning Board or Committee which controls
development, and usually maintains a high standard. It promotes work to enhance the landscape and provides extra facilities for people using the park; these include information and
warden services, camping and caravan sites, and access arrangements.

Areas of Outstanding Natural Beauty are of broadly similar
character to National Parks, but are not usually quite so extensive and generally do not contain so much of the wilder
countryside or of facilities for outdoor recreation. By September 1968 there were twenty-four of these covering many fine
stretches of the coast and areas such as the Sussex Downs and
the Cotswolds. They are designated by the Commission, but
do not have a special body to administer them. The local
planning authority is responsible for protecting and improving
the landscape and for making arrangements for public access
to open country.

Areas of Great Landscape, Scientific or Historic Value are
designated by local planning authorities and depend on the
authorities' readiness to seek and accept the best advice available and to show such areas on their development plans. The
authorities usually require developers in these areas to achieve
higher standards of design and to pay particular regard to the
appearance of the landscape.

Long-distance Routes are paths for ramblers and horseriders and are protected within the planning system. The Pennine Way was the first to be completed (in 1965) and negotiations are well advanced for other routes over long stretches of coastline. The Commission handles most of this work itself, subject to Ministerial approval and liaison with local planning authorities. It can create new paths to complete a route and provide hostels and related facilities. The 1949 Act also provides further measures for access to coast and country. Local planning authorities must survey and record footpaths and other public rights of way, and they have powers to provide facilities by means of access agreement with owners or by orders if agreement cannot be reached. The new Acts also included more powers to deal with footpaths.

Nature Reserves are frequently referred to as 'living museums' and 'outdoor laboratories'. They contain habitats for the conservation of animals and plants and are areas of the greatest scientific interest for research and education. National Nature Reserves, which are the most important, are chosen and administered by the Nature Conservancy. There were 124 Reserves in Britain in July 1968, covering over 257,000 acres; 183,000 of these are in Scotland. The Reserves are given virtually complete protection within the planning system.

Local Nature Reserves (17 in July 1968) are established by local authorities in consultation with the Conservancy. Thirteen forest nature reserves are managed for research and conservation by arrangements between the Conservancy and the Forestry Commission and certain other major landowners. Together with approximately 2,000 Sites of Special Scientific Interest (S.S.S.I.s) they form a second tier of much educational and scientific value to the nation and ensure the conservation of many habitats and their animals and plants. The security of local nature reserves depends on the legal tenure and powers of the local authority concerned. S.S.S.I.s are, however, not safeguarded against agricultural operations or afforestation, and their interest has only to be taken into account by the local planning authority before determining a planning application.

Wildfowl Refuges, selected by the Conservancy and wildfowlers, give special protection to the main breeding and wintering grounds of wildfowl, although controlled shooting is permitted in some of them. They are linked in a national chain, which fits into a European pattern, and are supported by regional refuges. Although a few wildfowl refuges are National Nature Reserves, more of them are designated Sites of Special Scientific Interest; additionally, some are also statutory bird sanctuaries under the Protection of Birds Act, 1954.

Finally, in the main categories of land receiving special consideration within the planning system are the Green Belts. These were originally set apart to limit the spread of towns and to stop them merging to form conurbations (as in the Black Country) or to maintain the special qualities of a town, such as Bath. More recently it has been recognized that these lands must be positively managed to prevent their deterioration and that they can provide for many of the country pleasures sought by townspeople. The local planning authority proposes green belts, which then require Ministerial confirmation.

Conservation of clean air is increasingly within the scope of the planning system. As shown in Chapters 6 and 7, many experts consider that the best long-term solutions lie with physical planning. This is particularly important in preventing new pollution and in ensuring that sources of air pollution are sited where they can do least harm. By concentrating industry in certain zones and prescribing distances from roads and dwellings, by avoiding valleys where air pollution can be penned in, by providing open spaces and green belts, and by favouring housing and other urban development with centralized heating systems, the planner can help to ensure clean air. Generally, there is wide scope within the planning system for the planner to support the measures described in Chapters 6 and 7.

Water conservation affects most proposals of the local planning authority and, in turn, is materially influenced by town and country planning. The shortage of planners able to evaluate the highly specialized functions of the River Authorities limits the full integration of measures for water conservation in the development plan. Another problem is the coordination between the twenty-nine River Authorities in England and Wales and the 175 local and park planning authorities. It is, however, essential that there should be close integration, both in strategy – when plans are made for dispersing population, relocating industry, and preparing barrage schemes – and in the more tactical detailed inter-authority joint schemes for, say, the recreational use of some local waters. In particular, river projects such as those proposed for the Tyne and the Great Ouse, and the landscape design of new reservoirs like the one at Dove Valley, offer great possibilities within the planning system. It is, however, probable that support for the strategic planning of the Water Resources Board, and the implementation of national and regional policies by the River Authorities, can best come from full-scale regional planning.

Wild-life conservation is obviously supported by all these measures within the planning system. There are also many other functions of county and county borough councils – the planning authorities – which have a direct impact on wild life. For example, many county councils had bird protection and sanctuary committees until their powers were altered by the Protection of Birds Act, 1954; some still have them. Most councils have by-laws to control or prohibit the picking of wild flowers. The flora and fauna of roadside verges are influenced by the way in which Highway Departments carry out road maintenance. Education departments can acquire and manage sites for field studies and other outdoor activities. Many planning departments are very active – often with the help of county Naturalists' Trusts – in conserving local nature reserves and sites of scientific interest, in making tree preservation orders and enhancing the value of open spaces, green belts and amenity areas, and in reclaiming derelict land.

A tremendous network has been built up here of central and local agencies engaged in improving the quality of the environment. The measures set out in this chapter reveal just why Britain is generally accepted as having the most comprehensive and advanced system in the world.

CHAPTER 17

PLANNING: ASSESSMENT

DESPITE this tremendous fabric of authorities and powers, British planning has disappointed. But before analysing the reasons for this, it is only fair to consider some of its achievements.

Inevitably much planning has been restrictive and the public do not readily appreciate the great contribution it has made to the quality of the environment. Planning has saved the countryside from a great deal of thoughtless urban sprawl, unwise expansion of villages and despoliation of the countryside. Unsightly advertisements and ribbons of houses cannot now be erected to obscure the best views or create hazards for traffic.

Few of the results of planning are spectacular. Improved layouts of housing estates, better communications, interspersed parks and greens, and better siting and design of public and private dwellings all too frequently gain no credit for the planners but only for their builders. The inter-war years showed the kind of development that can occur where there is no planning control.

More obviously, new towns have been established, national parks have been created, motorways are being built, town development has gone ahead and most war-damage has been eliminated. Planning also contributes to the provision of clean air and pure water and to nature conservation. Perhaps its main achievements, on which all the rest hinges, are the development plans which now cover the whole of Britain. These plans are very much the key to the success or failure of planning.

But the achievements are dwarfed by the problems which still have to be faced. The first of these stems from the planners' failure to anticipate and to deal with the effects of the population explosion. Unfortunately, many planners do not think of population numbers as coming within their philosophy. In all fairness it must be added that until 1957 the general assumption was that Britain had a static, ageing population. The

Minister of Housing and Local Government made this point at a meeting in April 1964 on the Government's *South-East Study*, and went on to say:

It was only from 1957 onwards that the rise in the birth-rate and the acceleration in the rate of household formation, due to younger marriages, longer living and increasing prosperity, made themselves evident, and it was not for a couple of years that these trends were validated.

Planners obviously need reliable projections of population trends for as long ahead as possible, but these they have not had until recently.

Despite the efforts of the planning network, the huge growth of population and industry in the south-east of England has continued; the blight on the older industrial areas and their centres remains; the finances of planning – the compensation–betterment problem – are still unresolved; land for development is scarce and almost prohibitively expensive; the decay of the landscape and changes in the countryside under a bewildering succession of impacts are being tackled in an *ad hoc* and fragmented manner; decisions about the uses of agricultural land, the problems of living and working in the countryside, the demands of those seeking enjoyment in the countryside in their leisure time – all these are more complex and urgent than ever before.

Although so comprehensive, present planning legislation is inadequate for rural land with its many special problems. Doubtless this still reflects the static approach of the pre-war period with its relatively 'stagnant' agriculture. There is, nevertheless, still insufficient coordination between the many interests concerned with rural land – forestry, water, recreation, conservation, amenity and so on. Often, each one has had to prove separately that its need for a particular piece of rural land is more important than leaving that land to agriculture, with the result that some areas are still being farmed which might, in fact, have been more valuable to the nation if put to other, combined uses. On the other hand, there are numerous cases where best-quality agricultural land has been taken, particularly in the south-east area, as the Study showed. The agriculturalist complains that little or no thought is given to the needs of farmers and their workpeople, and the prime use of the countryside, which is to grow food, is ignored.

The measures for conservation give rise to many difficulties. The farmer may find them a source of inefficiency. The industrialist, when faced with a map of these special areas, must wonder where he can develop. How can he take a pipeline, overhead cable or road through such a maze? The prospective developer sees the areas set aside as reserves and green belts as a demand on land and water which must be justified in the overall national interest. The active sportsman finds some of the restrictions in national parks are irksome. Yet in many areas these restrictions must become tougher: the coastline, for example, is a constant source of concern. More positive powers and resources are required by the Countryside Commissions and the local planning authorities. What we must guard against, however, is allowing 'conservation' to lapse into 'preservation' and thus imperil the nation's economic strength.

New policies and procedures are required to expedite the finding and development of suitable sites for industry and leisure activities. In March 1966 Mr Neil Wates, a director of a major firm of building contractors, said:

We are left with the feeling that the whole emphasis of town planning in this country is on the static side of the 1947 Act, and not on the dynamic; upon preservation rather than provision, with the apparent aim of preserving this country as a sort of second-rate outdoor museum.

The measures adopted for the support of industry (see page 208) need to be operational for many years, for frequent changes are unsettling to an industrialist. (Recently he has been given little chance to plan ahead in peace. Over sixty Acts and numerous orders affecting industry have been passed since 1947.) But within agreed strategy there should be more flexibility and selectiveness, and much more account should be taken of all the resources of an area.

Why cannot planning cope adequately? Inevitably the reasons lie in every facet of society – in laws and their administration, in the organizations and professions concerned, but most of all in the attitudes of the people who accepted the trends or led them.

Undoubtedly, too much was expected of planning by the public and by those engaged in it. In retrospect, we can see that it was both grossly unfair and naïve to imagine that the handful of qualified planners available could remedy the mistakes and wrongs of the past, ensure that current development did not repeat these errors, be alert to new evils and act as prophets to diagnose trends and predict the best solutions.

People in power were also a problem. Many in central departments or local authorities did not take kindly to being planned, integrated, or even helped, by the planners. Inevitably consultation meant delay and often changes in their own plans and projects. Members of old-established professions often disdained to accept the comprehensive approach of this new race of synthesizers.

And the people themselves? The man in the street reserved his traditional rights: to have his cake and eat it; to grumble about 'them' holding up development and being impractical; to complain bitterly when a project of personal interest was affected; and to demand better standards and services. But would he participate in the processes of planning, through the normal social channels? In most cases he would not! Yet to get a good relationship between the individual or the public and the planning authorities (especially in local government) is crucial to the task of achieving a high-quality environment.

Planning legislation has been, and is still, regarded by many people as an encroachment on personal liberty. They believe it is wrong to interfere with market forces and the interplay of private initiative and the profit-motive. The concept that legislation can provide a framework for better living and create a healthy environment does not yet command sufficient support. The subject-matter of much planning legislation is technical and complex, even to experts, and over much has been attempted centrally and not enough power and encouragement given to the enterprise of local authorities.

Much modern legislation fails to treat the environment as a unity. Too many principles and policies are polarized around the attitudes of ministries and agencies. Pressure groups seek to resolve or alleviate urgent problems without regarding their full impact on a wide range of related issues. Undoubtedly it is a difficult operation to integrate the entire body of law relating to the physical environment. Without question, the problems inherent in coordinating the work of the modern nation-state are great and tending to increase. But they have to be tackled.

Inevitably, therefore, the actions of central departments do not reflect the unity of environmental issues. The conflicts openly aired in the press, such as in the correspondence columns of *The Times*, are but the tip of the iceberg. Although on occasions a bulwark against misuse of power, departmental attitudes can seriously hinder effective planning. The antagonisms tend to be fiercer and more difficult to modify than those of the individuals in whom they are often focused. Also, too many decision-makers are reluctant to use the end product of modern research and survey. Their unwillingness often arises from that lack of understanding of scientific principles and distrust of quantitative data which is common to many administrators. These shortcomings affect most aspects of central administration, but they are particularly important in planning, because no environmental situation is ever static. Whether decisions are taken or not there is a changing situation, and failure to take a decision at a given time often means that desired aims can never be achieved.

In planning legislation the central ministry was undoubtedly involved in too much detail. A report of the Planning Advisory Group (P.A.G.) of the Ministry of Housing and Local Government published in July 1965 stated:

Finally, the attempt to process all these detailed plans through a centralized procedure, including provision for objections (of which there may be hundreds or even thousands on a single plan) and public local inquiry, has inevitably led to very serious delays which tend to undermine public confidence in the system. The average time taken by the Ministry of Housing to deal with a development plan submission is two or three years, but some cases may take considerably longer – some sixty town map submissions have been with the Ministry for more than three years. The result of these delays may mean both that necessary development or redevelopment is held up pending approval of the plan, and that the plan once approved is already in some respects out of date.

Many of these problems arose from the dismantling of the war-time regional structure. The central Ministry lacked adequate 'antennae' on planning problems, yet became overwhelmed with detail. Coordination deteriorated and strategy suffered. In particular, economic and physical planning tended to operate in separate compartments and there was no national plan or strategy for either. Apart from a few projects, such as the plans for Greater London and the Clyde Valley, there was a dearth of regional plans. In consequence, there was no adequate conceptual framework within which local planning authorities could function.

Whatever the deficiencies and inadequacies of the central bodies, those of the local planning authorities are worse. There are 175 in England and Wales,* with the Peak Park and Lake District, and 57 in Scotland. The counties range in size and capacity from the Greater London Council, which has the scope and resources to attract some of the finest talent in the world, to the County of Sutherland in Scotland with only 13,500 people in an area of over 2,000 square miles. County boroughs range from Birmingham to Canterbury.

With a few exceptions, such as the Greater London Council, the local planning authorities in England and Wales are based on the structure established by the reforming Local Government Act of 1888. The ancient Norman counties and the large towns of the Industrial Revolution were then made the major units of democratic local government. Although conditions now bear almost no relationship to the ones prevailing when they were created, and countless books have been written on their shortcomings, these units have remained, against all probability, the authorities responsible for local planning. From the outset the antagonism between county and county borough shatters the interdependence of town and country and has often created and intensified an antipathy between urban and rural communities. This nullifies much modern planning.

* Including 32 Greater London Boroughs.

In November 1965, the Minister of Housing and Local Government, addressing a reunion celebrating World Town Planning Day, said: '. . . effective planning is rendered almost impossible by the battle for rateable values between rural-minded counties and urban-minded boroughs . . .'

A characteristic of many authorities is their (inevitable) pre-occupation with rateable value; that is, the money they derive from property in their area. This is often not only half their total income but also the source of any real independence they claim. Many authorities are too small in area, have too little money, knowledge and staff, to take account of the economic and technological demands inherent in dealing with traffic, location of industry, water, refuse disposal and sewage, and many other services. There has been a dismal post-war record of the allocation of major services to *ad hoc* bodies. Joint boards and committees are a poor substitute for proper long-term planning and integration of major services, hence, to get effective action, numerous reports in recent years have recommended a special authority should be set up. A proliferation of *ad hoc* authorities makes coordination and synthesis – the essence of planning and the spirit of creative development – almost unattainable. The planning authorities would face immense difficulties even if they had been given a national strategy setting out principles and policies in planning, and full coordination between all the agencies of central government. But they have had neither.

The planning process itself – with its key instrument, the development plan – has been the target for great criticism, and the P.A.G. Report was primarily concerned with re-shaping it to meet current and anticipated demands. The development plan was held to have acquired 'the appearance of certainty and stability which is misleading'. The original intention (to indicate general principles for promoting and controlling development), seems to have been forgotten, and recently it has accumulated too much detail and spurious precision.

Development plans have frequently become out-of-date and unresponsive to the rapidly evolving trends emerging from an affluent, mobile and leisured society. As discussed earlier, it is

expected that by the year 2000 there will be a one-third increase in Britain's population, a fourfold increase in car ownership and a fourfold increase in average individual income.
All this is not allowed for sufficiently in many plans and the
situation is made worse by the lack of guidance on national and
regional strategy. The development plan fails to measure up
to the demands of regional-scale services because it is based on
out-of-date local government boundaries. The approach of
many plans to the complex problems of rural landscape is negative and preservationist. They contribute little to the quality
of the environment, whether in the way of standards of design
or criteria for dealing with competing or incompatible uses. With
substantial changes occurring in the patterns of living and human
settlement, the development plan must itself change or atrophy.

The control of development suffers inevitably from the
defects of the plan. The usual criticism is that the control
is too complex and too slow: it may take six years to get
all clearances to work a gravel pit, ten to build a reservoir.
Giving the existing county districts a say in many decisions
is bound to take up the time of people who can ill be spared
from other planning tasks, yet it is the policy of the National
Association of Parish Councils to obtain for parish councils
'the opportunity to comment upon planning applications
before they are determined'.

But a report* on development control in 1967 recommended
that, in the interests of efficient management, parish councils
should not be extensively consulted on applications. It favoured
decentralization to groups of District Councils and specific
delegation to officers.

These are not the only problems. The shortage of qualified
planners and the many pressures upon them mean that their
creative capacities for influencing and promoting higher
quality in development are inhibited. They do not have adequate time – or support – to explain to the public the context of
development control and the scope there is for contributing to
a better environment.

Certain developments not at present subject to control should
be controlled, such as traffic engineering, some constructional

* Management Study on Development Control, H.M.S.O.

work and certain changes of uses. One particular problem of some concern has been that agricultural departments gave grants for ploughing-up Sites of Special Scientific Interest which the Nature Conservancy and local planning authorities go to some pains to protect. These weaknesses in the pattern of control, although separately important, are not central to the basic issues of the relationship over development control between planner and public.

The P.A.G. Report says that the present system 'tends to make physical planning appear a very dull and pedestrian business . . .'. This, if generally true, would be desperately unfortunate because planning has unlimited creative scope and requires a great capacity for understanding people. A planner has to see that the quality, utility and variety of the environment are maintained and enhanced. The way he is educated and the opportunities he is given to use his skills are therefore matters of great importance. Many of the planners are so hard-pressed that they cannot keep abreast of the increasing demands of an exacting profession. Neither have the authorities sufficient staff of the requisite intellect and training. A survey by the Town Planning Institute in 1962 showed that out of 3,689 technical planning staff employed by the local planning authorities in England and Wales, only one third had a planning qualification and half had no professional qualification at all. Estimates of the number of extra planners required vary from 3,000 to 5,000 and the P.A.G. Report speaks of 'the present acute shortage of qualified planners'. Many of the smaller authorities cannot afford to pay for talent appropriate to their problems; they cannot get the staff they need nor employ the right consultants. An article in *The Times* of 6 January 1966 was headlined: 'DESPERATE LACK OF PLANNERS'. The Town Planning Institute in February 1966 criticized the P.A.G. Report for placing too much emphasis on procedures and too little on manpower shortage.

Most planners, therefore, dare not spare much valuable working time for talking to laymen about the issues involved and for generally encouraging public interest. It is not surprising, therefore, that people tend to think planning is a mystique, that planners are introverted and exclusive and that, especially in the counties, they are remote and bureaucratic. Thus people fail to see how the quality of their environment can affect them, and do not grasp how they might be able to make a personal contribution to its enhancement. The divorce between planners and public is made sharper by the failure of many local councillors to lead and inspire their citizens. This is not necessarily their own fault, but often reflects the great practical difficulties which face the public-spirited councillor. That these can be overcome is demonstrated by the success of authorities, such as Coventry and Newcastle, which have promoted activities to secure public involvement in planning schemes. But whatever the cause, few people seem to feel that enthusiasm and sense of participation which are the ingredients vital to the process of adult education called local government. And planning suffers most.

Until the necessity of planning is fully accepted and people are actively involved in its processes, it will continue to treat symptoms and not get down to basic issues such as environmental standards and criteria. In attempts to get public participation, a prime factor is that of timing – plans of the right stage must be publicised at the right time to avoid *faits accomplis*. And information must be presented suitably. Perhaps the old truism might be rephrased to read 'the public gets the planning it deserves'. But this is not really true. Today there is so much specialization and expert knowledge required that, unless all officially concerned are imbued with a belief in the vital nature of 'grass-roots' participation, the public is unlikely to get its chance either to understand what is happening or to say what it feels. The desired approach is well illustrated by the arrangements for the Lee Valley Regional Park and the Landscape Plan for the Town Moor of Newcastle upon Tyne (see p. 178).

To imagine that the individual does not care would be a gross error. One of the most encouraging features in Britain today, particularly in respect of the countryside, is the strength and depth of feeling about its conservation and enhancement. People do care – the shortcomings and blemishes can be removed through teamwork and leadership. But without question, the country is not devoting enough of its top talent to these tasks.

In Other Countries

In almost all countries planning is a function of the State. Inevitably, factors of history and geography lead to differences in planning policies and practice, but more important today is the philosophy of each society. For example, planning at national level is more comprehensive in the U.S.S.R., Poland and Hungary than in the U.S.A. and many South American countries; in some socialist countries physical and economic planning are already integrated. But few countries can equal the Netherlands for comprehensiveness and development and yet this country is obviously of 'Western' philosophy.

At the top level in government and the professions, the work of many international associations and conferences confirms there is a common approach on principles and policies. Greater integration of economic and physical planning is sought to deal with the dominant problems of population control and distribution, and the location of industry. Strategic planning, and ways of harmonizing policies for agriculture, forestry and urban needs are emphasized. Most countries face in varying degree problems created by urban sprawl, the pressures of traffic and leisure, the contamination of air and water, the loss of wild life and a deterioration in the quality of the environment.

It is, however, over powers and procedures that the greatest differences emerge. Britain's comprehensive system of planning administration is the envy of most countries. Undoubtedly, it reflects the fact that this crowded island was the first to suffer the excesses of the Industrial Revolution and has therefore developed a relatively greater public acceptance of planning. But in all countries, public support and participation appear inadequate to sustain the systems required to deal effectively with today's environmental problems.

Recommendations about these problems formed part of the 1968 report on Regional Planning by the Council of Europe. The report deals with the main needs of regional planning in member countries and within the fast-emerging European entity. It reviews the present state of cooperation between member countries (there are numerous bilateral planning schemes), stresses the gaps and lack of cohesion and proposes the institution on a permanent basis of a European Conference of Ministers responsible for regional planning.

If, then, the powers and processes are still inadequate for modern needs, not only in Britain but elsewhere, what are the changes which all countries should make? What can be done to improve the whole position, especially to ensure fuller citizen participation? These are the issues discussed in the three following chapters.

CHAPTER 18

REQUIREMENTS AND PROPOSALS – I

Philosophy · Principles · Legislation · Administration

> I have been ever of the opinion that revolutions
> are not to be evaded.
>
> Benjamin Disraeli

THIS chapter and the next consider how it might be possible
to place the structure of planning on a firmer long-term basis.
The proposals go beyond suggesting reforms merely in the
processes of planning because these in themselves will only
'paper over the cracks'. What is needed is a framework conceived differently from the present one.

PHILOSOPHY

> I repeat . . . that all power is a trust – that we are
> accountable for its exercise – that, from the
> people, and for the people, all springs and all
> must exist.
>
> Benjamin Disraeli

In most countries the State maintains law and order and seeks
to guide social development by political, legislative and administrative means. The need for the State to create a framework
for individual and cooperative effort is now taken for granted.
What is in question is its extent and detail. Planning, not only
of the physical environment but of most economic and natural
resources, is not yet wholly accepted as part of this framework.
Some regard it as a keystone of ideologies – for example, Com-
munism or Socialism – which they may abhor. Others regard
it as a factor inhibiting the free play of market forces. To some
it is a panacea for the ills of society, an opportunity to create
their own particular Utopia or a means of imposing their own
concepts upon an inarticulate and apathetic public.

All this is particularly unfortunate because essentially planning is neutral. It is primarily a process for making a deliberate

choice about future relationships between man and his environment. It is not antithetic to freedom. Where men have a choice, they usually choose to plan their affairs. In a community planning helps to provide the ways and means of achieving social objectives, just as in all modern industry it is a prerequisite for continued commercial existence, development and profit-making.

No one today questions the need for communal action in the field of, say, public health, or in the compilation of population statistics. But for years these were regarded as gross infringements of personal liberty and were hotly contested in Parliament, Press and Pulpit. What really has not been widely accepted is the premise that a healthy environment requires the positive efforts of the community to create it, and rules to prevent individuals or groups from marring or destroying it. It seems essential, therefore, to state some of the philosophy and principles underlying the policies and procedures suggested in this book.

The first of the philosophic issues is summed up in an extension of the old adage 'A healthy mind in a healthy body' to include 'in a healthy environment': for those who prefer a Latin tag – *Mens sana in corpore sano in vicinia sana*. If man is to achieve real fulfilment and satisfy his highest aspirations, then clearly a healthy environment is vital. The tragedies which came from his forgetting this can be seen in any of the unhealthy slums of the world. Fortunately today he is remembering it more often, as the many discussions on land use and conservation which are taking place in most countries now show.

Acceptance of this extended adage requires an awareness of man's creative and destructive capacities. It demands a sense of personal responsibility for the curbing of the destructive forces and the wise use of the creative powers. It demands an understanding of the individual's inheritance and of his obligation to hand on to his children an enhanced heritage. Each generation should take particular care to leave its successor some scope for choice in the creation of a healthy environment.

Environmental issues need to be appraised in ethical terms. Such an ethic embodies responsibility for the maintenance of the productive capacity of land, air, water and wild life, for their integrity and stability, and for the aesthetic qualities of the landscape. It requires the formulation and acceptance of environmental standards and codes of behaviour, together with a constant vigilance to ensure that they are put into effect.

It is essential to make people feel that they are trustees for the environment and to infuse this attitude into all activities of the State. Conservation for posterity must become a built-in aim of central and local government. Members and officials must develop the right attitude of mind so that they constantly seek to maintain and enhance the resources and qualities on which society depends. That this approach is not common to-day is well illustrated in most countries where sectional battles over land and water resources are common. A danger to guard against here is the philosophy of a corporate State. As many large organizations – of government, industry or workers – learn to speak the 'same language', there could emerge a system of 'package deals' which, in the long run, would be self-defeating. But once society has developed a philosophy demanding a healthy environment, based on ethics and trustee-ships, planning can really become positive and purposeful, creative and imaginative. But it must be established on certain principles.

PRINCIPLES

Unity

A primary principle is that the environment is a unity. Town and country are within one society and one civilization. In all spheres – economic, social, physical and probably moral – there is clear and continuing interdependence, between those who live and work in the countryside and those who use it, and be-tween agriculture and forestry, industry and commerce. The people are concerned with one land. Most social activities, urban or rural, are enjoyed by most people at some time.

The physical environment has been shown to be a complex and interconnected system, both a web and a continuum. It is dynamic and ever-changing, and any action in one part affects others. Planning should recognize this unity of physical forces and people and seek to create a synthesis guiding changes to desired social objectives. To do this effectively, it must assess policies and developments affecting the environment not only for their impacts on natural resources but for all their inter-relationships.

Wetlands are particularly sensitive to apparently minor changes. Each part is uniquely interdependent with another. The cases studied in Chapter 12 show that their ecological balance is so delicate that any action not based on a thorough appraisal of all aspects, and a comprehensive approach to their planning, management and development, may be fatal to them.

And this unity embraces man.

Comprehensiveness

Coupled with the principle of unity should be that of com-prehensiveness in environmental planning. Hitherto, much rural planning has been *in* the rural area – for villages, services, or minor uses. Rarely has it been *of* the countryside. Yet it needs to take account of such a wide range of demands: for agriculture and forestry; for industry and housing; for traffic, tourism and outdoor recreation; and for the requirements of a changing rural population. All future plans must assess the capacity of the land to meet these demands. They must also recognize that people cannot withstand an indefinite increase in the pressures of city life. Again, urban and rural planning must be synthesized.

To do all this requires a comprehensive appraisal of en-vironmental issues, particularly economic and ecological. Any future for the countryside must be based on a sound economy. Agriculture needs to be closely integrated within economic and physical planning so that limited resources are used in the best interests of society. If the nation expects rural landowners and occupiers to fulfil extra obligations – for example, to create new landscapes for general enjoyment – these must be paid for. A complementary need is to consider all developments in terms of their effects on the ecological health of the country-side.

The effects of air pollution at Haverton Hill, discussed in Chapter 7, grimly demonstrate man's capacity for getting one product at the expense of many other qualities – human and environmental. Few people would question the need for a comprehensive approach if they were aware of the implications of such cases.

Quality

The third principle is that the quality of the environment is part of the heritage of the nation.

Quality has been proclaimed for years as an objective for urban areas. Perhaps its most publicized expression was in the report *Traffic in Towns*. This spoke of the need for environmental management to maintain the quality of the towns in face of the all-engulfing traffic. Brilliant practical illustrations of planning for quality, which embody the principles of unity and comprehensiveness, are the Lee Valley Regional Park and the Newcastle Town Moor project. The Tyne Landscape Report, published in 1965, also seeks to set a high standard. There are about twelve miles of open land facing the river, containing numerous derelict industrial sites and much blight. The main objective is to replace this depressing scene, to conserve the river and its banks as a natural resource and to harmonize all legitimate demands in a new, imaginative and unified landscape.

At the same time, the quality of rural areas has been taken for granted, but it has probably altered more since 1945 than has that of urban areas. Some consider the changes of the past decade to be greater than those in the fourteenth century following the Black Death or in the eighteenth century following the enclosures. Recognition of this, and that even more sweeping changes are on the way, inspired the 'Countryside in 1970' Conferences in Britain in 1963 and 1965; the White House Conference in the U.S.A. in 1965; and European Conservation Year, 1970; with their call to conserve quality.

The quality of the environment would be greatly diminished if there were no healthy wild life, yet Chapter 10 shows that the world is in danger of losing the abundant wild life of Africa just as it almost destroyed the bisons of North America. The application of science and technology in Britain is in-

exorably eliminating certain plants and animals and their
habitats, and population pressures are affecting coast and
country. Yet this need not be, if conservation and enhancement of quality were accepted as a basic principle. The
situation is unlikely to get better till people perceive quality
as being of personal value and voluntarily do things to
achieve it. The individual gain will add up to overall human
satisfaction, which, in the final analysis, is the ultimate test of
society.

These three principles are essential if the State is to safeguard resources for the needs of future populations. How are
they to be implemented today?

LEGISLATION

To get the State to act as a trustee and to develop a unified
approach to environmental problems will require substantial
changes. These will obviously take time and can evolve only at
a pace dictated by the strength of public confidence in the
objectives. Much can, however, be done to adapt and equip all
levels of the constitutional structure, and many countries
already have valuable experience of how to do this.

At the top, it seems vital to secure more active participation
in environmental issues by the elected representatives in
Parliament. One method being tried in the late sixties is the
use of Parliamentary committees parallel with the major departments. Such committees have been in operation for years
in many countries – for example, the U.S.A. and France – and
were formally proposed in Britain by the Haldane Committee
in 1919. Opposition to them in Britain frequently appears to
arise from the executive's reluctance to disclose objectives and
motives and their inadequate response to constructive criticism.
Possibly other methods may be found acceptable both to the
executive and the legislature, but it would be a great step forward if Members of Parliament were able to contribute more
fully to major environmental discussions.

Many European countries have a ministry and staff specially
entrusted with the task of securing law reform. Recent developments in Britain include the setting-up in 1965 of a Law Com-

mission which is already dealing with major social questions of law reform. This Commission should be equipped to maintain a continuous review of the state of British law and to be the focus for the study of law-reform proposals from other countries. One central ministry should be made fully responsible for the physical environment. This department and the Commission, working closely together, could ensure the appraisal and integration of legislation affecting the environment. Future legislation should contain clauses to require those operating under it to have full regard to the nation's duty to posterity.

To carry out the longer-term and more complex tasks of integrating a wide spectrum of environmental legislation the central ministry will need to have access to the sources of new knowledge and ideas in the relevant fields. A continuous and effective administrative link should be developed between these sources and the departments responsible for the inception of new legislation. In this, experience of how similar problems are handled in other countries should be valuable, and both the central and law-reform departments could gain from, and contribute to, international cooperation in these fields. Already there are substantial areas of law which have been studied by international bodies, many of which have led to international conventions. International experience during the late fifties and early sixties shows the great value of pooling ideas, techniques and procedures. The widespread administrative practice of creating 'action teams' to study traffic, education and other subjects in other countries and then modify and apply the lessons learned at home, needs to be extended to legislation. Britain has no monopoly of the best.

ADMINISTRATION

> The power of the Crown has increased, is increasing, and ought to be diminished.
>
> Lord Ashburton

This Motion in the House of Commons of 1780 is today relevant to the activities of central government.

How can more strategic and comprehensive resource planning be combined with greater delegation locally and more scope for individual initiative? This question of getting a balance between central and local government, and between public and private initiative, and of creating a partnership in which each does what it can do best, is at the heart of all democratic government. It is particularly significant in the determination of social priorities and the policies and processes of a 'mixed' economy.

Central government must obviously decide the broad allocation of national resources, settle the priorities between investment and expenditure, and the deployment of activities over the country. These decisions are particularly important for land and water, which are always scarce at any time in relation to the demands upon them. But to go beyond this leads to the failures and frustrations outlined in Chapter 17. Central government should, therefore, concentrate on strategy, the formulation of national standards and on seeing that the nation's intentions are effectively carried out.

To achieve these aims requires considerable reform of central government, both in structure and personnel. As the Civil Service in Britain was reviewed in a major report* published in 1968, it will be sufficient here to express the hope that its recommendations will lead to the development of an executive qualified for the positive, operational role demanded by the modern State. But the structure of central government needs streamlining. The number of ministries should be greatly reduced and those remaining should concentrate on strategic tasks, such as economic and physical planning, foreign affairs, public order and defence and the social structure. Much of the work presently undertaken should be handed over to regional government. This trend to integration and delegation is international and is found in many other countries.

As noted, strategic planning of the environment would be the responsibility of a central ministry. Before setting up this department, it would be worth while studying the conflicts that marked the birth of the Ministry of Town and Country

* Cmnd 3638 *The Civil Service* (the Fulton Report).

Planning in the forties and the short-lived Ministry of Land and Natural Resources of 1964–7. Political and administrative vested interests should not be allowed to prevent the strategic coordination of policy so urgently needed. Housing, transport, agriculture and the other major land and water users should submit their broad proposals to the central planning ministry for appraisal and synthesis. The fiscal and economic measures of the Treasury and Department of Economic Affairs would have to be assessed by this ministry for their implications for the environment. Equally, of course, the physical planning strategy would be evaluated by the central ministry for economic affairs and policies coordinated accordingly. Placing responsibility for the quality of the environment squarely on to one central ministry necessitates substantial re-shaping of the structure and responsibilities of the various levels of government.

In this context it is worth quoting Goschen, who, speaking in 1872, said: 'We have a chaos as regards Authorities, a chaos as regards rates, and worse chaos than all as regards areas.' The situation today is little better. Fortunately, the whole structure and administration of local government are undergoing critical examination. Two Special Committees * have reported upon the situation of members and staff in local government. Reorganization in Wales was started in 1967 (see page 301), as early action was urgently needed. Royal Commissions were set up in the spring of 1966 to make comprehensive reviews of local government in England and Scotland. These far-reaching assessments were due for 1969. The evidence pointed to some form of regional government based on the comprehensive authority. If posterity is to be left any choice at all, the new organization must be designed for multiple functions and be flexible enough to adapt to changing circumstances. An *ad hoc* body is inevitably limited and in time creates further problems as new needs dictate fresh priorities. The past two hundred years in Britain have seen an oscillation between the *ad hoc* and the comprehensive authority. But in a country as small as Britain, and with modern means of communication,

* *Staffing of Local Government* (the Mallaby Report) and *Management of Local Government* (the Maud Report).

there is no excuse for not bringing all State activities into a systematic and coherent whole.

A century ago, John Stuart Mill pointed out:

Another equally important principle is, that in each local circumscription there should be but one elected body for all local business. . . . The local, like the national Parliament, has for its proper business to consider the interest of the locality as a whole. . . .

The allocation of functions between central and local government requires comprehensive, democratic regional authorities for long-term planning of major services and strong local authorities for their implementation. The case for regional government rests partly on the whole value of democratic local government and partly on the fact that many services today require large areas to support them. There is an extensive literature on the subject, most of it arguing that democratic local government can provide an effective, responsive administration which will limit the powers of central bodies. It offers great scope for training in civic leadership and citizen participation. Many local authorities cannot now fulfil these aims. Perhaps their most serious weaknesses are that they have failed to attract local people; cannot contribute to or influence national economic and physical planning; nor manage to carry out national strategy in planning and the major services. Hence a reform of local authorities is urgently required.

Regional authorities and a stronger sub-regional tier – replacing the present structure of county and county boroughs – could meet these objectives and help to reduce the marked variation in the economic, social and physical conditions of different parts of the country. Such authorities are essential in the total structure of the nation's government if a synthesis of social and environmental issues is to be achieved. Several countries, notably France and Germany, are creating a regional structure for planning. These authorities prepare plans for all resources and take the rural sector as a vital part of the whole economy, requiring as much attention as the urban one.

There are many possible definitions of regions, depending very much on the character of the functions to be carried out,

21 Economic planning regions (Crown Copyright)

and it is a complex technical and political exercise to determine the most suitable areas. Clearly, there can be a greatly extended delegation of powers to Wales and Scotland; the economic plan for Scotland involves five sub-regions. Additionally, Scotland has the Highlands and Islands Development Board, whose Chairman favours regional government and regional planning and has proposals for developing the Highlands which include a new university and a major new city in the Moray Firth area.

The regional authorities in all three countries would take over their major responsibilities from central government and free it for its primary tasks of strategy and coordination. It should be far more practicable for central government to guide strategy and development within such regions than within the present multitude of major authorities. In particular, the regional functions of central departments and many specialist agencies (including the new *ad hoc* bodies – such as Rural Development Boards and the Land Commission) could be taken over by, and integrated into, the work of the regional authorities. Details of a revised structure of local government are given in Appendix 3. To provide each comprehensive authority with an area large enough to make the system work means that some compromise is needed over the boundaries for most services.

The regional authorities would be responsible for the general framework of population and employment, for the broad planning of major regional services, for all policies affecting the environment, and especially for the integration of urban and rural interests. They would be given the power and money to deal with areas of depression, sites for new cities within national strategy and for 'overspill' within the regions, derelict land, the creation of new landscapes and all the major tasks now beyond the scope of the counties and cities and clearly not suitable for central government. The authorities would be able to take the wide view; for example, they could plan traffic and other services to clear congestion from living areas and fine landscapes. Perhaps, above all, they would be large enough and have the powers to attract and keep first-class civic leaders and to secure participation by their citizens.

Regions already have a sense of identity and cohesion; giving them their own government would soon increase this feeling. Some still evoke memories of the ancient Anglo-Saxon Kingdoms – such as the Iceni (locally called 'ickennies') of East Anglia – whose areas in some cases seem surprisingly more apposite to today's needs than those of the Norman counties or the 'upstart' cities of the Industrial Revolution. The war-time regions showed, and the current regions of the Department of Economic Affairs are confirming, that there exists a strong basis for regional government. The system offers great scope for harmonizing national objectives with regional resources and for encouraging the maximum delegation of powers to local authorities.

As the regional authorities are organized, local government will need to be radically reformed. As much as possible of the work and practical decision making should be done by the next tier down – created from the reform of county and county borough. The aim would be to create a greater sense of interdependence between town and country, and to see that in civic affairs the large city and its hinterland is treated as an environmental unity. Perhaps the term 'county region' may be better suited to describe this idea than 'city region', though the objectives sought are broadly the same. The county is, in practice, the authority more accustomed to dealing with the larger areas, to delegating work to a lower tier, and to considering the needs of the countryside. It also usually has experience of urban affairs in the boroughs in its area. But in view of the present rivalry of county and county borough, a new term may be required. Some second-tier areas would be virtually all-urban counties, such as that proposed in late 1965 for the area around Manchester. These authorities, combining the best traditions of the counties and cities, could be made responsible for all government functions and services in their area. They would also be able to join in a two-way flow of ideas and data which would enable them and the region to plan and coordinate effectively on a regional basis.

Third in the hierarchy, below the region and the sub-region, there is a need for a local authority to stimulate wider public participation in government, and to act as a cornerstone against bureaucracy. There are today vast numbers of minor local authorities in Britain – around 1,700 county districts (non-county boroughs and urban and rural districts) and 7,000 parish councils. These could be regrouped and simplified, yet at the same time strengthened, to meet the need for local leadership and participation, particularly in the personal services and in the formulation of local plans and environmental standards (see Appendix 3). In practice, this reformed third-tier authority should be the 'front line' in the efforts to create a better-quality environment. Some of the larger urban authorities have a well-established organization for carrying out the day-to-day work for most county services. To these authorities delegation should be continued as fully as possible but, particularly in those fields where the interdependence of town and country is most obvious, they should be given the opportunity to take on functions outside their urban area.

In addition to the reforms of central departments and regional and local authorities, advisory bodies are required for major sectors of environmental planning. Private initiative should be encouraged by the creation of development agencies to bring together functional specialists from government and commerce, the economist and ecologist, the architect and engineer, the public relations officer, the land agents and managers, the developers and so on. These could help to fuse into a harmonious pattern the various qualities essential to planning. The requirements for research into the 'built' and 'natural' environments and the social sciences are discussed later, but one of the problems in planning not touched on elsewhere is that of distinguishing the quasi-judicial function from the executive. Some think that in time a separate branch of government will be needed to handle appeals against planning decisions. For the time being, a redefinition and allocation of tasks as suggested here, leaving the central ministry free for this appellate function, would probably lessen present discontent with the system.

The full implications of all these proposals will take a long time to work out. The essential thing is that they should be firmly based on the philosophy and principles set out earlier.

CHAPTER 19

REQUIREMENTS AND PROPOSALS – II

Resource Planning · The Planner

THE term 'resource planning' is used in this chapter to embrace economic and physical planning. Broadly, governments work through two main lines of policy: financial and fiscal measures controlling investment and subsidies, and physical controls over development. In November 1965 the Minister of Housing and Local Government spoke of '. . . a strangely lopsided planning system . . . without the accompanying fiscal and financial structure that gave it strength and purpose'. Most of the measures now being essayed in central, regional and local government seek to remedy this situation through a more unified and comprehensive approach to creating a better environment.

In the past, fiscal policies have often been put into effect without adequate account of their long-term impact on the environment. But to achieve coherence in such measures is a large task. Consider, for example, the problems involved in creating a synthesis of the effects of subsidies and price supports in agriculture; tax concessions in forestry; national and local government action in water supply and use; the exploitation of minerals; the reclamation of land and the use to which it is put; the location of new towns; and the creation of traffic and communication systems. All these separate and often conflicting activities are helping to shape the environment. Yet somehow their planning, management and development must be made consistent with society's general desire to preserve natural resources.

As noted earlier, the Government's proposals for investment incentives are intended to secure better geographical distribution of industrial growth. To promote the balanced growth of regions, extra inducements will be made available to encourage industrial development and economic growth. Agriculture will be helped to effect further productivity and to save manpower.

The clearance of derelict land by local authorities will qualify for an eighty-five per cent grant if it can be proved to contribute to the development of industry. All these measures could obviously give rise to substantial changes in the environment. For example, population redeployment and expansion of industry require an infrastructure of sites, communications and amenities. All economic and physical decisions interact. Clearly, therefore, national strategy and regional integration are required if these and other fiscal and economic measures are not to nullify much physical planning. The Regional Boards and Councils of the Department of Economic Affairs have prepared plans which clearly reflect the indissolubility of economics and the natural resources of land, air, water and wild life.

Equally, physical planning has often failed to take adequate account of real economic values. For example, to site factories which depend on vast quantities of water in the drier east of Britain may give rise to indirect social costs which might equal or exceed the benefits from other factors, such as easy access to skilled labour and communications. Policies for the use of land and water resources should seek the maximum total satisfaction of present and estimated future needs. The optimum value of resources for specific uses must be assessed; for example, the capability of various soils for different crops. Most areas will be able to support multiple uses and the aim should be to get that combination of uses which, in the long term, gives the best return while yet maintaining the quality of the resources.

This inter-relationship of economic and physical planning may be simplified, perhaps crudely, into a relationship between demand and supply factors. Most immediate demands, though not all – not, for example, the community's need for leisure space – can be translated into cash terms; but to assess the cost of maintaining for posterity the required supply of natural resources is very difficult. Nevertheless the continuing nation-state has to attempt this. Somehow much more account must be taken of the long-term scarcity-value of resources as their quantity and quality tend to decline. This is more and more important as Western civilization becomes an inverted pyramid, with the point a reducing proportion of workers (currently about one tenth) engaged in dealing with the natural resources on which all else is based. Economic and physical factors must be considered together all the time – this is imperative. Probably the best current example of this dual approach is the Government's White Paper* *The Scottish Economy, 1965–70: a Plan for Expansion*. This gives a grand strategy for the economic, physical and social planning of Scotland, and, in fact, has employed some of the approaches advocated in this book – planning is done on a regional and sub-regional scale, and appraisals have been made of resource potential.

The White Paper on the 1966–7 Estimates published in February 1966 states:

> The new methods should ensure that the main Government services will be expanded on a scale which can be accommodated within the nation's resources and taxable capacity. Once the total has been established, to spend more on one item means spending less on something else; and this is a true system of economic and social priorities. It is for debate and discussion how these choices should be modified in the years ahead. . . .

The points made here are equally relevant to all resource planning. A major aim must be to define and assess the main alternatives that may not be implemented in the given circumstances. It is equally important to identify and evaluate the factors preventing the optimal utilization of resources and to seek to relate their cost – or the outlay required to resolve them – to those benefiting from the course of action adopted.

It is, however, essential to stress that the best economic and physical planning can only operate within defined limits. It is not possible to get a clean slate for a new blue-print environment. Past conditions and ingrained attitudes exercise a continuing influence. Despite the pace and scope of technological advances and the scale of information and propaganda, methods of land management as old as the Bible are still found side by side with chemical and factory farming. Folklore still plays a significant part in the work of many agricultural communities. Furthermore changes of policy – for example, in the type of trees planted – take generations to come to fruition and may have been superseded by new policies long before their end-

* Cmnd 2864.

result is visible. As a general rule, substantial improvements
to the landscape take a long time – destruction is rapid.

At the moment, official bodies, industrialists and private
citizens who seek some place where they can get answers about
the implications and implementation of their projects find
they are entering a labyrinth. Undoubtedly, the local planning
authority is at present the only effective focal point for such
information and for the coordination of a vast range of factors
affecting the environment. What can be done to improve the
planning system so that it may meet the criticisms set out in
Chapter 17?

PLANNING POLICIES AND SYSTEM

The main features of the 1965 Report of the Planning Advisory
Group (P.A.G.) were accepted in a White Paper in June 1967,
and included in legislation in 1968. The primary objectives are
that development plans eschew detail and 'should deal only
with the broad physical structure of the area and the principal
policies and priorities for its future development'. The new
system frees the Minister to deal with strategy and major
issues of policy, but still requires him to approve the new
'structure' plan (see Appendix 4).

Further improvements could be made with the emergence
of the democratic regional authorities discussed earlier. These
would be responsible for the planning of the major services;
producing the strategic development plan would be one of
their primary tasks. The more detailed plans for the next
tier – the sub-region – would be prepared within a regional
framework and be approved by the regional authority. In
answer to the accusation that the Ministry would get out of
touch with realities, it can be argued most strongly that the men
at the top should be able to grasp the policies of, say, ten to
twelve major regions far better than they can those of the
numerous planning authorities – at present around 230 in
Great Britain.

The 1968 legislation recommends the preparation of local
plans for action areas and for towns not otherwise dealt with.
These will provide a detailed basis for positive planning and

development control. The action area plans, a primary responsibility of the local planning authority, would be for areas which need to be treated as a physical entity and where development on a large scale should take place within ten years. They would be indicated on the main structure plan so that a basis for resources programming would be provided, but they would not be submitted for approval, simply requiring adoption by the council of the appropriate local planning authority.

The prospect that local plans might be handled more quickly and be related more directly to development, plus the feeling that local opinion could have a genuine influence on decisions, should bring substantial improvement in development control. In general, the reforms arising from the P.A.G. Report do much to meet criticisms of the current planning process and offer considerable scope for participation by the public. Backed by a dynamic regional strategy, such detailed plans should soon acquire qualities sadly lacking in much present planning.

One major weakness of the P.A.G. Report is its approach to rural planning. This is currently neglected and insufficiently related to the actual use and management of land and water. The P.A.G. Report rightly refers to the County Development Plan being prepared with a broad brush and proposes that it should cover the needs of conservation, recreation and landscape. But it proposes the preparation of local action area plans for villages only 'as and when resources allow', and it hardly touches on the need to plan rural areas on a long-term basis to meet changing demands. No longer should large areas of the development plans be left without any conscious policy for their use or enhancement. In the past the physical planner has been little concerned with agriculture and forestry or with the leisure activities of townspeople in the countryside. Planners should now be able to formulate and to promote policies which can take full account of the primary roles of the countryside, in particular of the needs of those living and working there. The third-tier authority should be encouraged to provide facts about local conditions and developments, and about the community's own aspirations.

No environmental planning would be complete without the integration at all levels of measures to provide for traffic and leisure. The national level provides motorways and trunk roads; regional and local coordination of traffic is needed in relation to this national network. To achieve this, the Minister of Transport started in 1966 studies and consultations with the many bodies concerned. A series of White Papers in the next two years culminated in the major legislation on transport in 1968 (see Appendix 4).

In rural areas, road and traffic planning, access and facilities require special care and standards if the countryside is not to be despoiled. Technological development in the short term can destroy the rural scene; planned on a long-term basis it can often enhance it. Modern technology now enables coastal barrage schemes to be developed and major areas of land to be reclaimed from the sea. All these possibilities, and the great surging waves of people moving over the countryside, require more, not less, planning. Although the air traveller over Britain can still see lots of apparently untouched and beautiful countryside, there is a great need at ground level to plan, manage and conserve this part of the national heritage in face of the impacts threatening it.

Implementation of the regional plan should be the primary task of the next tier – the county or city region. These authorities must guide development, both by direct action through partnership with industry and commerce and by providing inducements for commercial bodies, such as sites for factories and accommodation for staff. In promoting such developments this authority must cooperate fully with specialist bodies like the river and navigation authorities. It should be able to obtain from the region powers to rectify any shortcomings if the bodies concerned cannot fulfil the plan.

Regionally and locally much greater effort is needed to encourage the positive use of resources. The authorities must be given the staff and power to enable them to start special projects for the enhancement of the countryside, preferably by cooperative schemes with landowners; to clear and landscape derelict land and eyesores; to restore or redevelop land after mineral working; to use and dispose of waste and by-products; to provide intensive recreational areas in towns and leisure parks in the countryside; and to advise agriculture, forestry and other development in certain selected areas. In all this, there is great scope for comprehensive plans to create new landscapes, particularly in and around older industrial towns.

Development control should be the responsibility of second-tier authorities which would cooperate with the third-tier authorities not only on developments of importance but also over the collection of data on which regional and local plans can be based.

RESEARCH AND SURVEY

Knowledge is required for all these tasks, much more than exists at present. In November 1965 the Joint Parliamentary Secretary to the Ministry of Land and Natural Resources said: 'We had as a nation done virtually nothing to find out even the basic facts about our resources and had been almost criminally negligent.' Research is required not only into the distribution of resources but also into their quality and quantity. New techniques and methodology must be devised. Land-use data banks are needed. Research into systems for classification and inventory is required for all physical factors. And much study of personal and social motives and attitudes is long overdue.

Millions of people now go into the countryside; what is the real nature and impact of their activities? How will these develop? For example, should outdoor recreation be regarded as a use in its own right? How will the country-dweller respond to these developments and what changes are required in economic and social policies? Not to answer such questions will inevitably result in changes desired by no one; to answer them requires much more knowledge than at present exists about the physical environment and about the behaviour and attitudes of people. In turn, people need to know more about the processes of government, especially planning, if they are to participate fully. All this requires research and surveys – sociological, economic, ecological.

The Land Utilization Survey of the 1930's and that now under way only describe current uses. They need to be complemented by thorough classifications and inventories of soil capability and the possibilities for multiple use. These assessments of resource potential should be processed and stored regionally and nationally by computers. Such data banks would provide a much firmer basis for decision, speed up development and facilitate a concentration of effort on the enhancement of 'key' areas. Comprehensive inventory of all features of interest is required. Work of this kind which has already been done in Britain and the U.S.A. (discussed in Chapter 20) shows that these features are often grouped together in zones or corridors. The planning process should, therefore, provide for more effective control over them; and the executive arm of local government – perhaps a special committee – should have responsibility for their conservation. The voluntary bodies should be encouraged to participate fully in this work. With suitable measures for effective intercommunication between all sectors of society, such research and survey could give zest, meaning and depth to the quest for a high-quality environment.

It is important that most of the research and survey necessary for the re-shaping and creation of a new urban landscape should be *pari passu* with that for rural planning. Data collection, the deployment of manpower, the capacity of the construction industry, commuting, people's choice of residence and surveys of land use – these and many other fields of 'urban' research are all interlocked with the economic, physical and sociological material relating to the 'natural' environment. Urban planners have to decide, on the basis of their research into resource demands, where certain types of development should be located, taking care to consider all the while how the maximum benefit to the whole society can be obtained. This approach is equally relevant to rural planning and can best be developed by integration of research at the outset in both regions and counties. But it is also essential that there should be close liaison over policies and techniques at national level between the Natural Environment and Social Science Research Councils and the Centre for Environmental Studies set up in 1967 as an independent charitable trust to advance education and research in the planning and design of the physical environment.

PARTICIPATION

A better environment is today expected by many people and countries as an essential part of their standard of living. Until resource economists and social scientists can provide adequate ways of evaluating the costs and benefits of the necessary measures, many of the policy decisions will be purely political. These often place a strain on the relationship between the short-term interests of individuals and the continuing interests of the community. It is, therefore, essential for all citizens to participate fully in the formulation and determination of the criteria which will influence policies and action. This requires the knowledge and support of universities, churches, chambers of commerce, voluntary bodies and other social groups.

In this field, the Civic Trust helps to secure public participation by means of exhibitions, discussions and publications.

It has been involved in some of the major planning issues of the decade: successful opposition in 1960 to proposals for the piece-meal redevelopment of Piccadilly Circus; expert studies on re-planning town centres; proposals for the rehabilitation of the Rhondda Valleys; and the Lee Valley project (see page 166). It has organized pilot-schemes for transplanting semi-mature trees, and in 1966 launched a national campaign to plant millions of trees in towns. The Trust played a leading part in the pro-motion of the Civic Amenities Act, 1967 (see Appendix 4).

Such activities and those of the parish councils and numerous voluntary bodies need to be encouraged everywhere and new measures developed for informing and involving the public. This would soon greatly improve local amenities and stimulate civic pride. Above all, it would use the enormous reservoir of human energy and goodwill in the community in work *for* the community.

Citizen participation is also essential if the dangers inherent in planning – over-centralization, bureaucratic tyranny, 'the great mistake' and its waste of resources – are to be avoided. If planning is to work the public must have a say in it. Its officers must be accountable to the public – no sheltering be-hind Ministers or committees – and the voices of local demo-cracy must be strong.

Measures to ensure more effective publicity over development applications and all plans are long overdue. The third-tier authority has a vital role in this work. The more it is in touch, the more likely it is that it can handle proposals quickly and at the same time prevent leaks about matters which must be kept secret. Members, supported by officers and information from the regional or second-tier authority, should initiate public forums on all major and controversial issues. Each authority should continually seek to be aware of the needs, aspirations and environmental problems of its citizens. The planning process must ensure this, hence the importance of the new philosophy enshrined in the 1968 legislation.

THE PLANNER

> . . . logic and learning and all mental activity . . .
> have been understandable only as a process by
> which man puts himself *en rapport* with his
> environment.
> Norbert Wiener, *I am a Mathematician* (1956)

There are many types of planners: the economist who helps to formulate the national economic plan; the specialist who plans the programmes of a nationalized industry or a major private concern; and the scientist or professional who plans natural resources. All of these obviously have to take account of many issues. But they do not have to cover the whole range of social, economic and physical factors, which is the task of the town and country planner. This planner has, in fact, to comprehend all the factors which make up the total backcloth to life. He must not only know the requirements of his own profession but also be aware of the contribution to planning of other professions and be capable of creating a synthesis of related concepts and data. The planner should be in frequent contact with universities and research councils and be aware of scientific knowledge bearing on land and water resources. He must understand and use assessments of the ability of land and water to sustain, without detriment, the uses to which they are put.

About half of the 3,900 members (in 1968) of the Town Planning Institute are engaged officially and directly in central and local government planning. The heads of the major departments directing the preparation of development plans and town maps are the key figures. These really do have to apply to the environment the principles of unity, quality and comprehensiveness. About twenty per cent of the qualified planners are engaged in private practice, many as consultants. They employ similar methods to the ones of their official colleagues. Although not all have the resources of the major local planning authorities, their greater freedom from official and routine commitments enables them to make a valuable contribution to the thought and practice of planning. A number of these consultants are undertaking plans for new cities and towns, some of which are mentioned in the next chapter.

Most planning on any scale is carried out by teams which include people skilled in many professions – architecture, estate valuation and engineering, for example – and sciences such as economics, geology and, recently, ecology. Their leader seeks to synthesize the main elements emerging from the work of the whole team. Members usually have the training and capacity to seek out and to identify those issues on which a judicious contribution can be crucial in creating a good three-dimensional environment. In effect, the planner develops a special quality likened to sophisticated 'antennae'.

Different requirements are needed at the three main levels of government. At national level, the planner must be able to identify the relevant principles, to apply them to complex masses of information, and then to formulate strategy and policies for the nation. At regional level, the planner would contribute to the shaping of national policies. Within these he prepares a strategic plan to take into account the special characteristics and resources of the region. He will be required to plan for population policies; the distribution and development of industry; communications; regional services, such as water and drainage; major landscape features; and generally bring into balance with human needs the economic and physical resources of the region.

At the level of county or city region, the planner is increasingly concerned with the detailed design of the environment. He should work out more fully the policies of the region. He must prepare plans to implement them and to deal with any issues not covered in the regional plan, including policies for the smaller towns and villages. He also organizes the procedures for the control of development in his area.

Many qualities are obviously required for this exacting work. To those of first-class judgement and a sense of political issues must be allied the discipline of many professions and sciences. National-level planning makes its own specification, but at regional level a knowledge of economics and ecology appear to be indispensable to the planner. At county level, more emphasis on architectural, engineering and landscaping considerations is essential and executive capacity becomes important. At all levels the planner has to have the ability to understand and to get on with people. He must be able to communicate with, and be acceptable to, a wide range of citizens.

One of the most important problems facing society is that of relating its human talent to its priorities. This is particularly so in environmental planning. The intellectual requirements for planners are obviously high, and the qualities of dynamism and persuasiveness are scarce. With so few fully qualified planners to take on this exacting work it is essential to place them at the key places. There should be a greater concentration of professional talent at regional level; rarely is it efficient to employ planners at the level of the existing county districts although there is a pressing need for more employment locally of design skills. The in-service training and education of the planner must be organized to enable him to keep abreast of the rapidly increasing and changing knowledge relevant to his work.

The planner's task is to spear-head man's response to human impacts on the environment. To do this effectively requires readiness to accept great responsibility, to make decisions, to argue a case with those concerned – publicly if necessary – and to lead, persuade and inform.

CHAPTER 20

REQUIREMENTS AND PROPOSALS – III

Land Ownership · Zoning · Standards

THE past two chapters have set out guide-lines and measures for action. This chapter is concerned with three issues of great topical and yet continuing interest – land ownership, zoning and environmental standards.

LAND OWNERSHIP

The intention here is not to advocate any ideal solution or to give a comprehensive picture of this vast and complex problem, but to indicate some of the most interesting features and current developments about land ownership and betterment.

Few people can discuss land ownership and betterment without emotion or prejudice. It raises a host of technical problems and the only point people generally agree upon is that there is no solution wholly acceptable to everyone. Proposals to resolve these problems vary enormously. At one extreme are the people who favour complete public ownership; at the other are those who seek complete freedom. Others would settle for annual taxation of site values or a scheme to return to the community part of the extra value created by its actions, especially by planning decisions. Those who oppose interference with the free play of market forces in land trans-actions overlook the fact that complete freedom in the use of any natural resource is against the interests of the State; history – long past and recent – has amply proven this and the inadequacy of the collective 'wisdom' of the market, particu-larly in relation to land. Additionally, in very few sectors of the modern 'mixed' economy is there untrammelled bargaining and land especially is subject to restrictions of one kind or another. In some situations its qualities give it all the features of an effective monopoly product. It therefore requires special consideration, not least because few people now question that the wise use of land is vital to a healthy society. This inevitably brings in criteria of ethics and social justice.

Complete public ownership is no panacea. There are about six million acres of land in Britain owned by public authorities; decisions still have to be taken about the planning, management and development of this land. Conflicts rage, not only secretly in 'corridors of power' but openly in public, at inquiries and in the press. Often a decision based on the facts of a case is baulked by someone pleading a higher degree of 'public interest' or being more expert in the 'committee game'. Sometimes the major conflicts over land and water use are between public bodies with the landowner a third party living under the threat of compulsory purchase from either side. Experience in countries where most or all of the land is owned by the State, as in Russia, does not suggest that public ownership, in itself, resolves conflict. And when the State makes an error of judgement, its effects are usually widespread.

Whether public or private, a landowner is still faced with many of the same problems. Economic considerations obviously come into play at the outset, but the town and country planner should initially assess the potential of the resources available and their capacity to sustain heavy demands without becoming debased. Obviously, private ownership and market values of land affect public decisions and social priorities. But these are not thereby rendered insoluble and market value may, in some cases, give a better 'yard-stick' than the often subjective assessment of relative public interest. Although the power of a landowner may have political and social repercussions, it is little different from that of the organized 'lobbies' of other pressure groups.

If the primary aim is to determine the long-term optimum use of natural resources, then the fact that in the process some people make money from land is inevitable; society's concern is to keep this within reasonable limits. Critics rail against betterment and the unearned profits of the land speculator, and forget about 'worsement': sometimes land becomes less valuable through the action of the community and this may be serious, especially for the individual landowner. For example, traffic facilities, such as flyovers and airports, impair privacy and create noise; an arbitrary line on a map may enable one person to develop and make a large profit and another, refused permission or finding his land is zoned for a purpose of lower value, will sustain a loss. In justice, there should be some transfer of cash here, as most social action consists in redistributing wealth on one or other principle of equity or need. In practice, the complications of such a concept would probably render it unworkable. Additionally, since 1946, the increase in British land values and the various planning provisions make it even more difficult to assess whether any such worsement or 'planning blight' has occurred on any appreciable scale.

Land Commission Act, 1967

This Act came into force in April, 1967. Its stated objectives are:

1. To secure that the right land is available at the right time for the implementation of national, regional and local plans.
2. To secure that a substantial part of the development value created by the community returns to the community and that the burden of the cost of land for essential purposes is reduced.

To achieve these aims a Land Commission was set up in 1967. The Commission has wide powers to acquire land compulsorily and by agreement, on the basis of its market value less a proportion – a levy of 40 per cent – of the development element in that value. As the Commission will often acquire land in anticipation of it being needed for development, it has been given power to manage and improve the land meanwhile. It will be able to dispose of its land by sale or lease, as appropriate.

To bring other land broadly into the same financial position as that acquired by the Commission, it is subject to a levy on the development value. This levy applies to most land transactions and, initially, is 40 per cent of the development value, with the prospect of being increased. It is collected by the Commission and paid into the Exchequer.

Inevitably the Act has aroused strong feelings; the strongest relate to the methods rather more than the objectives. The main target for criticism is the Land Commission. Undoubtedly, opinion in favour of the community taking a proportion of the value of betterment is now stronger than it was just after the war, when the hundred per cent development charge which was imposed then failed to survive the first five years of post-war planning. An important practical distinction is that the previous charge was levied on a person who might have paid full market (development) value for the land; thus there was an unfair element of 'double taxation'. The new levy is, however, intended to be taken from the person who has actually realized the development value.

Opposition to the Land Commission is based on many grounds. It is seen as a measure for the nationalization of land by stealth; as a body nominated ministerially it is held to be undemocratic. Some people argue that it will be cumbersome and use up scarce resources of talent (it will need just under 2,000 staff when fully operational); that the Inland Revenue is better equipped to collect the levy; that its powers of compulsory purchase are too wide and, in any event, unnecessary; and that local authorities are better placed to exercise the powers for land acquisition. To these criticisms the Government replied:

1. But the compulsory purchase powers of local authorities are vested in some 1,500 separate authorities which differ widely in their willingness and in the effectiveness of their ability to use compulsory purchase powers. Anyone with experience of local government knows well that this is so. Thus, if the Government is to be able to ensure that in these circumstances land is to be available at the right place and at the right time for the implementation of national, regional and local plans which involve private as well as public development, then it must provide a national agency with the duty and with sufficient powers to ensure that land is indeed brought forward as required.

2. The Land Commission will be able to buy substantial areas of land well in advance before its value has significantly risen at the prospect of development, thus ensuring that an even greater part of betterment accrues to the community.

If effective democratic regional authorities were in existence
now, it would seem more appropriate to vest these powers in
them. It would also be desirable to vary the levy from region
to region in order to encourage development in the areas
where it is most needed. This should, of course, be within a
national plan on similar lines to the Investment Incentives
noted on page 209. It is feared, too, that the levy will be 'lost'
in Treasury funds and not applied to environmental renewal,
particularly in urban areas, in which Britain lags behind many
other European countries. Leaving the money with regional
authorities would help to provide another source of local
income and perhaps, independence.

It is to be hoped that some measure of political agreement
over the principles by which the legislation is to be implemented will soon be achieved. Without this, planning will
continue to be bedevilled and the quality of the environment
will suffer.

ZONING

To explain fully all the concepts included in modern resource
planning would need several books, but as zoning is the subject
of many new ideas it must be considered. In its basic form,
zoning is the defining of an area for specified purposes. To
survive, a concept must evolve and adapt to meet changing
circumstances. Ideas about zoning well illustrate this process.
It started as a rough, rule-of-thumb guide in the early town
plans; now it has become an integral part of all planning,
including that for traffic.

The word 'zone' rarely appears by itself but is usually accompanied by some other term which indicates the use or
activity assigned to a particular area of land or water. In urban
areas there are zones for industry, obnoxious trades, education
and open spaces, housing, public services and for clean air.
Frequently these are intermixed. In the older towns this is
usually due to inadequate planning and the result is often
unsatisfactory. Where mixed zoning occurs in new towns it
generally takes advantage of the inconspicuous nature of
modern light industry buildings and other facilities: for the
sake of compactness and convenience small factories are

placed in or near residential areas. Often zones permit several compatible uses.

The report *Traffic in Towns* proposed zoning based on activity and function. It suggested a cellular structure for environmental areas, set within a network of highways specially designed for the free flow of vehicles and for safety. Pedestrians and traffic were to be separated. Sufficient data exist to specify zones for some natural resources, such as for most minerals, and these are now usually kept free from development which might prevent future exploitation. Other forms of zoning are the green belts, National Parks and the measures described in Chapter 16. Zoning has been used over countries as a whole. Already some people talk of England as becoming one big city, with zones for parkland and other uses, and with access to wilderness areas in Wales and Scotland.

The greatest long-term value of zoning is its contribution to the creation of a high-quality environment, particularly in the countryside. Here it should be applied on a regional scale, as in Germany and Holland, to provide the framework for the sound management of natural resources and the aesthetic and functional development of the environment for work and for relaxation. Regional authorities should relate economic needs to major resources for agriculture, forestry, urban development, water, minerals, science and recreation. They could specify 'growth' zones – that is, areas where investment and development could be concentrated. Within regional development plans, the second-tier authority should define smaller zones and the measures necessary for special landscapes, sites for intensive recreation, countryside 'treasures' and other features contributing to the economic and ecological quality of its area. To keep some flexibility and to facilitate forward planning, the effects of zoning need to be continuously monitored on a regional basis. Models should be devised to project the impact of change on an area for, say, five to seven years ahead. Data about the main components of a region or town should be stored in a computer, together with a range of criteria for formulating alternative courses of action. As changes are noted, they should be fed into the computer and the plan reassessed accordingly.

The more that zoning can be applied to an inventory of classified resources, the more likely it is to be successful. Much land is already classified on the value of its soil and other features for agriculture and forestry, and (on the basis of ecological factors) for natural systems, wilderness areas, 'wild' rivers, and wild life. Zones for air sheds may become definable like water catchments. Mineral deposits are well-defined. Much of the 'bad' land – derelict, twilight and so on – is also well known. These assessments should be correlated and then similar information about all the main other features of the environment should be added to them.

An inventory of this kind has been carried to a very advanced stage in the U.S.A., notably in Wisconsin. This State is larger than England yet survey teams have already mapped its natural and man-made features of interest. The maps reveal a network of 'environmental corridors' which can be traced back to the Ice Age. Inevitably, man settled in these – in the U.S.A. the Indians, in similar areas in England the Celts. Subsequent developments by man and nature have intensified the values in these 'corridors', which are notable for their pure air and water. They have become zones of quality, and this in turn helps to determine planning policies. Today even the forest and land patterns in Wisconsin are linear. Inevitably, the conditions are very attractive to would-be developers and to tourists and recreationists.

In Britain there are also identifiable zones of high quality – the various National Parks, large stretches of the coastline, the Broads, the Gower Coast, the Cairngorms and many other attractive landscapes. Detailed survey in certain counties in England reveals smaller 'resource zones', comparable to the Wisconsin 'corridors'. Several may be found in a typical English county. Within them there are specific features of interest – archaeological, scientific, historic, landscape and so on – usually protected in various ways by official and voluntary bodies. Surveys and studies are in progress on the type and distribution of such resources, both by central and local authorities. Some local planning authorities have undertaken 'character' surveys of selected localities – Cornwall, for example, have examined Polperro. The experience gained in these surveys should help further appraisals and conservation of quality.

Stricter control and higher standards for development should obviously be applied in such zones and localities. This would, of course, intensify the differences between resource zones and other areas. As the areas of relatively poorer quality thus become more obvious, agreements about their development – for example, by industry – should be reached more easily and quickly; or, in some cases, special remedial treatment could be arranged. Developers would welcome the greater certainty arising from the clear identification of the main resources and their zoning. The regional authority, or the Land Commission, could make available in appropriate zones large areas of land for relocation of industry and dispersal of population. Development clearly needs to be encouraged, say, in parts of Scotland and Wales, and doubtless expansion in the south-east of England would be very strictly controlled.

Other examples of large-scale zoning may be seen in the plans to provide for the expanding population. To meet the needs of the south-east region, three major cities are proposed – near Bletchley, Swindon and on the Solent. Several large towns are planned; for example, 22,000 acres will be required for Milton Keynes, the North Buckinghamshire New Town.

In 1966 the Government initiated a study of Humberside as a first probable site for major regional development. Other studies now cover the Severn and Tayside. This work could lead to new cities of from 250,000 to 1,000,000 people by A.D. 2000, facilitate long-term distribution of population and enable the development of transport systems based on these estuaries.

Some planners propose linear cities. These would be urban developments three to four miles wide, using existing towns to form a chain along major road and rail routes linking the great ports. Such a linear city stretching from Liverpool to Cardiff has been proposed by Leslie Ginsberg. He claims that this would give easy access to the countryside and help in its conservation. Its opponents see it as ribbon development disfiguring the land. New dispersed cities are favoured by some planners, in fact, of sub-region size, with buildings and countryside intermixed and the whole reflecting the importance of the car in modern life. Other proposals include the creation of clusters of four or five villages of a few thousand people around existing centres, such as market towns. These and linear cities are held to be better alternatives to the gradual congealment of the conurbations into vast, amorphous cities.

Preference for the concept of corridors is shown in *Strategy for the South East* (see page 60). This makes far-reaching proposals for corridors of growth based upon major lines of transportation leading from London to new cities, which should become counter-magnets to the capital and be large enough to promote two-way flows of traffic. Between the corridors would be country zones, where good agricultural and amenity land would be more positively safeguarded than at present.

Proposals for care of the countryside include more intensive management of National and Country Parks and green belts; the safeguarding of wilderness areas; the enhancement of air and water zones; and the multiple use of land reclaimed from dereliction or from the sea. The coastline is being zoned by many countries as a major natural resource. Great scope exists for zoning small areas of land or water. For example, certain parts of a lake can be allocated to different activities – field study, angling and boating – this is zoning in space. Or an area can be let for different functions at separate times or seasons – zoning in time. These methods can obviously be combined. Such zoning, particularly on water, is urgently necessary for recreational activities. Its success depends largely on the co-operation of the individual and this is usually best obtained through clubs. Liaison to promote these objectives provides an excellent basis for planner–citizen relationships. It would facilitate the most efficient use of the limited supplies of land and water in suitable locations, and thus get to the heart of the problem of maintaining the rural environment's quality.

ENVIRONMENTAL STANDARDS

For nearly a century, public health, housing and factory standards in Britain have been codified in regulations and by-laws. Although still valuable, they are relatively clumsy and are not always relevant to contemporary needs. In recent decades standards have been prescribed for many social activities; for example, the area of playing-fields is related to the number of schoolchildren. But so far the rule books offer little guidance about standards for the carrying capacity of land and water, for wild life, or for man. These should be related to performance and need and based on ecological and sociological research. The *South-East Study, 1961–1981* grimly illustrates the grave danger of drift in the absence of such criteria. They must be formulated as soon as possible if planning is to become fully effective.

Population

The President of the Royal Society, Lord Florey, O.M., in his final anniversary address on 30 November 1965, stated that: 'It may be that to relate population to environment optimally is the greatest technological task of the end of this century.' As shown in Chapter 15, this involves national and individual factors such as family planning, selecting space for work and play, and the problems which arise when a high proportion of the population is either very young or very old. It requires the efforts of many professions and sciences, with information on economic trends, technological change, the physical capacity of resources and, above all, on the wishes of people.

The public sector in Britain (that is, the nationalized industries, defence departments and so on) accounts for about forty per cent of the national output and twenty-five per cent of the manpower. It should be required to estimate the resources needed to support different levels of population. To these national projections could be added those of major private organizations, such as I.C.I. Local planning authorities should provide estimates of the population they can either 'import', or, in some cases, should 'export' on the basis of yard-sticks specified by central government. Decisions about many technological and production projects have to be based on estimates of what the market and developments will be like in twenty years' time. Their planners have to make some assumptions about population growth, both national and for specified localities. In turn all these planners, whether fiscal or physical, can contribute when the criteria required for population numbers are being determined. Bringing together such estimates, and relating them to resources and trends, should give a global figure for population. This could then be used for national strategy: broad allocations of population between the regions could be indicated and they could serve as a basis for their development plans. The regions would prescribe in more detail the population numbers for the counties.

Research is urgently required into criteria for assessing in a community the balance of working, travelling and leisure time and the needs for open space and outdoor recreation. The advertisements of places, such as Northern Ireland, seeking developers refer to:

The good life. Not only business, but families, too, thrive in Northern Ireland. Better housing. A high standard of education. Carefree motoring in beautiful countryside. Cheap golf, fishing and sailing – all on the doorstep. A more natural environment that helps executives work better and enjoy a fuller life.

The Location of Offices Bureau offers similar inducements when trying to persuade firms to move out of London. Once standards can be properly formulated and become generally accepted, they should be used for evaluating the population appropriate to any area.

Natural Resources

Some urban planners argue that agriculturalists have conserved land at the expense of the town-dweller, who consequently suffers lower standards of housing and amenities. But the farmers can retort that once the first-class soils are built on they are lost for ever and that science cannot economically upgrade poorer lands to the productive quality of the best. Arguments of this kind should no longer be necessary. As discussed earlier, we do already possess the scientific and technical means to categorize all land and water and to relate their quality, location and potential for improvement to known demands. The criteria then are relatively simple and are based on a conservation approach. Further possibilities should emerge from ecological studies of the renewal of natural resources.

Standards are required for air. Conditions vary widely. Some authorities are very progressive and are well ahead with their programmes for preventing pollution. Other authorities lag behind. Similarly, standards for water for consumption and use need to be made mandatory, perhaps with a short period of grace for those areas where major reorganization or re-equipment is necessary.

The environmental zones and 'treasures' discussed earlier must also be regarded as natural resources. Experts in the various bodies responsible already have criteria but these need to be codified for wider acceptance and use. National legislation and local by-laws exist for the protection of many animals and some plants, but (except in a few cases – for example, birds) they are generally inadequate. There is available, however, expert knowledge on which standards could be prepared, if only the contribution of flora and fauna to the quality of the environment were generally understood. Much more education and information would be required to secure whole-hearted public acceptance of newly devised standards and of the higher level of behaviour required to implement them.

General

Many outdoor recreation activities are paid for directly – for example, the angler pays for the lease of a river and water-ski clubs for the use of a lake. The owner obviously follows the practice of charging what the market will bear and doubtless sees to it that the source of his income is properly maintained, but for many outdoor recreations this arrangement is not yet possible. Classifications of land and water for recreation have been mentioned earlier. Development plans are to include measures for the improved care and use of these areas in relation to the numbers of people visiting them. Some planning authorities who seek to maintain a few areas of spaciousness and solitude have already decided not to allow gregarious facilities, such as cinemas, dance halls and marinas, in certain localities. In this context, the Wilson Committee on the Problem of Noise (Cmnd 2056) was pioneering in a vital field – human capacity to sustain certain modern pressures and led in 1968 to noise standards for motor vehicles.

The Buchanan Report on *Traffic in Towns* gives some criteria for relating the amount of traffic allowed in a town to the quality of the urban environment; these are urgently wanted for rural areas. In some localities, such as National Parks, volume of traffic, speed and engineering considerations must be subordinated to the needs of amenity. In others, traffic must be segregated to allow for the enjoyment of walking, bicycling and horse-riding.

Appreciation of design is mainly subjective and often depends on local tradition and preference. The standards proposed, say, for estate layouts, street furniture and landscaping should, therefore, relate primarily to functional efficiency. In this the British Standards Institution (B.S.I.) has developed many widely agreed standards. The Royal Fine Arts Commission (R.F.A.C.) has been advising on urban design for many years, and has many criteria. The Central Electricity Generating Board (C.E.G.B.) has formulated several standards for its massive constructions. All these should form guide-lines which could, in time, be used when considering the whole environment. But most important is the possibility of using modern techniques of social survey to assess individual reaction to various qualities in the environment from street furniture to landscape. These are being used by authorities such as the C.E.G.B. and B.T.A., and from the picture that they give a valuable code could be built up to complement those of the B.S.I. and the R.F.A.C. These codes should also indicate where levels of aesthetic appreciation need improving in the schools and professions.

There are many other fields where criteria are required. One is time. Often it is the vital factor: when, say, an industrialist is trying to organize a new development, when a struggling community is in danger of losing its younger members, when an area is being eroded. If the time required for the implementation of a plan is not to render it out of date before it is completed, then economic and physical planning must be highly anticipatory. In particular, planners must resist the temptation to seek perfection. Trying to achieve this can inhibit citizen participation.

The implications for environmental planning of all standards should be fully worked out and kept under constant review by the strategic ministries to ensure their responsiveness to change. They should be disseminated through the information services and subjected to a continuing dialogue in society.

APPRAISAL: CHAPTERS 18–20

Planning as envisaged in this book embraces all resources in a strategic sense. The proposals touched on in these chapters are intended to indicate the spectrum – from philosophy to processes – for action. It is widely recognized that to design an environment for the twenty-first century demands extensive changes in the structure, functions and operation of central and local government in most countries.

It is vital that these changes are based not only on stated philosophy and principles but also on a psychological appreciation of how people behave in situations of power. Lord Acton's dictum 'Power tends to corrupt, and absolute power corrupts absolutely' is reported to have been modified by one African leader to 'Power is enjoyable, absolute power is absolutely enjoyable.' Whether this is wholly true or not does not really matter. Common sense dictates that there must be a system of checks and balances running through all forms of government. This is particularly vital in planning. The expertness required, the long time-scale, the scope for arbitrary judgements, the idiosyncrasies of taste or form and the certain fallibility of planners – these and many other factors confirm the need for maximum delegation and fullest citizen participation.

The best solution, therefore, seems to be to create a streamlined central government and to put it at the head of an administration in which centralization is opposed on all fronts except policies and standards. Many powers now lodged at the centre should go to democratic regional authorities, who should concentrate on strategy and the planning of services, leaving all possible implementation to reformed local authorities. The principles of unity and comprehensiveness must be stressed at all levels, otherwise specialization may lead to fragmentation. This is important for the citizen. Too many people now function and enjoy themselves effectively in only one or two ways – as managers, workers, recreationists and so on – and not enough as whole persons. So another aim here is to strengthen those organs of society, especially Parliament and local government, which represent the citizen. In this way the developing threat of the corporate State may be avoided.

The way to rouse people's interest is to give them more personal responsibility and scope. People must grow to expect their environment to be both beautiful and functional. Physical planning, in particular, offers a great challenge to planner and citizen alike, since most of its measures are revealed in the visual character of the environment. It is in the State's best interests to encourage the maximum personal effort by every citizen; it is both good government and in the long term good economics. Common acceptance of policies depends primarily on common involvement. Success here could lead to a great release of individual energy of lasting benefit to the nation.

Harold Wilson, speaking at Carlisle on 26 February 1966, said:

the New Britain, industrially and socially, must be conceived and created not on the basis of dictation from Whitehall, but by releasing all the different, the excitingly different, energies to be found in the different regions of the country. Regional decentralization through the new Regional Boards; the dynamic which is provided by the new Regional Councils; these are needed if industrial development and the renewal of our social fabric are to go ahead as one operation, with vigour, with vision, with intelligence.

CHAPTER 21

INTERNATIONAL

INTERNATIONAL influences – whether economic, ecological or social – have an enormous if often uncomprehended effect on the life of the average man. Since the time of the Roman Empire, with its legal code, and the establishment of the Roman Catholic Church, with its canon law, the institutions of the Western world have always had an underlying unity. This common heritage has not been substantially affected by the political changes of the intervening years. There has been a broadly similar approach to dealing with the physical environment which has led to a distinctive European husbandry of natural resources. There are inevitably differences of emphasis; for example, the Germans excel with their forests, the British are great protectionists of birds, while the Dutch tame their waters and use every acre of land.

In Europe particularly, there are in force numerous conventions between countries on social and political, economic and physical standards. For example, in the political field, in December 1965, Britain decided to accept (for a trial period of three years) the compulsory jurisdiction of the European Court of Human Rights. In this court a citizen may even complain against his own government! Conventions reflect the increasing sense of unity which animates leaders and pervades policies in all sectors of European life. In land planning, the trend is towards selecting large regions to facilitate comprehensive planning of all resources. For air, a major European conference in 1964 revealed widespread agreement on the policies to be adopted and the action to be taken. For water, there are numerous arrangements to deal with the major rivers, like the Rhine, and with catchment areas that overlap political boundaries. For wild life, a comprehensive network of practical measures includes, for example, agreements on legislation for protecting birds and a wildfowl refuge system which covers most of Europe. Throughout all these major fields there is close cooperation between the experts of many countries and a striking agreement on fundamental aims.

Trends and current problems reinforce this unity. The impact of outdoor recreation and tourism on European coastlines and wilderness areas demands urgent action to conserve them as part of the European heritage. From Norway to the Mediterranean, governments are seeking to control development along coastlines and to encourage and enforce higher standards of behaviour from visitors. This work is strengthened by cooperation between governments, particularly in the Council of Europe* and other European agencies. These organizations have formulated agreed principles for action – one of the most important, for instance, is on the use of pesticides. They are cooperating in education, have arranged to pool much of their data, and are holding the first European Conservation Year in 1970. In 1966 the Council of Europe awarded its first Diplomas to the Peak District National Park in England, the Hautes Fagnes Reserve in Belgium and to the Camargue in France.

In all these European activities Britain takes a prominent part. Although historically the forms of cooperation have varied, Britain has always been a part of Europe intellectually and socially. Now these links are strongly reinforced by political and economic moves towards a strategic unity.

European culture has, of course, spread over the world. Much of what has taken place in Europe has been repeated, with variations, in the U.S.A. and many other countries. But the emergence into world affairs of numerous Afro-Asian countries, many of them new nations, has created complex situations. Most of these countries have few or only superficial roots in the culture, social mores, law and religion of Europe and many have very differently based systems.

The developing countries contain about eighty per cent of the world's population and this percentage is increasing. And they have by far the greatest part of the fifty per cent of the world's population suffering from hunger and malnutrition. In such circumstances, their priority must be food production.

* See *Man in a European Society*, published by the Council of Europe.

For these reasons and the social ones just considered, Africans adopt criteria for the management of their great herds of wild animals different from the European conservationists', who regard them as part of the world's heritage. In Asiatic countries the potential long-term dangers to people, soils and wild life through misuse of persistent organochlorine pesticides are outweighed in the short term by the need for increased food production.

Nevertheless, despite these basic differences, a much greater degree of world unity is developing. This stems from the recognition that now disease and pestilence – the ancient controls over population numbers – are being eliminated and the threat of nuclear war may reduce the number of conventional major conflicts, the danger of over-population is the dominant threat to mankind. Everywhere governments are concerned about the multiplying pressures on food supply and natural resources. As the biologists uncover the importance of territory-consciousness in the forces motivating animal behaviour man's need for adequate space also becomes apparent.

Environmental issues affect almost every activity. For example, the management of British nature reserves provides information of direct value to Africa and many other parts of the world. The drier countries, who have experimented for many years in an effort to find new conservation techniques, can now advise a wet Europe facing serious water shortages. Contamination by radio-active gases and dusts and traffic fumes, oil pollution of the seas, control of ocean fisheries, the effects of space programmes, and many other environmental problems require action on an international basis. Perhaps meteorology offers the greatest scope, the most promise, and the most complexities. If weather can be controlled on a large scale, then the potential for good and evil may exceed that from the development of nuclear energy. But without close international cooperation and control, anarchy could rapidly prevail.

A further powerful force for international unity (although also a possible source of contention) is the revolution in expectations. With the great increase in communications, particularly the spread of films and television to the market-places and bazaars of the East, people see the living standards of the

West and want the luxuries for themselves. These expectations are also reinforced by the desire for more economic democracy, a factor underlying incomes policies in Europe. The complex of motives towards unity includes fear of disease from inadequate public health measures, religious and humanitarian beliefs, and of course, the traditional strivings after collective defence against the current potential aggressor – real or imaginary.

The inter-relationships of economics and the physical environment, the political and social factors, the problems of conserving resources for future populations, all combine to throw up common problems and needs which can best be resolved by cooperative action. It is not surprising, therefore, that there are already over seventy international organizations concerned with the conservation of nature and natural resources. Probably there are even more involved in town and country planning and air and water problems. The 1966-7 edition of *The Yearbook of International Organisations* lists 199 inter-governmental and 1,935 non-governmental organizations covering almost every aspect of human endeavour.

Overshadowing them all, of course, are the United Nations and its major agencies, notably the Food and Agriculture Organization (F.A.O.) and the United Nations Educational, Social and Cultural Organization (Unesco). F.A.O. launched its 'Freedom from Hunger' campaign in 1960 and has prepared an Indicative World Plan for agricultural development; all its activities affect the physical environment. Unesco promotes the discovery and spread of knowledge across the world and exerts an increasingly significant influence on environmental affairs.

All international bodies obviously provide a meeting place for the exchange of ideas and experiences, and stimulate that evolving together of solutions to common problems which will always be an important justification for international activity. They formulate agreed standards and codes which become part of the social fabric of the countries adopting them. They promote training and education and the dissemination of information in a whole range of subjects. Both within national programmes and in special international centres, they plan and carry out important research programmes like the ones promoted by C.E.R.N. (European Organization for Nuclear Research).

In the past decade major international projects on environmental issues have included the International Geophysical Year – held in 1957–8, but the research is still continuing; the International Hydrological Decade; the United Nations Development Decade – started in 1960 for capital investment and major projects, such as irrigation; and the current International Biological Programme (I.B.P.). The periods for these exercises reflect the great time usually required to obtain results in environmental affairs and the complexity of the problems involved. For example, I.B.P. is promoting worldwide studies of biological productivity and of human adaptability to changing conditions. These embrace a tremendous range of natural systems including the woodlands, moorlands and grasslands of temperate zones; the savanna woodland and lowland rain forest of the tropics; and freshwater and marine communities. The programme includes a world classification of ecological systems. The general aim of these studies is to increase knowledge about the long-term possibilities for human welfare (and particularly food production), arising from the rational management of natural resources. Applying internationally agreed methods of study to such a large variety of environments is expected to lead to new knowledge of great value, particularly to the developing countries. In Britain an extensive programme, backed by government funds, is being carried out under the auspices of the Royal Society and the Nature Conservancy.

The I.B.P. is government supported, but there are also very many independent professional and voluntary bodies active in international affairs, and they exert great influence on governments. For example, a voluntary body, the International Council for Bird Preservation, has made and is still making a vital contribution in the convention governing oil pollution of the seas. The International Union for Conservation of Nature and Natural Resources (I.U.C.N.), whose members include governments and voluntary bodies, is playing an increasingly important role in the conservation of natural habitats and in environmental education. The World Wildlife Fund, an entirely voluntary body, carries out vital rescue operations to save animals in danger of extinction and gives leadership through major world conferences. Organizations such as the David Davies Memorial Institute of International Studies pioneer new fields of cooperation in international problems: the Institute has, for example, brought together members of the legal profession and the environmental sciences, and has initiated studies to prepare the basic material for conventions.*

All these activities are emphasizing at every level, from international to local, the inter-dependence of living things and their relationship with land, air and water. These environmental issues and the increasing knowledge about them are providing a firm and lasting basis for a strategic approach to achieving a high-quality world environment. Everywhere the development of regional groupings – in Europe, in North and South America, and in Asia – confirms the trend to unity. Cooperation at this level is facilitating and stimulating activity on a world plane. Everywhere experts recognize the need to pool resources, especially those of human talent, in the attack on common problems. In his final anniversary address as President of the Royal Society (30 November 1965), Lord Florey remarked '. . . much more I believe could be done to forward discovery by making use of selected environments throughout the world in which concerted efforts could be deployed'. He favoured concentrating effort on the creation of international centres of excellence, which would further the goals of international cooperation and economy in the use of scarce resources, especially brain-power.

The International Centre for Theoretical Physics at Trieste, founded in 1964, shows one possible method of development. It fosters international collaboration in science and particularly helps physicists in the developing countries. Another line of approach is that proposed by Harold Geenen, chairman of one of the Committees set up for the International Cooperation Year. He advocates a world centre of knowledge. Equipped with computers and other modern techniques for the 'collation, retrieval and dissemination of knowledge', it might lead

* See *Principles Governing Certain Changes in the Environment of Man*, published by the Institute in 1968.

(subject to the problems of optimum size) to a world-wide system of intercommunication. This would further stimulate the cosmos of ideas and be of direct benefit to the developing nations.

There is today a world renaissance. The re-emergence into world affairs of the ancient civilizations of the East, the restlessness of the new nations, and the product of two millennia of European culture, are combining to create fresh and dynamic human and environmental situations. To all this Britain has a substantial contribution to make, perhaps most of all in the development of standards and in the creation of a public both informed and articulate.

CHAPTER 22

CONCLUSION

Whatever makes the past, the distant, or the
future, predominate over the present, advances
us in the dignity of thinking beings.

Samuel Johnson

To achieve a continuous improvement in the quality of the
environment demands perception, education, economic
strength, research, plus policies and administration geared to
the right aims. A process of constant appraisal and adjustment
is necessary, for as the scope of existing imponderables is reduced new ones will arise. Fresh discoveries will bring fresh
difficulties – and will always do so. As Goethe said, 'Every solution of a problem is a new problem.'

PERCEPTION

Of first importance is the capacity to perceive the essentials of
society's existence, to be able to analyse the factors that create
and enhance the environment and to relate these to the contemporary situation. If people are to understand, they must be
offered ideas which widen their horizons; ideas to excite them
to an awareness of a deeper purpose in their living and to a new
relationship within their environment. The challenge is to find
and capture these ideas and to put them over with the *élan* to
hold and inspire people.

Although much remains to be understood, we do have a
sufficient basis of knowledge and ideas to make it possible for
us to create a new fabric for man and his physical environment.
All the time we must remember that man is both part of nature
and yet able to influence its processes; that he, like other
animals, needs space and repose; and that all his actions have
far-reaching effects on other living creatures.

Man has made vast changes on the earth with relatively
primitive tools and limited knowledge. What is he going to

achieve with the vast power now at his command and the explosion of knowledge under way? Here it is important to note
that, while between 1840 and 1940 man created better food,
clothing, housing and hygiene for millions, he also contaminated the land, air, rivers and sea and eliminated much wild
life. Now we believe that he need not have done so, that in the
next century greater progress can be achieved without the
accompanying despoliation, and the old dereliction and waste
can be cleared away. Such a creative approach requires perception of the significant and lasting features of the national
inheritance. These are, of course, inter-related. As understanding increases, more values will be identified and cherished.

People must know the implications of their tastes and preferences: for example, that consuming vast quantities of news-
papers and magazines imperils the forests; that veneering
furniture requires the chopping down of certain trees; that
growing speck-free fruit and vegetables needs the use of chemicals; that using certain types of indestructible plastic involves
special methods of refuse disposal; that an open coal fire leads
to air pollution; and so on. People cannot both demand a
product and oppose the means of getting it and the damage it
may cause. Knowing what lies behind the chosen product is
not, in itself, enough. People must be helped to develop some
criteria so that they can demand alternatives and can judge
what shortcomings may be due to plain mismanagement.

EDUCATION

Such levels of perception demand an alert, educated and
participating citizen, responsive to the environment and conscious of his responsibilities to others and to posterity. He must
have much higher standards of education and information and
a highly sophisticated level of awareness. It will take time to
achieve this state, but a comparison of, say, the civilization of
1914 with that of today suggests that it can be done.

People need varying depths of knowledge to carry out their
aims, but everyone needs some understanding of the 'natural'
environment – even the people who see the country only at weekends. It is particularly important that the decision-makers

in government and commerce, all the workers whose activities affect the countryside, scientists and teachers, and members of the professions who plan, manage and develop the land should appreciate the forces at work there. To educate them to do this will require a new approach in the schools. Children must learn respect for other forms of life and that caring for their environment is essential to their own personal status and to a proper enjoyment of their heritage. This must start in the schools.

> All who have meditated on the art of governing
> mankind have been convinced that the fate of
> empires depends on the education of youth.
> Aristotle

Aristotle would, doubtless, apply this to the fate of environments. Children should be taught the scientific facts about natural processes and the role of such major elements in the landscape as agriculture and forestry. Education should make full use of the countryside as an outdoor laboratory or classroom, on the lines developed by the Field Studies Council. Where this is not practicable (say, for primary schools in a large urban area), city parks can be used and waste land and school gardens developed imaginatively, as pioneered by the National Rural Studies Association, to give real scope for the teacher and child. The Association has much to offer in this general context.

In all this activity the aim should be to stimulate inquiry into the factors governing the environment and the interactions between it and man. Man's powers and responsibilities and his capacity to alter and re-create society must be explained. To these ends, the importance of the teachers' role must be recognized, and the positive and creative character of education encouraged. Refresher courses with other professions and co-operation with visiting or part-time teachers from industry and agriculture, science and the land-linked professions, should help. The Council for Environmental Education, set up in 1968, should also have a major role to play. But formal education is not enough. The levels of adult awareness at any time will always lag behind those of the leaders in educational and professional knowledge. So the educational process must be

continuously reinforced by a sustained campaign of information. This should interpret and disseminate national policies,
persuade people to learn about new developments, and encourage a wider involvement in civic affairs, particularly those
concerning the enhancement of the environment. To achieve
these aims will require new interpretative skills and measures
to maintain better inter-communication.* Television has a
great capacity to stimulate, but the most vital need is for
sustained 'follow-up' in all media of information.

Clearly education and information on this scale, while increasing a nation's will to create wealth and a better environment, itself costs a good deal of money, and this fact reminds
us inexorably that economic factors can never be ignored.

ECONOMICS

> You take my life
> When you do take the means whereby I live
>   Shakespeare, *The Merchant of Venice*

Prosperity is essential to the objectives proposed in this book.
A hungry man has his own priority – food. Economic considerations are one half of the environmental equation – the other is
ecological capacity. Any worthwhile national economic plan
must invest a proportion of the resources available in the maintenance and enhancement of the environment – in effect, the real
capital of the nation. Land is still the primary source of food and
raw materials – only one per cent of the world's food comes from
the sea – and this will remain so for some time. Conservation
of the best soils and pure water is vital to future prosperity.

To achieve the continuing economic expansion necessary to
meet the rising demands of a growing population, new measures
are required to expedite development in suitable areas. New
levels of cooperation with industry are essential to the planning, management and development of land and water. Also,
the success of any national economy, but particularly the British
one, depends very largely upon the wise use of available talent.
Manpower must be deployed in those areas and on those

* The European Information Centre for Nature Conservation, set
up in 1967, should help in this work.

activities calculated to produce the maximum benefit. For example, as agricultural productivity increases more manpower will move into industry. Since there are few people who are professionally skilled in the management of land and water, their talents must not be wasted on trivial work; they must be employed on deciding national and regional strategy. The total national outlay on design is high and is not always well-deployed. Any over-fussy regulation imposes a burden on industry and impairs the nation's ability to enhance the quality of the environment in more appropriate ways and places. The Central Electricity Generating Board spend vast sums of money on amenity; for example, new cooling towers erected at West Burton in Nottinghamshire were specially coloured at an extra cost of £33,000 – with a result described by Ian Nairn as 'fruitless'. All this money represents human effort, mostly of a high quality. The nation must continually be asking if its scarce resources of human skill are being deployed to the best advantage.

The use of all resources is competitive, both in quantity and quality. The choice in quantity is more widely understood than that in quality. But when the resources to plan good towns, clean air and pure water are assessed, it will be obvious that some other desirable goods must be forgone. This elementary economic premise is, of course, subject to the qualification that dirt and dereliction are often symptoms of inefficiency and their removal might also cut costs and wastage of resources. Generally, however, quality costs money and must be a conscious choice; the classic illustration is provided by *Traffic in Towns*: it will cost a fantastic amount to implement the report's recommendations, and, perhaps, even more not to do so.

RESEARCH

Science is organized knowledge.
Herbert Spencer

Research is required into all these economic issues if imaginative new landscapes and industrial progress are to go ahead together. The primary need is for research into the real cost of a given result in terms of the benefits obtained – social cost–benefit analysis. It was used in 1963 to help the Minister of

Transport decide about the proposed Victoria underground line in London. The line would not be economic in terms of passenger fares, yet the value to society of reducing congestion and saving time were thought to outweigh the direct costs. Pesticides are another case for cost–benefit analysis. Far too wide a use is made of them without considering whether, in fact, the loss from pest damage actually justifies the outlay. Taking account of side-effects and accumulating environmental contamination, there is obviously a *prima facie* case for fuller research into the economics of their use.

Techniques are required for assessing the costs of the unintended effects of industrial development; for example, the damage done by river pollution could be evaluated and part or all of the cost of remedying it placed on the originator. This would lead to a truer assessment of production economics and perhaps, in time, a better deployment of resources. If the real price of obtaining congestion-free cities, clean air, pure water and fine landscapes can be assessed, then society may make a better choice of priorities. Ways and means of getting people to pay more directly for a particular use or activity must be devised. This applies to outdoor recreation and to the enjoyment of country and city parks, coastlines and wilderness areas where management is necessary to maintain the quality of interest. In some cases the only practicable levy may be on the taxpayer and/or ratepayer. But the more that use and enjoyment can be paid for directly and related to people's capacity to pay, the more likely it is that the money will be forthcoming to manage and enhance the environment.

The social aspects of a high-quality environment are, perhaps, even more elusive than the economic. In Britain the Social Science Research Council * covers the relevant fields and has a major contribution to make in evaluating people's attitudes to given situations, in assessing trends in human activities and in determining, with ecologists, the values of repose and space to the individual. Too little is known about the social functions of environmental features, such as forests, wetlands, open country, and the individual need for and response to them, or about the effects of concentrating people into cities, towns and holiday camps.

* See its Newsletters.

The impact of policies and practices is not always known or understood. The dynamic flows and the long 'production' scales of environmental processes are not appreciated by most people, including many concerned with the planning and development of land and water. Inter-disciplinary teams are needed to study the components of environmental situations. Laboratories are required in which models can be created and studied to find parameters and to detect relationships. Once criteria and methods have been established, techniques must be developed to exploit them. Countries know too little about environmental contamination; of the capacity of land and natural resources to sustain given demands and about what tomorrow's trends are likely to be; of how to detect and develop resources for the future; of how to maintain a continuous audit of social change; about how to control and direct the knowledge explosion; and of how to communicate to all types of people an understanding of man's environment and of his responsibility for it.

Although so much research is still necessary, enough is already known to make a substantial improvement in society. But policies and administration and *all* decision-taking must be more scientifically based. It should not, however, be assumed that even with all available knowledge there could or should be policies to cater for the detailed planning of every resource. The variations in the major factors involved are too enormous; for example, population numbers and settlement, agricultural productivity and its relation to world trade, capacity for industrial exports, the disposition of national and individual wealth, the motivations for leisure – having so many variables means the scope for error is wide. The economic forecasts published before Budgets amply demonstrate this. What is avoidable, however, is the failure to diagnose the long-term national interest. Nor is there any excuse now for not settling criteria or publicizing the results of scientific research so that people can evaluate the possible courses of action. The real aim is to provide for continuing research into policies affecting the environment, to make a determined effort to bring them into harmony and to create a synthesis for further advance.

ADMINISTRATION

> Government, even in its best state, is but a
> necessary evil; in its worst state, an intolerable
> one.
>
> Thomas Paine

Many people oppose planning while contending for the benefits which only planning – of one form or another – can provide. Car-owners want better roads and traffic conditions, yet
they often impede the controls necessary to produce the flow
which will help all drivers. Farmers are annually locked in
negotiation with ministry officials to get subsidies, grants and
other aids vital to a healthy agriculture; these must be planned
and administered, yet at many stages there is often bitter
opposition. Commerce states a preference for competition and
itself plans rings, monopolies and so on, seeking government
intervention if conditions become 'unfair'. Above all, many
individuals abhor the thought of population control while demanding the fruits of medical and social service which make it
necessary. They take for granted the social planning all
around them which has helped man to eliminate diseases and
many of those other checks that, so far, have staved off the
rigour of Malthusian correctives.

The paradox is that, without population planning, the rapidly
increasing pressures could be too much for land, water and
man himself, and so lead to panic followed by more and more
government regulation. It therefore seems better to control
births, to agree on a strategy of choice for numbers related to
activities and agreed living standards, than to become subject
to the regimentation of the *Brave New World*. This means a
clear understanding of the choices available and the priorities
on which resources are to be deployed. So a social plan is required to weave together resources, ideas and people and to
provide the basis for a continuing appraisal of priorities.

Such a plan for all the nation's resources must be in broad
terms and initially would be a synthesis of the policies of the
national and regional economic plans, the county development plans and those of major industries and services. As the
central and regional inter-disciplinary teams of planners,

economists, ecologists and many other professions gain experience, so it should be possible for central government to
take the initiative and give clear guide lines. A strategically
planned and positively encouraged use of resources should reduce the need for detailed regulation. For example, family
planning and allowances should be related to population objectives, and agricultural and industrial economic policies
should reflect the community's need for a 'social' landscape.

Much more self-government must be encouraged. Central
government should concentrate on strategy and ensure that
there is real delegation to regional and local authorities and
effective devolution to officers. The land users and owners
should participate in the processes of decision. Associations
and clubs, such as those for recreation, should be encouraged to
educate and inform their members, to be responsible for their
behaviour and to participate in the shaping of the environment.
The processes of decision-making need to be the subject of
continuous scrutiny. They should be more widely based and
yet more expeditious – not incompatible objectives with modern
techniques.

PREDICTION

> . . . the one fact about the Future of which we can
> be certain is that it will be utterly fantastic.
>   Arthur C. Clarke

Logically, the first prediction is that in the twenty-first century
Europe will become a single unit for strategic planning and
administration. All over the world regional 'blocs' are evolving
and nowhere faster than in Europe, not only in the economic
field but also in the whole range of social activities. In a Europe
planned as a physical entity, see Figure 22, the Scandinavian
coastline, much of Scotland, the Black Forest, the Alps and
many similar areas would receive priority for conservation and
enhancement. Perhaps most of England and Belgium would
be accepted as primarily industrial; possibly southern Sweden
would be the location of half a dozen new cities, each of a
million population taken from the overcrowded areas of Europe.
The planning of six new cities would call for new patterns of

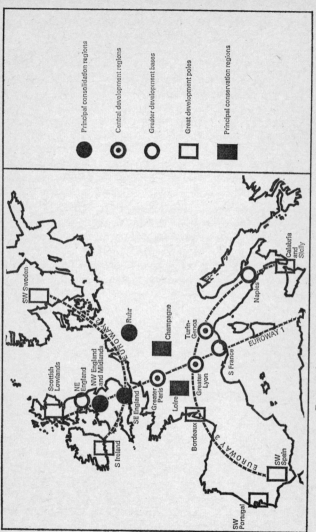

22 Proposed regions for planning in Europe (D. Rigby Childs)

● Principal consolidation regions

◉ Central development regions

○ Greater development bases

□ Great development poles

■ Principal conservation regions

SW Sweden

Ruhr

Champagne

Turin–Genoa

Naples

Calabria and Sicily

Scottish Lowlands

NE England

NW England and Midlands

SE England

Greater Paris

Loire

Greater Lyon

S France

S Ireland

Bordeaux

SW Spain

SW Portugal

EUROWAY 2

EUROWAY 1

EUROWAY 3

thinking for no country in the Western world has so far attempted anything on this scale. Development for six million means deliberately setting out to create a new environment for more people than at present live in the whole of Scotland. One planner, Derek Rigby Childs, has been thinking along these lines for some years now and has put forward a new conception for city development, designed not in terms of individual cities but on the scale of regions. He has devised a new kind of region with an area of around 14,400 square miles. This greater region is roughly the equivalent of the area of the whole of the Lowlands of Scotland. He believes that an overall population of around nine million could live comfortably in such a region, designed to contain new types of cities, a national park, a wide variety of farming and sub-urban type areas, with man's works and nature's activities in balance with one another.

With the development of techniques like atomic blasting, vastly more nuclear power, and underground sources of oil and gas, it should be possible to create landscapes on a European scale. Resources could be developed in a vast and excitingly imaginative way – agricultural zones could be related to the value over centuries of the best soils and climatic conditions; fish farming be developed in barrages created for water supply; and hydro-electric schemes be combined with new motorways, as was proposed to cross the Channel.

More knowledge of the environment should lead to measures for the elimination of ailments like bronchitis, which are associated with particular environmental conditions. Great scope exists for the detection and control of illnesses related to the mineral and other content of soils. Biogeochemistry has already found some areas which are conducive to cancer or heart problems. Preliminary indications relate these to a wide range of environmental factors, including soil. Perhaps planning will exclude certain activities or uses from such areas or require the dangerous conditions to be remedied before development takes place.

Computorized inventory and processing of all resource information will have become an accepted feature of man's relationship to his environment. Research will increase in importance; its role in decision-making may be extended to promote the examination of basic assumptions and personal prejudices. Decisions should thus be based more on facts and known preferences and less on vague intuition. Although the imponderables will always count, in respect of physical issues, many could be eliminated in the twenty-first century. Design-awareness centres will be an accepted 'institutionalized' part of the educational process as the public-health values of a high-quality environment are accepted. As more is learned about the diversity and quality of intelligence and man's potential for increasing it, so it may be expected that environmental conditions will be improved to enhance this most vital of all resources. The population pressure itself becomes the source of new qualities and quantities of human ability, provided that its growth is related to the development of man's intellect and his resource productivity, and that it is always borne in mind that he may have to occupy this planet for millions of years.

Albert Schweitzer said: 'Man has lost the capacity to foresee and to forestall. He will end by destroying the earth.' He must be disproven!

How then to conclude? In such a vast field and with so much at stake, it is perhaps most important to emphasize man's responsibility, and to stress the challenge he faces now.

RESPONSIBILITY

> . . . every interest is partly conservationist and partly destroyer.
>
> H.R.H. The Duke of Edinburgh

Is man responsible? The Book of Genesis and the Epistle to the Hebrews certainly state that man has dominion over all nature, because he is made 'in the image of God'.

Does man really have such powers? Until this century the subjection of all things to man has been potential – never actual. Today, his powers are enormous. Science has become the mainspring for the exercise of vast control, whether based on religious, humanist or other beliefs. What evidence is there that man has the capacity for this supreme responsibility?

Surely everything points the other way. Man has not to date acted responsibly. His arrogance as an urban species, disconnected from and unaware of his interdependence on nature, the lack of humility betrayed by all classes of society – these hardly demonstrate his responsibility. And the results confirm that he does not live wholly wisely nor look after the interests of living creatures. The evidence of environmental contamination is widespread: wild life extinguished, air and soil poisoned, land eroded, waters polluted and other natural resources (coal, oil, metals) wasted. This is not a single major problem but the result of myriad acts of thoughtlessness or ignorance. Each individual pollutes and suffers from pollution. All have an effect on the quality of the environment. As President Johnson said, in 1966: 'It [the menace of pollution] poses a major threat to the quality of life in our country.'

It took millions of years to form the present reserves of oil, gas and coal, and centuries to create the top soil on which life depends. The pace of man's growth and the pervasiveness of his activities threaten to exhaust these resources and many other vital features of the environment within two or three centuries. That is, within the lifetime of the grandchildren of the reader's grandchildren.

But will not man develop new powers to resolve these problems? Will not his venturing into space open up fresh vistas of unprecedented expansion? For a certainty man will develop new powers but whether he will have them in time is in doubt. The pace of change is so rapid, his population explosion and activities so great, and the psychological problems of expectation so deep in the mores, that his present civilization may collapse under economic and ecological pressures. And even if he does export himself into space, the likelihood that there are stars capable of sustaining some life may well lead him into conflict with another species, perhaps one which will not tolerate man fouling his habitat wherever he goes. Man should know more about himself, his attitudes, limitations and capacity, and about the earth he lives on, before he seeks to populate other planets.

Luckily, the activities of leaders in all sectors of society give hope that man is responding to the challenge of his powers.* Most social institutions – governments, churches, professions – recognize that man is responsible for the environment. Professional and social groups now press their demands for action and themselves make a more active contribution. Governments, both nationally and internationally, devote an increasing part of their effort to maintaining and enhancing the environment. A few are pioneering research into the discovery and production of resources for the future. Probably the weakest points in the chain of social responsibility are at the level of the operative in a particular industry and of the citizen who feels his only duty is to grumble. Once the individual has accepted his obligations, then, indeed the 'Age of Responsibility' will have arrived. Thus at the centre of all this – present or future – is man. He cannot abdicate responsibility for using his creative powers to guide the evolutionary process. He must seek stability and challenge in a new relationship within his environment and a new rapport between leaders and people.

CHALLENGE

A state without the means of some change is without the means of its conservation.
Edmund Burke

Historically, the Renaissance is seen as a time of great intellectual activity and change in the systems of ideas. New movements emerged then which charted the course for centuries. It seems probable that, as suggested by E. M. Nicholson, this present era may qualify as the start of a new Renaissance. Everywhere there is a ferment of thought, a consciousness that ideas are on the move, that the world is an exciting place to live in. The capacity of man to communicate is intensifying the rate of inter-penetration and interaction of all ideas. Men and nations are being transformed. And there develops a great

* See U.N.E.S.C.O. Intergovernmental Conference of Experts, September 1968, on 'The Scientific Basis for Rational Use and Conservation of the Resources of the Biosphere'.

unitary cosmos of thought, which becomes itself a force of global significance: 'One person with a belief is a social power equal to ninety-nine who have only interests' – J. S. Mill. Even if only one hundredth of tomorrow's population is needed to get the right policies working, that will still be a great number of people with beliefs! But it is necessary to create in all an awareness of their stake in life and to encourage their contribution to it. That in itself is one of the ideas which may later distinguish this Renaissance from its predecessor.

To accept responsibility and to have ideas is sterile without action. Man must get the measure of the challenge. Its *pace* now is breathtaking. It took 1,000 years to transform the forest and swamps north of the Alps into fertile farmlands; to change the west of the U.S.A. took only fifty years. The *scale* of the challenge is fantastic. The next forty years will see the creation of human settlements greater than in all recorded history and far exceeding those which now exist. In this, man must fulfil certain prime objectives: he must eliminate poverty; create a healthy environment; and provide for posterity. It will require insight into the continuing processes of adaptation, competition and reconciliation between man and the environment, between man-made and natural systems. Environmental change must be seen as a continuum, as a constant interaction between all elements of the environment in a three-dimensional web. Man has the great advantage of being able to look at the whole and to influence both the interaction and the continuum.

But to achieve it a healthier human ecology will be needed. This should embody a true partnership between leaders and people; it must encourage each individual to accept responsibility, to articulate his ideals and to seek to achieve them in co-operation with his fellows. Democracy must become real in political terms and extend into economic and social fields. This is vital to counteract the obvious dangers for the individual, as the powers of society, through the State, industry and organizations of one kind or another, are increased. A central problem of the next century may well be the reconciliation of personal liberty and democratic action with the power of the State. As man obtains more power to control his environment so he must exercise greater vigilance over its use.

Failure in this context could lead to vast unrest and human suffering, and perhaps the debasement of people. They might then even look back nostalgically to the glorious nineteenth and twentieth centuries!

Success in strategic planning, by people, for people, now and for posterity, could open the way to a 'Golden Age' for man. But time is running out. It is not on the side of man. Awareness, passion and an urgent determination to act are required of every one of us.

A CREED TO PRESERVE OUR NATURAL HERITAGE

Extract from President Johnson's message to Congress, February 1966

To sustain an environment suitable for man, we must fight on a thousand battlegrounds. Despite all of our wealth and knowledge, we cannot create a Redwood Forest, a wild river, or a gleaming seashore.

But we can keep those we have.

The science that has increased our abundance can find ways to restore and renew an environment equal to our needs.

The time is ripe to set forth a creed to preserve our natural heritage – principles which men and women of goodwill will support in order to assure the beauty and bounty of their land. Conservation is ethically sound. It is rooted in our love of the land, our respect for the rights of others, our devotion to the rule of law.

Let us proclaim a creed to preserve our natural heritage with rights and the duties to respect those rights:

The right to clean water – and the duty not to pollute it.

The right to clean air – and the duty not to befoul it.

The right to surroundings reasonably free from man-made ugliness – and the duty not to blight.

The right of easy access to places of beauty and tranquillity where every family can find recreation and refreshment – and the duty to preserve such places clean and unspoiled.

The right to enjoy plants and animals in their natural habitats – and the duty not to eliminate them from the face of this earth.

These rights assert that no person, or company or government has a right in this day and age to pollute, to abuse resources, or to waste our common heritage.

The work to achieve these rights will not be easy. It cannot be completed in a year or five years. But there will never be a better time to begin.

Let us from this moment begin our work in earnest – so that future generations of Americans will look back and say:

> 1966 was the year of the new conservation, when farsighted men took farsighted steps to preserve the beauty that is the heritage of our Republic.

I urge the Congress to give favourable consideration to the proposals I have recommended in this message.

(signed) LYNDON B. JOHNSON

THE WHITE HOUSE
23 February 1966

APPENDIX 2

SUGGESTIONS FOR ACTION

SOCIETIES

1. *Check* whether your local Planning Department has an up-to-date inventory of the natural resources of your area. Assess the role of these resources in local civic life and whether they are fully and wisely utilized. Ask your Councillors and Planning Office staff to explain the proposals in the Development Plan and, in particular, to show whether local natural resources are adequate for the next ten years, and until A.D. 2000. Check what is being done to ward off threats to them or to fill in gaps.

2. *Initiate or support action* with your local authority on practical works, such as surveys and pilot projects, fund-raising exercises and educational activities. In particular, help your authority to deal with:

   (i) canals, wet gravel pits and other waters, woodlands and commons which can be developed for field studies and recreation;
   (ii) derelict, degraded or waste land which can be reclaimed for other uses or landscaped;
   (iii) survey of, and perhaps measures for clearance of, derelict buildings and installations, and abandoned cars in your neighbourhood;
   (iv) measures to diminish air and river pollution locally;
   (v) measures to prevent local floods or droughts;
   (vi) cooperative schemes with local landowners and farmers to enhance the condition of roadside verges, areas of public access, etc. and to secure more responsible behaviour in relation to them.

3. *Allocate in your programme* a number of sessions every year for lectures and discussions on topics such as:

   (i) the quality of your local environment; in particular, the design and condition of its buildings, the pollution of its land and water, the availability of open spaces, environmental standards and measures to improve your surroundings such as tree preservation and planting schemes, and the management of local commons;

(ii) population numbers and control;

(iii) rural and urban settlements – their inter-relationship;

(iv) conservation of wild life and landscape;

(v) standards of responsibility and consideration for the enjoyment of coast and country;

(vi) the work of bodies such as your County Countryside Committee (especially over the 'treasures' of your locality), the Regional Sports Council, the other local voluntary organizations;

(vii) publicity and public participation in planning and management of your local environment.

INDIVIDUALS

4. *Check that:*

(i) you and your family know the country code and any special safeguards expected of you at the coast and country you normally frequent for recreation or holiday;

(ii) your family does not waste water and that your house and car do not pollute the air;

(iii) you do not misuse pesticides in your garden or allotment;

(iv) you and your family always place litter in an authorized receptacle or bring it home.

5. *Support:*

(i) one or more of your local voluntary bodies in measures to enhance your neighbourhood;

(ii) activities such as: National Society for Clean Air; The Noise Abatement Society;

(iii) measures to inspire the environmental education of your family, friends and local people.

6. *Undertake:*

(i) voluntary wardening to prevent vandalism and to encourage enjoyment of your town and country under arrangements made by your authority and/or society;

(ii) lecturing, leadership activities or other appropriate measures with local youth organizations.

REFORM OF LOCAL GOVERNMENT

LOCAL government employs over two million people and spends over £3,500 million a year. It provides services, such as planning, housing, education and roads, which affect the lives of its citizens during most of their daily round. Its wide-ranging activities enable it to exercise a crucial influence on the quality of the environment.

Yet interest in local government is low, if judged by the level of polling at local elections. This is not, however, a fully adequate barometer. In certain cities great interest has been evoked over educational changes and the re-development of town centres. Perhaps the most helpful current signs are the frequent and widespread calls for reform.

Chapter 18 touched briefly on the values and shortcomings of local government. As at present conceived, it is primarily administrative and executive, mainly responsible for implementing policy decided by central government. In this context, it should seek the optimal combination of efficiency and economy in relation to the quality of services demanded and local capacity to pay for them in whole or in part. Judged by these criteria it is usually assessed as inadequate, often unfairly. Since the present structure was laid down by legislation of 1888 and 1894, numerous agencies of government have been established. Their performance is considered by some to surpass, or compete favourably, with that of local government.

But no bodies have emerged which, even at the present low level of interest in civic affairs, offer better educational and political values than local government. It is on such criteria and on the principle of comprehensiveness that local government must be maintained and reformed to meet the challenges of modern society.

Before considering a few of the many proposals for reform, it is worth noting the main factors which have led to the present position. The first is probably the maintenance of the *status quo* under a different title. For example, the reforms of 1835 retained many of the ancient town corporations; the 1888 legislation making the county the large-scale unit retained the old geographical counties, little changed since the time of the

Normans; and the 1894 legislation, which broadly completed the present basis, kept many of the ancient parishes. The second factor is the rapid and increasing pace of technological and social change. This has led to *ad hoc* bodies, as the inadequate capacity of existing machinery for reform – a third factor – has prevented local government from adapting to changing circumstances. These defects derive from the vested interests of people, which are, nevertheless, often the obverse side of the motives which sustain local participation and loyalties.

All political parties stress the need for reform of local government, and today all contain proponents of reforms involving some variants of regionalism. Most of the experts in this field – in government and universities – have their own particular schemes for reform. The main distinction is that many of the practitioners of local government would make their type of authority (county or county borough) the basis of the reform, and some of those in county districts and parishes seek to perpetuate their own type of authority. The independent experts offer a greater range of possibilities, both in the grouping of regions and authorities and in the distribution of functions. Most of the schemes under serious consideration envisage:

  (i) extensive devolution to Scotland and Wales;

 (ii) fully democratic regional councils and some full-time paid members (taking account of the proposals of the Greater London Council);

(iii) greater attention to economic and physical planning, distinguishing the roles required at various levels, for example strategic, executive and so on;

(iv) reform of finance, notably the transfer of the cost of education to central government funds;

 (v) internal reforms such as, for example, the extension of the practice of council 'cabinets' and the city manager system (as in Newcastle upon Tyne).

All these factors are closely interwoven, but there is only space here to deal with the structure which is, as noted in Chapter 17, a major problem and the key to modern resource planning.

SOME PROPOSALS FOR STRUCTURAL REFORM

(To be read in conjunction with Chapters 18 and 19.)

1. A. The county borough concept to be applied throughout England, through the division of the country into single compendious (all-purpose) authorities.

1. B. Counties and county boroughs to be merged and regrouped to form about forty to sixty regions, with about 150 second-tier authorities; district and parish councils to be abolished.

Comment: These proposals leave too much power with central government; fail to provide adequately for the scale of planning required in modern services; and would be insufficiently responsive to local needs, particularly A, which places too much emphasis on the city.

2. The existing local government structure to be completely replaced by regions (seven in England), regional districts (population 100,000–500,000) and community councils (for villages or small towns). (See *New Life for Local Government*, a Bow Group Pamphlet.)

Comment: This meets most requirements but would lead to loss of the civic values in the present system, especially in counties and county boroughs.

3. Seven to twelve regions to be established for England; counties and county boroughs to be merged (leading to not more than ten second-tier authorities per region); and more management powers given to a third-tier authority, varying from a large town to a strengthened district-cum-parish (not more than twenty, generally less, per second-tier area).

Comment: This accepts some untidiness and a variation in functional efficiency, especially at the third-tier level, in order to maintain many of the values of existing authorities.

It differs from schemes 1 and 2 in the emphasis it places on removing the administration of most functions from central government (departments and boards) and in seeking maximum devolution to all levels.

FURTHER DETAILS ON SCHEME 3

(i) It envisages that a wide range of functions at present dealt with by central departments and boards will be taken over by the regions. Most of the work of the region will thus be 'ex-central-government', plus the strategic planning functions of the present counties and county boroughs as discussed in Chapter 19.

(ii) The final definition of the boundaries of regions should take account of the regrouping of the counties and county boroughs into second-tier authorities, as well as the reorganization of the functions taken over from central government.

(iii) As noted in Chapter 18 the primary functions of the regional authority would be the economic and physical *planning* of the environment, population, industry and all major services.

(iv) All possible *management* and *development* should be devolved to the second-tier authority. This would contribute data and ideas for the strategic planning function and undertake detailed planning for its area. It would be responsible for the implementation of services, including most of the extended range to be brought into local government.

(v) Further devolution of functions of a more personal and local character could be made to the third-tier authority. It should be encouraged to provide the facts about local conditions and aspirations necessary to the local planning undertaken by the second-tier authority.

(vi) All devolution and delegation need to be clearly prescribed to facilitate the maximum action by second- and third-tier authorities without reference 'upwards'. Close liaison between members and officers at all levels and active cooperation in the formulation of policies and standards facilitates delegation and scope for local initiative. In particular, the regional and second-tier authorities should avoid the setting up of local offices working on the same subjects as the next tier.

(vii) In certain cases – for example, a new town to be developed across local boundaries – it might be necessary for the regional authority to set up a special agency, but this should be abolished as soon as the new town has acquired civic viability and can be integrated into the normal structure.

(viii) Local government functions would be allocated on the lines indicated above and would include:

Economic and physical planning of the environment (urban and 'natural')
Population and employment – numbers and location
Industry – scale and location
Education, libraries and ancillary activities
Housing and related services
Highways and traffic, including bus services*

Hospitals and related services, including G.P.s*

Public health, sewage and drainage

Police and fire services

Welfare services

Research, intelligence and training services*

Water supply and conservation*

Entertainment, recreational and cultural provisions including sport and arts

Air – elimination and prevention of pollution

Conservation of man-made and natural features, including wild life

Rural Development Board functions*

Land Commission functions*

N.B. The functions asterisked have distinctive problems which may require special arrangements at second-tier level; for example, as noted in Chapters 8 and 9, the river basin is the best unit for the administration of water resources.

Whatever system is adopted, it must be sufficiently flexible to take advantage of new concepts and technologies. For example, the development of electricity from small nuclear stations may, in time, lead to the abolition of a national grid; local authorities might then re-assume responsibility for a service they once operated. The system must respond to the dynamic concept of the developing city regions, now extending over great areas in many countries. It is predicted that by A.D. 2050 over half of the world's population will live in cities whose social and economic influence, facilitated by transport and communications, will pervade and dominate the countryside more than today. Increasingly the city becomes a location for the varied and changing activities of society which require cooperation and confrontation, but more and more it demands a setting within the countryside which will provide repose and relaxation for its members.

A system of local government must also constantly seek new ways of tapping the wealth of local ability and pride so often revealed in the work of the voluntary bodies. In Britain today this *esprit* is frequently stifled by the elective process and by the methods of organization. The vital role of truly local government in creating a high-quality environment demands continuous appraisal and the active participation of all citizens – the system must ensure this or be replaced.

These features were very prominent in the wealth of evidence presented in 1966–7 to the Royal Commissions on Local Government. There was massive support for reconstituting the structure of local government so as to have larger and fewer local authorities, to eliminate the division of town and country and to reduce central control. Two main forms of regionalism were widely favoured: the large region and the city-region, as noted in paragraphs 3 and 1B on page 298.

The three tiers of the large region system should meet the increasing demands for more local independence. The top-tier itself would soon be able to take over some of the major public utilities, such as gas, electricity and hospitals. It should provide an effective link between central and local government and be able to coordinate, advise and plan on the scale required for modern services. The city-region should provide effective units for implementing most of the existing functions of local government. It would, however, be too small for the strategic planning of, say, land-use, water supply, police and many other services.

The need for some unit below Whitehall to handle regional strategy has been well illustrated in the work of the Standing Conference on London and South-East Regional Planning and the Economic Planning Council for the South East (see pages 59–60 and 262). An official circular in June 1968 stated that 'the Government attaches great importance to comprehensive regional planning' and stressed the close links between economic, physical and social planning.

Perhaps some pointers may be found in the Government's plans for the reorganization of local government in Wales.* These require extensive amalgamation of many small and weak authorities: 5 new administrative counties to replace 13; 36 new districts to replace 164 middle-tier bodies; and parish or 'common' councils to be amalgamated and strengthened and set up, where needed, in urban areas. Cardiff, Newport and Swansea should remain county boroughs, and a new Welsh Council is given a wide range of advisory and promotional functions.

Two major reports on Britain's welfare services published in July 1968 are also relevant. One, by the Ministry of Health,† proposed that the whole range of health services, then administered by nearly 700 local authorities, executive committees

---

* Cmnd 3340 *Local Government in Wales*, July 1967. H.M.S.O.
† *National Health Service. The Administrative Structure of the Medical and Related Services in England and Wales*. H.M.S.O.

for G.P. services, and hospital boards, should be unified under 40 area boards. The Seebohm* report recommended that local authorities set up a unified social service department to run all aspects of social care, with planning at national level under one central department. The administrative areas proposed for these functions should, in time, be made to correspond with those of local government – for example, the middle-tier of the large region or the city region itself, according to the system adopted. The new local authorities may become so effective and attract such a quality of leadership that these social services could be handed over completely to them.

Inevitably there are advantages and shortcomings with either system. The issues dealt with in this book will need to be worked out very thoroughly and applied with great regard for local *esprit* and achievement. Not only a more effective and efficient service is required but the gaps between government and governed must be bridged at all levels.

> I am certain we shall have to widen the scope of our local self-government in two different directions: towards regionalism and towards the parishes and wards.
>
> Sir George Stapledon

* *Report of the Committee on Local Authority and Allied Personal Social Services.* Cmnd 3703. H.M.S.O.

REFORM OF PLANNING

MOMENTOUS changes introduced by the Government are now 'resetting the stage for the next twenty years' in the field of planning, said the Minister of Housing and Local Government in an address to the Town Planning Institute in April 1968. They would involve a major and deliberate devolution of power and responsibility from Whitehall to local government. The Minister referred to legislation for the Land Commission (see pages 254–8), Civic Amenities, Transport, Countryside, and Town and Country Planning. Taken together, these would 'create conditions which are more conducive than ever before to the achievement of quality' in the environment, in which 'people should be involved from the word "go", so that they have a real chance of influencing planning of their areas'.

TOWN AND COUNTRY PLANNING

The White Paper (Cmnd 3333) of June 1967 noted three major defects in the system: its delays and cumbersome procedures; inadequate citizen participation; and its negative approach. It proposed a streamlining of processes and a concentration of effort on what is vital. Its proposals formed the basis for the first major reform of the system of administration stemming from the 1947 Acts. They were included in the Town and Country Planning legislation considered in Parliament in 1968.

Development Plans are replaced by a new form of plan, as proposed by the P.A.G. Report (see page 245), consisting of:

1. a *structure plan* submitted for ministerial approval. This would be primarily a written statement of policy, accompanied by a diagrammatic structure map for counties and major towns only, designed to expose clearly the broad basic pattern of development and the transport system. These structure plans would form the main link between policies on a national and regional level and local planning. They would indicate 'action areas', i.e. areas where comprehensive treatment (development, redevelopment, improvement or a mixture) was envisaged in the ensuing ten years;

2. *action area plans* to be adopted locally, showing the shape of development in those areas; and

3. other *local plans*, to meet local needs, also to be adopted locally.

Transition to the new system will be gradual. It will reflect the capacity of the present local planning authorities to deal with the 'new' planning and the need for the procedures to 'ensure fair treatment of those affected by planning proposals'. Clearly, the speed of advance will be influenced by the recommendations of the Royal Commissions on Local Government and by the inevitability that these will advocate some form of regionalism.

Development Control is improved in three major respects: dealing with appeals, enforcement of planning control and preservation of buildings of architectural or historic importance. Appeal arrangements (see page 206) in England and Wales are radically changed and simplified by delegation to selected inspectors of certain types of cases, to be defined by statutory instrument. This will be possible in Scotland, where other ways for expediting decisions are also being explored. Enforcement of planning control is strengthened by ensuring that it will not be possible for unauthorized development to become immune to official action by the mere passage of time. There are other supplementary powers for local planning authorities. Listed buildings (over 100,000) of special historic or architectural interest are given increased protection and covered by powers similar to those of a building preservation order.

Miscellaneous improvements and simplifications in the law are made to deal with numerous operational difficulties. A notable new provision arranges for *ad hoc* inquiries by special commissions into major development projects, such as airports, power stations and natural gas installations. Such commissions will precede a local inquiry and examine more widely the merits of the location proposed for the development, providing some of the 'openness' about decision-taking recommended by the Fulton Report. Additionally, local planning authorities will be able to delegate responsibility for making certain decisions to their planning officers (see *Management Study on Development Control*, 1967, H.M.S.O.).

More obligations are placed on local planning authorities to publish proposals and consult with local people. These should provide scope for the implementation of recommendations from the Skeffington Committee on Public Participation in Planning, set up in 1968 'to consider and report on the best methods, including publicity, of securing the participation of the public at the formative stage in the making of development plans in their area'.

TRANSPORT AND TRAFFIC PLANNING

1966 may be an important date in the history of traffic planning. March opened with two important measures. First, the Minister of Transport set up a Directorate of Economic Planning to initiate research for traffic policy and to undertake cost–benefit studies and the formulation of standards for traffic in towns. Secondly, the Minister invited the regional economic planning councils to send in their ideas on regional transport policies and to start pilot studies of various transport problems in the regions. In July there was a White Paper on Transport Policy (Cmnd 3057), which stated that public transport and its finance must be reorganized. It envisaged single authorities responsible for land-use planning, highways, traffic and public transport. 1967 brought a further quota of White Papers, with those on Public Transport and Traffic (Cmnd 3481) and British Waterways: Recreation and Amenity (Cmnd 3401) being particularly relevant to the planning of the physical environment.

The massive transport legislation of 1968 included provisions to implement these proposals. The general principles of this legislation are:

1. To make basic transport policy a function of local rather than central government.

2. To unify in a plan matters relating to traffic and transport – such as the local road network, investment and management.

3. To grant-aid investment in public transport.

4. To bring the basic network of local passenger services under public organization and control in order to facilitate its planning and rationalization.

5. To plan and operate public transport over larger areas than those of the existing local government authorities.

As the transport situation was so serious in some areas, the Minister of Transport could not wait for the reports of the Royal Commissions on Local Government and so the legislation provided for passenger Transport Authorities to be established in any area where the Minister considers that they are needed to organize and plan public transport. A National Bus Company and Scottish Transport Group were to be set up to bring together all public transport. New large-scale measures of government help for public transport were introduced; these include major capital grants for new tubes, monorails and the purchase of buses. Special consideration is given to rural bus

services. The Ministers concerned require local authorities in the
conurbations and larger towns outside Greater London to prepare
traffic and transport plans for the next five to seven years. These
must, in time, be integrated into the Structure Plans of the local
planning authorities.

In relation to waterways, the 1968 legislation provided powers
to implement Cmnd 3401, notable for its proposal for 'cruiseways' (see page 129). It set up an Inland Waterways Amenity
Advisory Council to advise the Minister and the British Waterways Board on the extent and use of cruiseways for amenity and
recreation and authorized the making of exchequer grants to the
Board, initially of the order of £1 million.

COUNTRYSIDE LEGISLATION

The *Countryside (Scotland) Act*, 1967, provided for the formation
of the new Countryside Commission for Scotland. (The National
Parks Commission set up by the 1949 Act related to England and
Wales only.) The Act made wide provision for the better enjoyment of the Scottish countryside and for the improvement of
recreational and other facilities, giving important powers to the
Commission and extending those of local planning authorities.
Numerous clauses relate to access to open country and to public
paths and long-distance routes, and the provision of country parks.

The *Countryside Act*, 1968, enlarged the functions and changed
the title of the National Parks Commission. It conferred new
powers on local authorities and other bodies for the conservation
and enhancement of natural beauty – widely defined to include
animals and plants – and for the benefit of 'those resorting to the
countryside'.

The functions of the Commissions are to keep under review
all matters relating to:

1. The provision and improvement of facilities for the enjoyment of the countryside.

2. The conservation and enhancement of the natural beauty
and amenity of the countryside.

3. The need to secure public access to the countryside for the
purposes of open-air recreation.

Important features of the legislation are new powers for:

i. Local authorities to set up country parks for open-air
recreation – to include sailing, boating, bathing and fishing –
and to provide picnic and camping sites.

ii. Local authorities to pay compensation under certain conditions in respect of tree planting arising from tree preservation orders.

iii. Statutory water undertakers or local water authorities to provide recreational facilities at their reservoirs and other waters.

iv. The Natural Environment Research Council to make conservation agreements with owners, lessees and occupiers of selected Sites of Special Scientific Interest.

v. The Forestry Commission to plant, care for and manage trees in the interests of amenity and to provide facilities for recreation.

vi. The appropriate authority to make traffic regulation orders for special areas of the countryside.

vii. The signposting of footpaths and maintenance of stiles.

OTHER LEGISLATION

The *Civic Amenities Act*, 1967, reflected the widespread mood of the country that more positive action was essential to conserve the quality of the environment. It provided extra measures to protect and improve buildings of architectural or historical interest and the character or appearance of conservation areas containing such interest. Local planning authorities were also given extra powers and duties for the preservation and planting of trees. A special feature of the Act was that it introduced powers to tackle 'eyesores'. Subject to certain safeguards, local authorities are required to remove and dispose of abandoned vehicles and to provide dumps for the deposit of bulky refuse by citizens; penalties are specified for unauthorized dumping.

The *Caravan Sites Act*, 1968, places a duty on local authorities, subject to certain conditions, to exercise their powers under the *Caravan Sites and Control of Development Act*, 1960, in order to establish caravan sites 'for the use of gypsies and other persons of nomadic habit'. Additional provisions are introduced to control unauthorized encampments.

Many other measures – for subjects such as Clean Air and Water – were included in the heavy Parliamentary programme of the late sixties and must be taken into account with the other legislation referred to in this book in order to get a comprehensive picture of the scope of resource planning.

COMMENT

Despite the great opportunities offered by the recent measures, which are undoubtedly among the most comprehensive and advanced in the world, most of the criticisms made in this book about the efforts to conserve and enhance the quality of the environment in Britain still apply, and many of its proposals remain to be acted upon.

Clearly, the economy of the country must be put on a sounder basis if the continuity of planning, management and development, essential to a positive approach to environmental problems, is to be ensured. Obviously, too, there is an urgent need to improve the machinery of government – central and local. But despite all this, there is wide scope for action now.

The planning profession must make rapid progress if it is to measure up to the challenge of the new legislation and the prospect that the new local government authorities will embrace town and country, thus providing scope to cover urban and rural areas in one coherent strategy. This requires the capacity to make a penetrating analysis of the resources of the countryside and the evolving inter-relationships of town and country. The knowledge and creative possibilities thus gained need to be related by new skills and techniques to the formal legislative provisions. For example, the 'structure' plan will require a broad evaluation of numerous uses of the countryside, such as agriculture, forestry, landscape, wildlife and open-air recreation. This will involve the efforts of many professions and sciences, and the harmonization of the activities of many organizations concerned with specific resources, such as the Ministry of Agriculture, Fisheries and Food, the Forestry Commission, the Nature Conservancy and the Water Resources Board.

It will probably prove necessary for the 'action area' concept to be applied to specific parts of the countryside. This will require more detailed and precise assessment of resource zones and their suitability for a wide range of activities. In some areas formal agreements may be needed to manage land and water for particular purposes.

To achieve these aims and to relate town and country harmoniously, planners and agriculturalists must find a true rapport. Much of the new legislation now enables public authorities to do what many landowners have already done, such as to create the great landscaped estates of the eighteenth century and the country parks of the twentieth century. It is important, therefore, that the professions and the processes of planning, management and development should encourage the positive, creative activities of private and public decision-makers. The divisive influences, starting at national level in separate ministries, must be resolved. Regional and local government should promote cooperation between urban and rural interests. Planning must stimulate and educate and, in turn, respond to the collective wisdom of enlightened land management, reinforced by new scientific knowledge, particularly that from the biological sciences.

There are, of course, many other professions concerned with the planning, management and development of land. Land agents and surveyors, engineers, architects, landscape architects, agriculturalists and foresters, are in close contact with it. Numerous others – for example, biologists, economists, geographers, sociologists – also have a significant contribution to make. All these must develop further the knowledge and skills required for effective conservation and extend their awareness of each other's contribution.

It is, therefore, particularly encouraging that, under the aegis of 'The Countryside in 1970', a permanent liaison committee was set up in 1968 to bring together many of these professions. The committee will keep under review, and arrange for consultation over, issues of common interest and will receive and disseminate professional information about the conservation of the environment.

For potential entrants to these professions, it is essential that universities provide more effective intellectual support, probably in the form of post-graduate courses and special chairs. Several have been started but more are required. A promising development is the Chair for Countryside Planning established in 1968 by London University. Particular fields which would repay study include methodology for the assessment of rural land potential, the development of urban land form and systems of classification for relating both (see page 248); codes for multiple use, particularly in difficult areas (see page 258); the role of green belts, countryside corridors and resource zones (see page 258); policies for settlement in rural areas, which should reflect the views of the Development Commission and its Council for Small Industries in Rural Areas (see page 188); techniques for the survey of social attitudes and preferences; and environmental standards (see page 262). All these are vital to resource planning and all are currently neglected.

The social and aesthetic elements in resource planning have been discussed at length throughout this book, notably in Chapter 14 and the sections on Research (pages 248 and 280). But hard facts and viable hypotheses are still in short supply. Are there really distinctive qualities of rural life and, if so, what weight should be given to them in a cohesive strategy for the new regions? How can one determine criteria for effective assessment of visual and other aesthetic values? How can the vast wealth of historic and aesthetic treasures of the environment be conserved without handicap to economic activity? All these issues merit urgent attention.

A particular sector for intensive effort by professions, sciences and universities is that of techniques for economic assessment (see pages 242 and 281). These are required at all levels: for example, nationally to assess the full implications for the environment of price supports, subsidies, taxes and tax concessions, systems of site values and land levies and a host of macro-economic factors; regionally, to quantify more effectively features such as investment incentives, location of industry and airports, and the costs of reducing environmental contamination; locally, to encourage people to pay more towards the creation of the town or countryside they enjoy. But, whatever techniques emerge – and social cost–benefit is as yet in its infancy – they are unlikely ever to eliminate or quantify wholly the aesthetic, ethical and emotive criteria which are an inherent part of land-use policies and actions.

For these and many other reasons there runs through the activities of these professions, especially planning, the most compelling demands for cooperation with landowners and occupiers and for participation by citizens. The recommendations of the Skeffington Committee should be a major action point from 1969 onwards for planners, as increasingly they have to justify their proposals. This requires persuasion writ large in the diary of every planner. And all measures should be taken with the fullest possible awareness of their implications for the conservation of the qualities desired in the environment.

The issues dealt with in this book will largely decide what the environment will be like at the start of the third millennium A.D. A philosophy of conservation planning, compounded mainly of economics, ecology and ethics, seems vital if it is to be of high quality.

> The art of life lies in a constant re-adjustment to
> our surroundings.
>
> Chinese Proverb

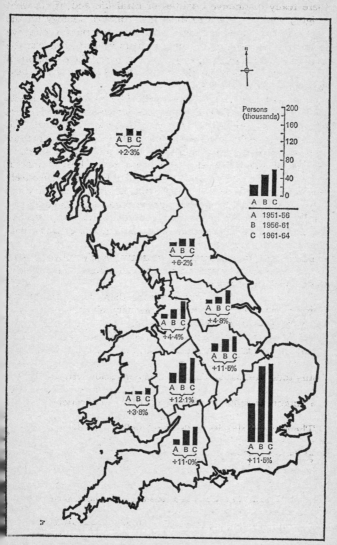

23 Total population change in Britain 1951–64. (*Architects' Journal*)

REFERENCES AND FURTHER READING

Extensive use has been made of the publications of the following bodies: Central Electricity Generating Board; Council for Nature; Council for the Preservation of Rural England; Council of Europe; Forestry Commission; National Parks Commission; Nature Conservancy; International Union for Conservation of Nature and Natural Resources; Ministry of Agriculture, Fisheries and Food; National Society for Clean Air; National Trust; Resources for the Future, Inc.; Study Conferences 'The Countryside in 1970'; Town and Country Planning Association; Town Planning Institute; U.N. Food and Agriculture Organization; World Wildlife Fund.

LAND

Advisory Committee on Pesticides and Other Toxic Chemicals, *Review of the Persistent Organochlorine Pesticides: Supplementary Report*, London, H.M.S.O., 1964. 8 pp.

Advisory Committee on Poisonous Substances Used in Agriculture and Food Storage, *Review of the Persistent Organochlorine Pesticides: Report by the Advisory Committee . . .*, London, H.M.S.O., 1964. 67 pp.

Best, R. H., *The Major Land Uses of Great Britain*, Ashford, Wye College, 1959. 113 pp.

Best, R. H., 'Recent Changes and Future Prospects of Land Use in England and Wales', *Geographical Journal*, *131*, 1965, pp. 1–12.

Best, R. H., *and* Coppock, J. T., *The Changing Use of Land in Britain*, London, Faber, 1962. 253 pp.

Blake, P., *God's Own Junkyard: the Planned Deterioration of America's Landscape*, New York, Holt Rinehart, 1964. 144 pp.

Bracey, H. E., *Industry and the Countryside: the Impact of Industry on Amenities in the Countryside*, London, Faber, for the Acton Society Trust, 1963. 261 pp.

British Broadcasting Corporation, *The Countryside for Use and Leisure*, London, B.B.C. Publications, 1965. 23 pp. (Booklet for a series of broadcasts Oct.–Dec. 1965.)

Burton, T. L., *and* Wibberley, G. P., *Outdoor Recreation in the British Countryside* (Studies in Rural Land Use, Report No. 5), Ashford, Wye College, 1965. 54 pp.

Civic Trust, *Derelict Land: a Study of Industrial Dereliction and How It may be Redeemed*, London, The Trust, 1964. 71 pp.

Crowe, S., *The Landscape of Power*, London, Architectural Press, 1958. 115 pp.

Department of Agriculture and Fisheries for Scotland: Advisory Panel on the Highlands and Islands, *Land Use in the Highlands and Islands*, London, H.M.S.O., 1964. 104 pp.

Dower, M., *Fourth Wave: the Challenge of Leisure*, London, Civic Trust, 1965. 68 pp. (Reprinted from *Architects Journal*.)

European Conference of Local Authorities, *Papers on Regional Planning and the Conservation of Nature and Landscape (Text of Resolution 43)*, Strasbourg, Council of Europe, 1964.

Food Supply and Nature Conservation: A Symposium, Cambridgeshire College of Arts and Technology, 1964. 51 pp.

Friends of the Lake District, *Traffic in the Lake District*, Ulverston, 1964. 11 pp.

Hedgerow and Farm Timber Committee (Chairman: the Lord Merthyr, T.D.), *Report*, London, H.M.S.O., 1955. 64 pp.

Hitch, A. S., *and* Sorenson, M., *Conservation and You*, Princeton, Van Nostrand, 1965. 126 pp. Bibliog.

Jacks, G. V., *and* Whyte, R. O., *The Rape of the Earth: a World Survey of Soil Erosion*, London, Faber, 1939. 313 pp.

Leopold, Aldo, *A Sand County Almanac*, New York, Oxford University Press, 1949. 226 pp.

Ministry of Housing and Local Government, *New Life for Dead Lands: Derelict Acres Reclaimed*, London, H.M.S.O., 1963. 30 pp.

Ministry of Housing and Local Government, *The South-East Study, 1961–81*, London, H.M.S.O., 1964. 145 pp.

Ministry of Land and Natural Resources *and* Secretary of State for Wales, *Leisure in the Countryside: England and Wales* (Cmnd 2928), London, H.M.S.O., 1966. 15 pp.

Natural Resources (Technical) Committee (Chairman: Sir Solly Zuckerman), *Forestry, Agriculture and Marginal Land*, London, H.M.S.O., 1957. 67 pp.

Outdoor Recreation Resources Review Commission (Chairman: L. S. Rockefeller), *Outdoor Recreation for America: a Report to the President and to the Congress*, Washington, O.R.R.R.C., 1962. 246 pp.

Pollard, R. S. W., *Law Reform and the Countryside*, Dorking, British Naturalists' Association, 1964. 24 pp.

Stamp, Sir L. D., *The Land of Britain: Its Use and Misuse*, 3rd edn., London, Longmans, 1962. 546 pp.

United States: President's Science Advisory Committee. Environmental Pollution Panel, *Report: Restoring the Quality of Our Environment*, Washington, U.S. Government Printing Office, 1965. 317 pp. Bibliog.

Wibberley, G. P., *Agriculture and Urban Growth: a Study of the Competition for Rural Land*, London, Michael Joseph, 1959. 240 pp.

Wibberley, G. P., *The Changing Rural Economy of Britain*, Ashford, Wye College, 1964. 14 pp.

Wibberley, G. P., *Pressures on Britain's Land Resources* (Tenth Heath Memorial Lecture), Sutton Bonington, University of Nottingham School of Agriculture, 1965. 12 pp.

AIR

Conservation Foundation, *Implications of Rising Carbon Dioxide Content of the Atmosphere*, New York, 1963. 15 pp.

European Conference of Local Authorities (Strasbourg), Fifth Session, *Regional Planning and Air Pollution* (CPL (5)15), Strasbourg, Council of Europe, 1964. 28 pp.

European Conference on Air Pollution (Strasbourg), *Effects of Air Pollution on Animals and Plants. General report by M. Tendron* (CPA/RG 2), Strasbourg, Council of Europe, 1964. 53 pp. Bibliog.

Gregory, P., *Polluted Homes* (Occasional Papers on Social Administration No. 15), London, Bell, 1965. 64 pp.

WATER

Central Advisory Water Committee: Sub-committee on the Growing Demand for Water, *Final Report*, London, H.M.S.O., 1962. 43 pp.

Conservation of Water Resources in the United Kingdom, Symposium 1962, *Proceedings*, London, Institution of Civil Engineers, 1963. 213 pp. Bibliogs.

Council of Europe: Committee of Experts for the Conservation of Nature and Landscape, *Water Conservation: Ecological Consequences of the Management of Catchment Areas and Influence of Forests on River Basins* (EXP/Nat (66)7), by Z. Salverda, Strasbourg, Council of Europe, 1966. 29 pp. Bibliog.

Council of Europe: Consultative Assembly (Doc. 1965), *Report on Fresh Water Pollution in Europe*, Strasbourg, Council of Europe, 1965. 177 pp.

Ministry of Housing and Local Government, *Water Conservation: England and Wales*, London, H.M.S.O., 1962. 14 pp.

Water Resources Board, *Annual Reports*, Water Resources Board, 1963/4, 1964/5.

WILD LIFE

Darling, F. F., *Wild-life Conservation: the Ethical and Technical Problems*, New York, Conservation Foundation, 1964. 7 pp.

Elton, C., *The Ecology of Invasions by Animals and Plants*, London, Methuen, 1958. 181 pp.

Fitter, R. S. R., *Wildlife in Britain*, Harmondsworth, Penguin Books, 1963. 191 pp. Bibliog.

Huxley, Sir J., 'Huxley in Africa', *Observer*, 13, 20 and 27 November 1960.

Wild Life Conservation Special Committee (England and Wales), *Report* (Cmd 7122), London, H.M.S.O., 1947. 139 pp.

UNITIES

Atkinson-Willes, G., *ed.*, *Liquid Assets*, Morges, International Union for Conservation of Nature and Natural Resources, 1964. 16 pp.

Central Council of Physical Recreation, *Inland Waters and Recreation: a Survey . . . of the West Midlands . . . by the Staff of the Physical Education Department of Birmingham University*, London, C.C.P.R., 1964. 99 pp.

Civic Trust, *A Lee Valley Regional Park: an Essay in the Use of Neglected Land for Recreation and Leisure*, London, The Trust, 1964. 48 pp.

Denman, D. R., *Five Crucial Years in the Destiny of Common Land, 1965–1970* ('Countryside in 1970' Second Conference paper), London, Royal Society of Arts, 1965.

Farb, P., 'Disaster Threatens the Everglades', *Audubon*, 67, 1965, pp. 302–9.

Franklin, T. B., *British Grasslands from the Earliest Times to the Present Day*, London, Faber, 1953. 173 pp.

Moore, N. W., 'The Heaths of Dorset and Their Conservation', *Journal of Ecology*, 50, 1962, pp. 369–91.

Nature Conservancy, *Report on Broadland*, London, The Nature Conservancy, 1965. 98 pp. Bibliog.

Pearsall, W. H., *Mountains and Moorlands*, London, Collins (New Naturalist Series), 1950, 312 pp.

Royal Commission on Common Land, *Report* (Cmnd 462), London, H.M.S.O., 1958. 248 pp.

Hilton, K. J., 'The Lower Swansea Valley Project', *Journal of the Town Planning Institute*, *51*, 1965, pp. 106–8.

PEOPLE AND POPULATION

Council of Europe: Consultative Assembly. Committee on Population and Refugees, *Report on the Problems Raised by Population Trends in Europe* (Doc. 1689), Strasbourg, Council of Europe, 1963. 33 pp.

Leyhausen, P., 'The sane community – a density problem?', *Discovery*, 26, 1965, pp. 27–33.

Osborn, F., *ed.*, *Our Crowded Planet: Essays on the Pressure of Population*, New York, Doubleday, for the Conservation Foundation, 1962. 240 pp. Bibliog.

United Nations, *Provisional Report on World Population Prospects in 1963* (Doc. ST/SOA/SER.R.7), U.N., 1964.

PLANNING

Ashworth, W., *Genesis of Modern British Town Planning*, London, Routledge (International Library of Sociology), 1954. 288 pp.

Cullingworth, J. B., *Town and Country Planning in England and Wales*, London, Allen & Unwin, 1964. 301 pp. Bibliog.

Ministry of Housing and Local Government, *The Future of Development Plans. A Report by the Planning Advisory Group of the Ministry of Housing and Local Government, Ministry of Transport and Scottish Development Department*, London, H.M.S.O., 1965. 61 pp.

FORECAST

Fisher, J. L., *and* Potter, N., *World Prospects for Natural Resources: Some Projections of Demand and Indicators of Supply to the Year 2000*, Baltimore, Johns Hopkins Press, 1964. 73 pp.

Landsberg, H. H., *Natural Resources for U.S. Growth: a Look Ahead to the Year 2000*, Baltimore, Johns Hopkins Press, 1964. 260 pp.

Nicholson, E. M., *Conservation and the Next Renaissance* (The Horace M. Albright Conservation Lectureship, IV), Berkeley, University of California School of Forestry, 1964. 19 pp.

SUPPLEMENTARY BIBLIOGRAPHY

British Waterways Board, *Leisure and the Waterways*, London, 1967. 44 pp.

Committee on the Civil Service (Chairman: Lord Fulton), *Report* (Cmnd 3638), London, H.M.S.O., 1968

Council of Europe, *Man in a European Society: Inter-governmental Work Programme of the Council of Europe 1967–68*, Strasbourg, Directorate of Information of the Council of Europe, 1967. 90 pp.

David Davies Memorial Institute of International Affairs, *Principles Governing Certain Changes in the Environment of Man*, London, 1968. 34 pp.

Development Commissioners, *Aspects of Rural Development: thirty-second report . . . for the three years ended 31 March 1965* (H.C. 100, Sess. 1965/66), London, H.M.S.O., 1966. 37 pp.

Management Study Team on Development Control, *Report*, London, H.M.S.O., 1967. 52 pp.

Mellanby, K., *Pesticides and Pollution*, London, Collins, 1967. 221 pp. (New Naturalist Series)

Noirfalise, A., *Forest Management: ecological consequences of the intensive cultivation of resinous trees in the deciduous zone of temperate Europe*, Strasbourg, Council of Europe, 1967. 18 pp.

South East Economic Planning Council, *A Strategy for the South East: a first report*, London, H.M.S.O., 1967. 100 pp.

Town and Country Planning Association, *The Citizen's Guide to Town and Country Planning* by D. W. Riley, London, 1966. 66 pp.

INDEX

MORE ABOUT PENGUINS
AND PELICANS

Penguin Book News, which appears every month, contains details of all the new books issued by Penguins as they are published. From time to time it is supplemented by *Penguins in Print*, which is a complete list of all books published by Penguins which are in print. (There are three thousand of these.)

A specimen copy of *Penguin Book News* will be sent to you free on request, and you can become a subscriber for the price of the postage – 4s. for a year's issues (including the complete lists). Just write to Dept EP, Penguin Books Ltd, Harmondsworth, Middlesex, enclosing a cheque or postal order, and your name will be added to the mailing list.

Some other books published by Penguins are described on the following pages.

Note: *Penguin Book News* and *Penguins in Print* are not available in the U.S.A. or Canada

POLITICS AND SOCIAL SCIENCE

W. J. M. Mackenzie

For as long as politics has been a human activity, it has also been a subject of serious study. Such names as Machiavelli, Hobbes, Montesquieu, and de Tocqueville have exercised enormous influence in the history of politics.

In our generation the study of politics has developed dramatically in new and fascinating directions. New ideas and techniques in the fields of philosophy, psychology, biology, sociology, and mathematics have all played a part in revolutionizing the world of academic politics and giving meaning to its new name of political science.

In this new Pelican Professor Mackenzie briefly reviews the history of the academic study of politics from Plato and Aristotle to Bagehot and Marx. But the most important contribution of his book is to give the ordinary reader the first opportunity to read a complete survey of the incredible diversity of modern political science in a book which never loses sight among the technicalities of method of the prime aims of the study of politics.

In effect, Professor Mackenzie ably interprets political science to the social scientist, and social science to the student of politics. In so doing he makes both clearer to the intelligent man in the street.

PROBLEMS OF THE WORLD ECONOMY

Richard Bailey

The whole system by which world trade is organized
under GATT was called in question at Geneva in
1964. The discussions of the United Nations Conference on Trade and Development underlined the
growing gap between rich and poor nations and inevitably cast doubt on the adequacy of arrangements
for providing aid and technical assistance and for
securing political understanding between them.

The development of relations between the West and
the 'Third World' are examined in this new Pelican
by an economist who for ten years headed PEP, the
research institute. Scrutinizing the agencies which
organize, and to some extent regulate, the economic
and political affairs of the world, he discusses the kind
of questions we are bound to pose: Are the international
institutions dealing with trade, money, and technical aid
equal to the tasks facing them? Is the formation of
regional blocs (such as the Common Market or EFTA)
likely to spread? Has a multi-racial British Common-
wealth a role to play in bridging the gap between the
West and the 'Third World'? And what part can and
will Russia and China take in the development of Africa
and Asia?